SIGNS & WONDERS

BERNARD EVSLIN

SIGNS & WONDERS

TALES FROM THE OLD TESTAMENT

DRAWINGS BY CHARLES MIKOLAYCAK

FOUR WINDS PRESS   NEW YORK

Library of Congress Cataloging in Publication Data

Evslin, Bernard.
    Signs and wonders.

    Summary: A retelling of Old Testament stories,
including some Apocrypha, in which the author has
tried to re-create the character through dialog and
description.
    1. Bible stories—English—O.T.   [1. Bible
stories—O.T.]   1. Mikolaycak, Charles.   II. Title.
BS551.2.E9   221.9'505   81-2188
ISBN 0-590-07686-8   AACR2

Published by Four Winds Press
A Division of Scholastic Inc., New York, N.Y.
Text copyright ©1981 by Bernard Evslin
Illustrations copyright ©1981 by Charles Mikolaycak
All rights reserved
Printed in the United States of America
Library of Congress Catalog Card Number: 81-2188
1   2   3   4   5   85   84   83   82   81

ABOUT THE MAKING OF THIS BOOK

Signs & Wonders was designed and illustrated by
Charles Mikolaycak. The typeface is ITC Novarese and
was composed by Printworks, Inc. of Norwalk,
Connecticut, and TypoGraphics Communications,
Inc. of New York City. The illustrations are pencil
drawings reproduced as duotones. The book is
printed on 60-pound P&S Offset by Halliday Litho-
graph Corporation in West Hanover, Massachusetts.
The book is bound by Halliday Lithograph Corpora-
tion in a three-piece binding of GSB Natural and
Multicolor Antique Quaker Grey. The end papers are
Multicolor Antique Jet.

*For Galeal, Jarah, Noah, Boaz, Eli, Luke, Nathaniel —
our new sons with the old, old names*

CONTENTS

SIGNS & WONDERS

INTRODUCTION

Once, a very long time ago, the world turned almost good for a day. For the space of twenty-four hours, there were no wars, no private murders, no rapes, no robberies — some small cruelties, but no major crimes.

Satan was displeased. He summoned the most reliable of his demons and said: "What's happening?"

"I don't know, my lord."

"Find out."

The demon flew up to earth, looked about, and flew back. Demons are quick. "It's a book," he said. "People have been reading it."

"What book?"

"I hesitate to use such a term before your dark majesty."

"The Bible, eh?"

The demon shuddered.

"The Bible. Very well, we'll take it away from them."

"How?"

"Make it unreadable. That's your job."

"I am at your service, my lord, but I do not quite know how to proceed. God's word is immutable, is it not?"

"God's word is immutable, but clerks make mistakes. Translators, too, are prone to error. That's where we come in. Am I not the father of error? Go up there and darken counsel."

"Can you be more explicit, my master?"

"That collection of books called the Bible is drawn from many different writings: Egyptian hieroglyphics inscribed on tomb walls, Chaldean cuneiforms on broken stone tablets, fragments of Hebrew script on rotting papyrus and moldering sheepskin scrolls. All this feeds confusion. Even better, ancient Hebrew was written without vowels, ancient Greek without punctuation or division between words. Translators reading Hebrew cannot really tell whether a word is *pet, pot, put,* or *pit, shut, shot,* or *shoot.* Take this sentence: 'Baalisnowhere.' Someone translating from the ancient Greek can choose between two opposite meanings: 'Baal is now here,' or 'Baal is nowhere.' See the possibilities?"

"Where do I start?"

"Start and end with the stories. Don't bother with the tomes of law;

1

nobody reads them. Excruciating detail of priestly vestment, description of temple architecture, chapters on ritual — forget it. Nobody looks at such texts except priests and scholars and other specialists. I want you to ignore all that material and concentrate on the stories. Stories are dangerous. They call up the reader's own experience and release energies of mind and soul, directing them in whatever path the author wishes. Stories grapple the imagination, engage the senses. A reader of tales absorbs instruction through his pores. Go up there and make the stories unreadable."

"How?"

"Mix up the scroll fragments. Butt them against one another at random so that a story starts and stops and starts again in a different place, and certain phrases repeat themselves endlessly."

"Yes, sir, I can do that."

"Find an exciting place in a story and insert a stupefying genealogy, a string of jaw-cracking names joined by *begat*. From time to time, rip out whole sections of law or ritual and plant them bodily in the stories. So much for sowing confusion; I also want you to do some editing. Here's a pencil red as flame. Search among the tales and destroy the sensuous fabric wherein events must dwell if they are to pierce the heart. Strike out physical detail. Get rid of any word that describes how something looks or sounds or tastes or smells. As far as possible, eliminate dialogue. You can't get it all, but every bit helps. Follow my thinking?"

"I believe so, my lord, and shall punctually perform your will."

"Make haste, my son. I don't know if I can bear another day like today."

The demon, whose name was K'miti, flew to earth and did what he had been told to do. It may be coincidence, but not a day since has troubled the Devil's mind.

Whatever the merit of this legend, it identifies the major problems of Bible scholarship and is accurate in its critique of those stylistic barriers that keep people from reading these marvelous Old Testament tales. Everyone has heard fragments, snippets, synopses. We know Eve ate an apple, Cain had sibling problems, Noah came in out of the rain, Goliath was big, and Solomon was wise. But how many of us have actually read these tales?

The fact is that they are often disappointing to read. The Devil did his work well. This book is an attempt to restore these stories to what they were before Satan stuck his pencil in.

What liberties have been taken? This is tricky ground. There are many who think it sacrilege to change a word of Bible text. They do not realize how that text has been mutilated through the ages. Mutilated not only in the ways already described but by a kind of popular insistence on certain detail. The apple Eve ate, for example, is never mentioned in Genesis. The word is fruit. It might have been a fig or an orange. In that climate it would more than likely have been an orange or a date or a fig or a pomegranate. But everyone knows it was an apple. Something demands an apple.

Elijah, starving in the desert, was fed by ravens. But in ancient Hebrew, written without vowels, the words for raven and Arab were identical: *oreb*. Was the old prophet fed by birds or nomads? For story purposes, birds beat Arabs. Ravens they remain. Drama dares where scholarship falters.

What liberties have been taken? There has been an attempt to restore what Beelzebub had deleted: dialogue, description, sights, sounds, smells. Phrases meaningless to a contemporary reader have been re-phrased. When Jezebel "tired her head," it does not mean that she wearied herself thinking but that she *attired* her head, put jewels in her hair. Sometimes it was necessary to change a phrase to restore its meaning.

About language: The Authorized King James Version is one of the glories of English literature. James convened his council of English poets and prose stylists in 1611, five years before Shakespeare s death. At least two of the phrases in the Bible are duplicated word for word in Shakespeare's plays: "A generation of vipers" and "Grave, where is thy victory, death, where is thy sting?" So it can be assumed that the Bard sat on this council and helped translate into immortal English older English texts, which had been translated from ancient Greek — which had been translated from much older Hebrew texts. In retelling these tales, I have attempted to preserve the deep organ notes of the King James Version, changing it to clarify what is unclear or to restore the original meaning to words that now mean something else.

My greatest regret is having eliminated *thou* and *thee*. In growing away from these intimate forms, our language has lost nuance. Nevertheless, they are fossil forms and make one more hurdle for the reader, so they have been tenderly laid to rest.

All the tales here retold are taken from the Old Testament, except for

Judith and some legends of Abraham. The Judith story is apocryphal. What does that mean? The word means "obscure," "of uncertain origin." But in Bible terms it means more. The priests and pundits who decided what went into the Old Testament arbitrarily closed the books about 500 B.C. Anything told thereafter, no matter how inspired, how beautiful, how exalted, was denied a place in holy writ. Thus, some of the best tales, some of those that have become the tissue of tradition, are apocryphal: Susan and the Elders; the Maccabees; Judith. Where would ecumenism be without Chanukah to be coupled broad-mindedly with Christmas? Where would Chanukah be without the apocryphal Maccabees?

Of the tales out of Apocrypha, Judith is perhaps the best. She is one of the all-time heroines and has inspired poets galore. Painters, too. Holofernes' gore reddens many a wall.

I have also gone beyond the Old Testament in some of the stories of Abraham — specifically, in the tales of his birth and his idol smashing. Here I have gone to those writings known as pseudopigrapha ("false writings"), which are folktales and legends about biblical figures. There is simply more to be said about Father Abraham than the Bible offers.

Keeping more or less to narrative event, I have tried to flesh out the giant bones. The intention was to undo some of K'miti's fiendish work and to make these indispensable stories more accessible.

IN THE BEGINNING

THE CREATION

I n the beginning there was only God who had always been. The rest was emptiness and darkness. Then God hung the sun in the sky, and said: "Let there be light!" The sun gave light; that light was Day. And God called up the darkness again to be Night. So ended the first day.

There was no earth yet, and no stars, only the great light of the sun shining on an endless waste of waters. Then God made the waters sink out of the sky, which He called Heaven, and prepared a place for the stars. He called back the darkness; that was the end of the second day.

On the morning of the third day He gathered the waters under Heaven in one place. Where the waters shrank away from His hand, dry land appeared. He called that dry land Earth; the place of waters He called Sea. Then He planted grass on the earth. He planted bushes and trees that bore vegetables and fruit of all kinds. God said: "These are living things, these flowers and trees that I have planted upon the earth. And I put upon them a special sign of my favor. From now on they will be able to make their own kind out of their own seed. So these living things that I have planted will live upon the earth until the end of time."

On the fourth night God punched holes in the sky to let the light shine through, and said: "These small lights shall be called Stars; they shall give a little light to the earth even at night. Then He hung the moon in the night sky between earth and stars. So ended the fourth day.

On the fifth day He breathed upon the seas and made them boil up into different kinds of life. There were fish in the sea, little fish and great whales. God lifted His hand; birds flew out of the water and sang with joy. He said: "You fish and birds shall bear my special sign. You will be able to make your own kind out of your own seed until the end of time."

On the morning of the sixth day God said: "Let the earth do as the waters have done and bring forth living creatures. I want animals of every kind, each one different, each alive in its own way." Whereupon animals appeared on earth and moved among the trees and the grass. Lions and tigers and bears and wolves, and deer and camels and horses. Also, crocodiles and snakes. Cows and bulls, too, and goats and sheep. Then God looked down on the earth and saw that the plains and forests were full of animals and the sea was full of fish and the air was full of birds, and He said: "My breath is life, and life is good. I have molded life

into different forms and given each form its own way to be, and have put upon each my special sign, which means that it may make its own kind out of its own seed over and over until the end of time. Now I shall make the most important living thing. I shall make man. And man will be unlike any other creature on earth, for I shall make him in my own image. He will have in him animal life and the spirit of God, and will rule over beast and fish and bird. He will rule the earth in my name."

God reached down and took a handful of dust and breathed His own life into it. There in the palm of His hand lay a man asleep. God set him down in a garden and let the darkness come. That was the end of the sixth day.

On the seventh day God rested. He looked down upon the earth, and upon the heavens, upon sun, moon, and stars, and all the living things of earth and sea and air — and upon man asleep in his garden. He said: "This is good."

THE GARDEN OF EDEN

The name of the first man was Adam. He lived in a garden God had planted in a place called Eden. This was the most beautiful garden that ever grew. Every kind of flower grew there and every kind of tree. A river ran through the garden and became four rivers. In the middle of the garden stood a tree, the tallest tree of all, hung with golden fruit.

"This is the Tree of Life," said God. "It bears twelve kinds of fruit, a different one for each month — orange, fig, date, quince, olive, apricot, and other kinds that nourish body and soul. If you eat of this tree and no other, you shall never die."

Then God showed Adam another tree, standing apart on a grassy slope. Red fruit burned on its boughs.

"You may not eat of this tree," said God. "It is the Tree of the Knowledge of Good and Evil. You must not taste this fruit, or you will die. Do you understand?"

"I obey," said Adam.

God said: "This is your garden and you must care for it. You must name its trees and flowers. For you are a man, and man is the only one of my creatures to whom I have given the power of the word."

"Shall I name the forbidden fruit?"

"Name it, but do not eat it."

"I name you Apple," said Adam.

He went around the garden naming the trees and the flowers. Before night came he had found names for the oak and the rose. Nor did he sleep when night came, but stood looking at the sky.

"You points of light," he said, "you are many, and I shall find a name for each of you, but not yet. Until then you will just be called stars."

He watched the moon climb, and said: "And you, yellow ball of fire that changes the night, I name you Moon."

God was pleased with these names. He took up handful after handful of dust and made new animals and birds. Each creature He made He took to Adam to be named. And Adam gave each bird and beast a name. Some were short names like cat and bear and lark. Others were long, like hippopotamus. But they all seemed to fit exactly.

When day was done, Adam did not sleep, but stood looking up at the sky, trying to find a different name for each star. He looked lonely standing there at night, and God said: "It is not good for man to be alone."

Then God made Adam fall into a deep sleep. As Adam slept, God took a rib out of his body, and that rib He made into a woman. Now a woman lay asleep in the garden next to Adam.

When Adam awoke he saw her and was glad. The woman awoke, and saw Adam, and smiled. Adam said: "You are bone of my bone and flesh of my flesh, and I shall call you Woman. Thank you, God, for making this woman to be my wife."

God said: "Because I made this woman out of your rib, she has become bone of your bone and flesh of your flesh. And from this time on, man and woman who choose each other shall belong to each other only and be one flesh. Man and woman, I put upon you the sign of my special favor. In the joining of your bodies you shall have the power to make your own kind out of your own seed, from now until the end of time. Man and woman have I created you. You are created in my image, and shall create your own children upon earth, who shall be born out of your love for each other, blossoming forth from the seed that man plants in his wife. I give you to each other in this garden of earth. Obey me, care for each other, and live in the blessing of the God who made you."

Man and woman looked at each other and were glad. They were naked and not ashamed. Adam said: "Because you are to be the great mother of all who come after us, I name you Eve."

Adam showed Eve all the trees of the garden and all the flowers, and taught her their names. He showed her the tallest tree, and said: "You may eat of the fruit of any tree, but do not eat the fruit of that one."

"Why?" said Eve.

"It is the Tree of the Knowledge of Good and Evil, and God forbids us to eat of its fruit."

"What name did you give that red fruit?"

Eve

The Apple

13

"I call it the apple."

"Do you not wonder why God denies us the apple?"

"It is for us not to question God, but to obey."

Eve obeyed. She did not eat the fruit of that tree. But it loomed above the other trees; she saw its topmost branches wherever she went. And of all the fruit in the garden — the orange, the fig, the quince, the apricot — Eve thought the forbidden fruit the most beautiful.

One morning Eve saw that the tree was quivering with light. Loops of golden light twined about the trunk and touched the fruit with fire. An enormous serpent unwound himself from the tree and glided toward her. His scales were red and gold and he burned like the morning star. His eyes were pits of blue fire. His voice was like the wind moving through the trees.

"You are Eve," he said.

"How is it you speak, O serpent?"

"I was like other beasts, without language. But I ate the fruit of a marvelous tree, and knowledge came to me."

Eve could not answer. She was striken with wonder.

"Do not be frightened, Eve. I see into the secret desire of your heart. It is good and natural, and you shall do it."

"Do what?"

"Eat the fruit you have not tasted, the red fruit named the apple."

"It is forbidden."

"How can fruit be forbidden? It is made to be eaten."

"If we eat it, we die, God says."

"He also promised that you would live forever. How can both things be true? Behold! I ate the apple. Am I dead?"

"Who are you? What is your name? Why do you shine there like the morning star, troubling me with light?"

"I have many names, but you are not ready to know them. My secret will be revealed when you eat the apple. Let us speak of you, Eve. You are the first of your kind, and of a beauty never seen."

"I do not understand."

"Do you not know that you are beautiful?"

"I know nothing so far but what I have been told. The names of flowers and trees and animals. Adam's name and Adam's ways. And that I must obey. I must obey God and I must obey my husband, Adam, who tells me what God wants."

14

The serpent, who was Satan, shifted his glittering coils closer to Eve and looked upon her with starry eyes, and said: "Do you not also hear another voice, an inner voice, whispering, 'Eat the apple. Eat the apple' ? "

"Yes."

"Perhaps that is God's voice, echoing in the deep of you. Perhaps it is you who sense His intention, not Adam."

"I have thought so. But can it be?"

"Yes-s-s-s."

"I am confused. I do not know what to believe."

"I am here to instruct you. I am here to give you the gift of knowledge, a greater gift than any you have been given. Knowledge hangs on that tree."

Eve looked at the tree. Globes of red fire burned among its dark-green leaves. She looked away.

"Look at me," the serpent whispered.

Eve gazed into the blue flame of the serpent's eyes. Fragrance of flowers swelled about her. She felt herself melting into particles of light; there was a taste of honey in her mouth.

"Yes-s-s," whispered the serpent. "That sweetness in your mouth is a foretaste of the apple."

"To eat is to die, God said."

"But I, who am His messenger, tell you that you shall not die. When you eat the apple you shall be as gods yourselves, accepting both good and evil."

"Tell me this, O shining serpent whose name I do not know: Does not the Lord God wish His commandment obeyed?"

"His ways are mysterious," said the serpent. "But I know Him better than anyone else. What would please Him most is for you to see behind His words to His real meaning, and to teach it to Adam."

"When God says 'Do not,' He means 'Do!' Is that His meaning?"

"In the matter of the apple, yes. He has created you man and woman, lords of the earth. Shall anything be forbidden to you that beasts may do? This apple I have eaten, shall you not eat it, also? It gave me speech. How much more will it do for you who already speak?"

"What is knowledge, serpent? I burn to know. What are good and evil? What do these words mean?"

"More than I can tell you. Only the apple itself will reveal the wonderful fullness of their meanings. I can tell you this: Attaining such knowledge, you will become like gods and fulfill God's unuttered wish. For, becoming godlike, you will walk with Him and converse with Him and assuage His gigantic loneliness."

"I don't know what to do."

"Please God, Eve. Obey the hidden intention that dwells behind His words. Go to the tree. Reach up your hand. Grasp the fruit. Put it in your mouth — and eat."

Eve went to the tree, took an apple, and ate.

Adam came into the garden and saw her eating the apple. She had taken just one bite. He seized her arm.

"Stop!"

"Too late. I have tasted the apple, and it is good. It is very good."

"How dare you break God's law? Now you must die."

"We shall be as gods. We shall not die."

"Forbidden! Forbidden! The apple is forbidden! God told me so."

"That was a test, Adam. He wanted you to read the true meaning behind His words. He was testing your love."

"How do you know all this?"

"God sent a messenger to tell me."

"What messenger?"

"A serpent, beautiful as the morning star."

"What does beautiful mean?"

"Look at me. Am I beautiful?"

"You are Eve."

"Eat of the apple, Adam, please."

"I dare not."

"You must eat of the apple or I shall know things beyond your understanding. Here. Take one bite."

"God has forbidden it."

"Then I shall live alone, for you will not know enough to be my husband. And if I have misunderstood God's will, then I shall be punished alone, and die alone. And you will dwell in your garden alone, as you did before I came."

"Give me the apple."

Adam ate. He looked at Eve and saw that she was beautiful — and that she was naked. He looked upon himself and knew his own nakedness, which seemed changed now, all strange.

16

"We are naked," he said. "You are naked and different. And I am naked and afraid."

She smiled at him. "Do not fear. We can clothe our nakedness in fig leaves. This is the beginning of such knowledge as the gods have. We do not know how to use it yet, but we will teach each other. And perhaps the wise serpent will come again and instruct us."

"Where is he now, this messenger who brought you the true meaning of God's word?"

"There he is, crouching in the grass behind the tree."

But the serpent had vanished.

Now the sun was falling, and the shadows closed in. They heard the voice of the Lord God, who was walking in the garden in the cool of the day. When Adam heard that voice he hid himself among the trees. He heard God say, "Adam, where are you?"

"I am here among the trees."

"Why are you hiding from me?"

"I am afraid."

"Why are you afraid? Come here."

Adam came from among the trees and Eve followed him.

"Why are you clad in leaves?"

"We saw that we were naked," said Adam. "And we clothed our nakedness."

"You have eaten of the Tree of the Knowledge of Good and Evil," said God. And His voice was like thunder coming out of the blue sky. "Man and woman, you have defied my will and eaten of the forbidden fruit. Why did you disobey me, Adam?"

"She told me to," said Adam. "The woman you gave to be my wife told me to eat the apple."

"The serpent told me to!" cried Eve. "Forgive me, Lord, but he came gliding out from among the trees, all glittering, and said he was your messenger, sent by you to tell me your true will. He told me to eat the apple."

God answered, saying, "No messenger was he, but the foul fiend who put on the form of a serpent to tell you lies. Prince of Darkness is he, and Lord of Lies. His name is Satan."

By this time, Adam and Eve were crouched on the grass, whimpering with terror.

"Arise now, and listen to me," said God. "Hear your punishment.

Because you have disobeyed me and eaten of the Tree of the Knowledge of Good and Evil, seeking to be wise as gods, you must leave this garden and the life you know. Everything is changed now. Because you have caused me such sorrow, you, Eve, shall know your greatest pain at the moment of your greatest creation. In pain and suffering shall you bear your children, and so shall all women after you, and that pain shall be the sign of your disobedience. For even the Lord of Lies could not make you believe what you did not wish to believe. You lusted in your heart for the forbidden fruit before Satan came; you made his way easy. But your way shall be hard.

"And you, Adam, first of your kind, you listened to your wife and ignored the word of your God. For this I sentence you to hard labor all the days of your life. You shall leave this garden, where everything grows without toil, and go to a place where the earth is dry, where only thorns and thistles grow. There in that cursed place little rain will fall. You shall water the earth with sweat and tears to grow a little food. And when you die, and die you must, you shall return to the earth. For of dust you were made, and to dust you shall return. Do you understand?"

They were weeping and could not speak.

"You understand," said God. "You have eaten of the Tree of the Knowledge of Good and Evil, and its fruit is bitter. You must go now. Leave this garden and go where you will."

So God drove Adam and Eve from the Garden of Eden. And to keep them from coming back he set an angel at the gate of Eden. This angel had four wings and four faces. His wings were made of brass, and his faces were those of lion, ox, man, and eagle. In his hand he held a flaming sword, which no one could pass.

CAIN AND ABEL

Adam and Eve went to live in another place. It was a dry stony place, where they toiled together, digging rocks out of the ground. When night came they fell into an exhausted sleep.

Adam prayed to God to forgive his disobedience and allow him to return to Eden. God answered, "You lost the Eden I had prepared for you. Now, if you wish another, you will have to make it for yourself."

Adam said to Eve:"By the God who made us, I shall not despair! His answer means that our heavy toil will bear fruit at last."

But now Eve could not help Adam because she faced a labor of her own. She was about to bear a child. Adam had to toil alone in the field, prying out rocks and breaking the ground so that it could take seed. He had to dip pails of water from a tiny stream and bear the pails back on a yoke across his shoulders to water the earth he had planted with seed. For in that place little rain fell.

Eve spoke to God secretly in her own fashion: "I know that it is too soon for you to forgive me. But, Lord God, hear my prayer. You have condemned me to bear my child in pain. And I can endure such pain without complaint, but in your mercy allow me to live to see my child."

God answered her with a secret sign, and she labored her child in suffering, and bore a son. And Adam and Eve knew the first joy they had known since leaving Eden, and named their son Cain. His hair was red; his brows were tufts of fire.

He grew into a tall, strong boy, level-eyed and unsmiling, who followed his father everywhere and did as his father did. Soon he was a great help to Adam in the work of the field. He wanted to help in the heavy work of prying rocks out of the ground and digging up stumps, but he was too young. He grieved so at not being able to help that Adam gave him the task of bearing water and chopping weeds. And Cain was content.

Then Eve bore a second son, whom they named Abel. This boy she kept close. He was a beautiful child. His cheeks were red, and his hair was dark, and his eyes brown as a lamb's. His voice was soft, and he was gentle in all his ways.

This second son, Abel, did not follow his father into the fields. His mother had given him a lamb as a pet, and he became skillful with sheep. He kept flocks of fat sheep, grazing them on the hillside. He sheared their wool and gave it to Eve to make clothes for the family.

Now Cain had grown into the full strength of his manhood. He was a mighty farmer, and his crops flourished. In the joy of a rich harvest he built an altar to the Lord and offered Him the first fruits.

Each morning he visited the altar to see if God had taken the offering, but the fruit lay there withered and dry. Cain saw that his offering had not pleased God, and he did not know why.

Then Abel raised an altar and offered the firstborn of his flock. Before his wondering eyes the wood burst into flame and the lamb was consumed. Abel rejoiced. And Adam and Eve rejoiced in the favor that had been shown him.

But Cain took fire. A murderous rage burned in his heart.

God said: "Why are you angry? Do you question my will? If I refuse your offering it is because I am not pleased, and you must study how to do better. And beware! If you close your heart to my will, you will be opening your heart to Satan, who squats always beyond the door. Put aside your pride, Cain, and heed not that fatal whisper."

Cain's wrath was not cooled. He said to Abel: "Let us walk in the fields."

They walked in the fields. Abel spoke of this and that, but Cain said nothing.

"You are silent, brother," said Abel.

Cain did not answer, but strode across the darkening field holding Abel tightly by the arm. The sun was falling, sending out shafts of light that were like spear shafts dripping with blood.

"Where are we going?" said Abel.

"Into the hills."

"Why must we go so far?"

"I have a heavy matter to impart. I do not wish to be near where we dwell."

"Brother, I am weary."

Cain did not answer, but strode up the slope of the hill toward the sun, which was bloodying the whole western part of the sky.

"Brother, you look so strange. I am afraid."

Cain said nothing. He tightened his grasp on Abel and strode up the hill.

"I am weary," said Abel. "I go no farther."

Cain turned on him and said: "Why did the Lord God refuse my offering and take yours?"

"I do not know."

"I know," said Cain. "And the knowledge is sore. You are a thief, born to steal whatever I have."

"No," whispered Abel.

"Yes! Oh, yes. I was happy until you came. I dug the fields with my father, and the earth prospered under my care. No one harmed me, and I harmed no one. But then, cursed day, you were born, and everything changed. For you immediately began to steal. First you stole my mother's love, then my father's. And now you have robbed me of God's favor — all in the same soft, false way and with that lying smile. Now I must punish you."

"Cain, stop! Do not raise your hand against your brother."

But Cain had seized Abel by the throat and held a rock raised over his head.

"Cain, forgive me. I did not mean to steal their love. I mean you no harm. I love you. You are my only brother."

"I hate you. You are my only brother and my only enemy. You must die."

Abel fell to his knees, sobbing. But Cain had no mercy. He smashed the rock down on Abel's hands, which were covering his head. The hands slid away, and Cain smashed the rock down again and again on the bowed head, until it was a mush of blood and bone. Then he took up rocks and covered Abel with them so that he could not be seen. Only a rim of the sun clung to the edge of the sky now. Cain reached his bloody hands to the bloody light and laughed a wild, bitter laugh. Far off across the valley he heard the lost voices of Abel's sheep. Then suddenly he was afraid.

God came down and said: "Where is Abel?"

"I do not know," said Cain. "Am I my brother's keeper?".

God said: "What have you done? Your brother's blood calls out to me from the ground."

Under God's glance the rocks fell away, revealing the broken body of Abel.

"You have murdered your brother," said God. "You have dared to take life from him whom I have given life. Now the earth itself shall curse you, because you have made it drink your brother's blood. From now on that

21

earth will be barren to your touch. You will till it and water it and plant it with seed, but it will not bear for you because you have blighted it with your brother's blood. You shall leave this place. A fugitive and wanderer you shall be till the end of time."

Cain said: "My punishment is more than I can bear. You drive me from your sight and from my home. I must go among strangers, who will kill me."

"No," said God. "Your death belongs to me. Whoever kills you will be punished with seven deaths."

Then God branded Cain's forehead with the letter M, meaning "murderer," also meaning "mine," so that all men would know that Cain was reserved for God's vengeance, and they would not kill him.

Cain traveled eastward. It was a terrible journey. The sun beat down on him. When he sought shade against rock or tree, the shade shrank away from him and he had no shelter from the burning sun. He was too thirsty to eat, and when he tried to drink the water shrank away from his lips. He was about to die, but God was not ready to accept his death. God clouded the sun and allowed a little rain to fall so that Cain might drink, and He allowed Cain to pick some fruit to eat.

Cain traveled to a land named Nod, which means "home of the wanderer," and there found a wife and fathered sons — who became fathers themselves. One became the father of all those who live in tents and raise cattle. Another became the first to play the harp and fathered all who play the harp and the pipes. A third, named Tubal-cain, became the first man to work in metal. He invented the forge, the sickle, and the plow, and became the father of blacksmiths. Cain lived to be very old, but the bloody sign never faded from his forehead, and he never saw Adam and Eve again.

23

NOAH'S ARK

Hundreds of years passed. Men multiplied upon the earth, but they had learned nothing from the curse put upon Cain. For they still killed their brothers and other men's brothers — and sisters and mothers and children. They robbed and murdered and did all manner of wicked things.

God grew very angry. "This race of man offends me," He said. "Their thoughts are evil, their deeds are evil, and I am sorry I ever put such creatures upon earth. So I will wipe them from the earth. I will wash them off with a cleansing flood of waters. Not one man shall be left, nor beast nor fowl that have breathed the air that man has corrupted. Yes, even the memory of a man's false and filthy habits will I wash away."

Now, in the midst of all this wickedness lived a man named Noah, who was gentle and kind and tried to raise his three sons to be good men.

God saw how Noah was living, and spoke to him: "You will see the end of all flesh. I have decided to blot man from the earth, for he is too violent and corrupt to live. But your life I will spare, Noah, and the lives of your wife and your sons and their wives."

"Thank you, Lord," said Noah.

"You must build an ark — a boat of cypress wood," said God, "the largest one ever built. It must be three stories high and as big as six of your houses put together — big enough to hold every kind of animal and bird, two of each. You shall take aboard, also, two of each creeping thing, such as snakes and crocodiles. You must stock enough food to feed your family and all the animals, for the beasts will not be permitted to eat one another, and your voyage through the waters of wrath will last almost a year. Work ceaselessly, you and your sons, for even now I am preparing my flood."

Noah did exactly what God told him. He and his sons, Shem, Ham, and Japheth, went to work building the ark. They worked night and day, stopping only for a little food and a little sleep, for they saw the black clouds rolling across the face of the sky and they knew that the terrible rain was soon to fall. Nor did they stop work to answer their neighbors, who came to jeer at them.

"You have gone mad!" they said to Noah. "Why are you building so huge a vessel so far from the sea? How will you launch it?"

"Perhaps the waters will come to us," said Noah. "Perhaps you should be building boats, too." But he kept working even as he said this. And the neighbors laughed and jeered and paid no heed to his warning.

Finally, the ark was finished. And it was built exactly as God had instructed — an enormous three-story houseboat, 450 feet long, 75 feet wide, and 45 feet high. A door big enough to admit the largest animal was cut into its side, and there were windows to see through. And the seams were caulked with pitch inside and outside.

When the ark was finished, Noah and his sons and their wives worked harder than ever, loading the cargo space with sacks of flour and dried meat and dried fish and great cheeses, with sacks of apples and oranges and figs, and with jars of honey.

Then God appeared to Noah and said: "You are a good man. Carefully have you prepared the ark of your salvation. It will keep you afloat when I drown the wicked. Now you have just seven days before I break the fountains of the deep and hurl the tides of my vengeance upon this earth. Herd together the animals, as I have commanded you, and gather the birds of air. Bring them into your ark two by two, then get aboard with all your family. In seven days the rains shall fall."

Seven days and seven nights Noah and the sons of Noah and their wives worked, eating as they worked, and sleeping not at all. But by the end of the seven days they had herded together the beasts of earth and gathered all the fowl of air, and marched them two by two — male and female of each kind — up the gangway and through the great door of the ark. God had given the animals a special wit for the occasion, so they did not flee their herders and did not attack them, but allowed themselves to be led tamely into the ark. Even the wildest beasts — even lion and tiger, gigantic elephant, and deadly grinning crocodile.

Then, at the end of seven days, when all the animals were aboard, Shem, Ham, and Japheth boarded the ark with their mother and their wives. When all were aboard, Noah took one last look at his home and his garden and his orchard, then walked slowly up the gangway and slid shut the great door.

His neighbors, who had watched the parade of animals with amazement, now fell into a terrible rage as they watched Noah climb into the ark.

"That's right, madman," they screamed. "Lock yourself into your stinking zoo. But don't try to come out, or we'll kill you!"

The sight of what they did not understand made their wickedness more wicked. But they did not have much time to think about Noah, for on that day the rain began to fall.

It was no ordinary rain. It did not fall in drops, but in thick foaming ropes like a waterfall — as if a mighty hand had lifted an ocean out of its bed and flung it down toward earth. And that is what was happening, for God had kept his promise and broken up the fountains of the deep and was hurling their great waters through the windows of heaven.

The water rose so swiftly that most people did not have time to climb to the roof of their house but were drowned inside. And those who were able to climb to the roof lived only a short time longer, for in an hour the water had climbed past the highest roof. Some people clung to wooden beds and planks of wood and floated awhile, but the water was whipped by the wind into a savage boiling torrent, and all who had managed to keep afloat were pulled under.

Noah looked out through the porthole in great wonder. He saw the houses being washed away, and the barns. He saw the fields disappear under sheets of water. He saw the water climb higher than the trees and cover the forests. But not a drop of water leaked into the ark. And he felt the great vessel rise comfortably as the water rose and float easily upon the surface. Nor did it pitch and toss when the gusts of wind hit it, but rocked gently and floated away north by west.

And Noah's heart was torn. He rejoiced in God's mercy, which had plucked him from the raging flood, but he grieved to see his neighbors drown. He forgot their wickedness when he saw them struggling in the water; he forgot the envy and hatred they had turned upon him, and pitied them as they fought to keep afloat and sank out of his sight.

He went to look at the animals. They stood quietly in the great hold of the ship. Some slept. All were peaceable. For God had laid his truce upon them to last all the time they would be in the ark, and the hunters did not hunt nor the hunted flee. The great cats ignored the cattle; the eagle did not pounce upon the lamb. Nor did any of the savage beasts fight among themselves. They obeyed God's truce and waited patiently to be fed.

Only the camel complained. He had been staring out the porthole and was made sorrowful by the great waste of waters. For he loved dry land; the hotter and drier it was, the more he loved it. The desert was his chosen place. So he uttered a loud, bawling, grating cry of outrage and dismay — and has spoken that way ever since.

It rained for forty days and forty nights. The water kept rising. Every man and woman on earth was drowned, and every beast and bird and creeping thing that was not on the ark. All living things perished, except the fish, and even they were very frightened, because the water had risen so high that they found themselves swimming over the tops of strange mountains. Yes, the waters rose above the tops of the highest mountains, and everything that had been alive was dead, except those aboard the ark.

At last the rain stopped falling. Noah and his family had become so used to the drumbeat of rain and the howling wind that they were shocked by the sudden silence. Now for the first time in forty days they were able to come up on deck. Three decks there were on the ark. The birds perched on the top deck. The beasts stood on the middle deck — all except the camel, who stayed below. And the men and women stood on the lower deck, drawing in greedy breaths of fresh air and looking at the sky, which was still covered with clouds.

God held back the waters now and stopped the great fountains of the sky. He blew the clouds away and let the sun come out. And Noah and his family, watching from the deck, saw nothing but an endless plain of water. The whole earth was one ocean, and upon the face of that vast sea the ark floated alone.

But the sun shone forth hotly each day and the waters began to shrink. Then, one day, Noah felt the timbers shudder and heard a grinding noise. He saw that the ark was resting on a rock. He knew that it must be a mountain top, and that the waters were shrinking.

But it took three more months for the water to sink far enough for Noah to see the entire mountain range. Beyond the mountains he saw nothing but water, and he did not dare to leave the ark.

By now ten months had passed since the rains began, and food was running low. Noah watched and watched as the waters sank slowly, but still he could see nothing but mountains and a waste of waters.

After forty days he loosed a raven, which flew away. But the raven did not return, and Noah did not know if it had found dry land, or had drowned, or was perched on another mountain. And now the food was almost gone.

He tossed a dove into the air to see if she could find dry land. But she found no rest for the sole of her foot and came flying back to the ark.

Seven days passed and the food was gone. Everyone was hungry and frightened.

"Do not lose hope," said Noah. "God promised that He would bring us safely through the flood, and His word is my faith."

Again he tossed the dove into the air. The bird winged off. They watched her disappear, and they were hungry and sad.

Noah stood watch all day. Just as the sun was setting he saw the dove fly back, and his heart lurched in despair because her return meant that she had found no dry land, and now they must surely starve to death aboard the ark. But, looking more closely, he saw that the bird was carrying something in her beak.

When she perched on his shoulder, he saw that she carried an olive branch, freshly picked. So Noah knew that the dove had found dry land at the foot of the mountain, and that trees were growing again. "Forgive me, Lord, for doubting," he said. "And thank you for your mercy."

Now God spoke to Noah, saying, "Go forth from the ark, you and your wife and your sons and their wives. Bring forth every living thing that is with you — wild beasts, cattle, birds, and every creeping thing. For I wish them to swarm upon the earth again and be fruitful and multiply."

Noah then instructed his sons to loose the animals. The birds flew off in a great rush of wings, darkening the sky again, as if the clouds had returned, and shrieking their joy. Then the beasts were led off the ark, two by two — the smaller ones first, then the sheep and goats and cattle. These were taken first so that they could descend the mountain and scatter in safety before Noah allowed the lions and tigers and wolves and bears to leave. For Noah knew that God's truce upon the animals ended at the foot of the mountain, and that once all the animals had gone down the hunters must hunt again and the hunted flee.

When the ark was empty of animals, Noah and his sons and their wives came down the mountain. The sun was shining, but the grass and trees were still wet and sparkled like jewels in the sunlight. The world looked all fresh and new, and very empty. Noah lifted his arms to the mountain and said: "Your name shall be Ararat." This meant "holy ground" in his language.

Noah's sons wished to raise tents for shelter. But Noah said: "We do nothing before we raise an altar, and sacrifice to the Lord and thank Him for His mercy."

They raised an altar of wood and made a burnt offering. The smoke arose in a sweet savor, and the Lord was pleased. He said to Noah: "I have drawn off the waters and spared you, Noah, you and your sons and their wives. Now you must be fruitful and bring forth many sons and daughters and renew the race of man. And since you are again first and alone upon earth, as was Adam, I will renew the pledge I made to Adam. Man shall rule. Beast of earth and bird of air and fish that swarm the seas shall serve your needs. All these shall be for your use, for milk and meat and honey and clothing. Green things that grow shall be food for you, also. But you shall eat nothing alive; this I forbid. And though you may kill animals for food, you may not kill one another. Whoever kills man, woman, or child shall pay a blood price. The killer shall be killed. That is my law."

"I hear your words and obey," said Noah. "And I shall teach my sons to obey."

"This, too, I say to you, Noah. I will never again curse the earth because man has displeased me. Some part of evil lay in the very dust of which I made him. So I shall not again blot him off the earth for the evil impulses of his heart. While the earth hangs in my heavens, seed time and harvest, summer and winter, day and night shall not cease."

"Thank you, Lord," said Noah.

God said: "Noah, blessed among men, survivor of my wrath, you stand here for all mankind on this day, and shall hear my vow. Never again shall the waters of my vengeance kill every living thing. I make this pledge to you, and to your sons after you unto the last generation, and to every beast and bird that came out of the ark with you. Never again shall the earth suffer a total flood, never again shall all life be blotted out. For I am the source of life, my breath is life, my intention is life. As a sign of this pledge, which I call a covenant, behold, I place a bow of many colors in the sky, a bridge of colored light arching from heaven to earth. After a storm of rain I shall fling these colors across the sky so that you and all living creatures may be reminded of my mercy, and that I, looking upon the rainbow, shall remember my pledge.

"There it stands in the sky, Noah, the rainbow, the bridge of many colors. Look upon it. Raise your tents and renew my world."

Noah and his sons raised tents and dwelt in them. They planted gardens and orchards and grazed their cattle upon the great meadows of grass. Noah planted a vineyard. He pressed the grapes and drank the wine — the first wine ever poured — and fell into a drunken sleep.

His son Ham entered the tent and saw Noah sprawled naked and snoring in his drunken sleep. Ham ran to his brothers and told his tale, jeering at what he had seen. But his brothers, Shem and Japheth, went to Noah's tent and covered their father's nakedness.

Noah awoke from sleep and knew what had happened. He said to his sons: "You shall be the fathers of nations. Your sons, Ham, will be known as Canaan. Cursed be Canaan! A servant of servants shall your sons be to the sons of your brothers.

"May the Lord bless Shem, and let Canaan be his servants.

"And you, Japheth, your tribe shall increase, and Canaan be your servants, also."

And all that Noah told his sons came to pass. For the sons of Ham were the Canaanites, who settled a fertile crescent of land on the eastern edge of the Inner Sea. And long, long after the Flood a son was born of the tribe of Shem. His name was Abraham and he fathered a mighty nation that conquered the Canaanites.

God kept his covenant. He never again sent a flood of that kind. Still today after a storm we can sometimes see the colors of the rainbow arching across the sky.

THE TOWER OF BABEL

After the Flood the sons of Noah had many sons and daughters, who bred many children and multitudes of grandchildren. The families became tribes. The tribes increased, and spread out from the plain beneath Ararat to other places. But all tribes of earth spoke one language.

One tribe, rich in flocks, went far in search of grazing lands and came to a plain of grass called Shinar. This great meadow was cut by a river swarming with fish. The river was remarkable, too, for the clay of its banks and the way its mud hardened in the sun.

The chief of the tribe was Nimrod, Ham's grandson, a mighty hunter and a fearsome warrior. He called his elders together.

"We are meant to be a great people!" he cried. "We must build a monument to our wonderful selves that will last for all time and be admired by all mankind. A tower it must be, high enough to pierce the heavens."

The people took clay from the river, and mixed mortar and piled brick on brick, building a tower. Through the seasons they labored upon it. It grew so tall it could be seen for great distances and struck wonder in the heart of the beholder. Men were drawn to the site from distant places and helped in the labor, for they, too, wanted to climb into the sky. The tower grew taller and taller. As high as a mountain it stood and higher still.

God looked down and saw what was happening. He was not pleased. "They are puffed up with pride," He said, "each man thinking himself a god, too good to live upon earth. They build toward the sky, neglecting all else."

As He watched the tower grew higher.

"This temple of vanity must fall," said God. "How shall I do it? Shake the earth and level their tower like a boy kicking an anthill? No. Their wits are so dulled by conceit that they will think the earth shakes of itself with no design, and they will learn nothing from disaster. A storm of wind? A tidal wave? These will serve no purpose, either. The tower will fall, but no lesson will be learned. Shall I wipe man's bold mouth of speech? No. For the word is the sign of my spirit dwelling within his animal flesh. If I take man's speech I take his manhood. Nevertheless, I must quench his arrogance."

He summoned His angels and told them what to do. They went down upon earth to the plain of Shinar where the tower was growing, and went from tent to tent confounding language. Invisibly the angels passed among the men, twisting the tongue of each tribe into a different mode of speech. The words of each man's neighbor became strange to his ears, nor could he make his own words understood. The work of building fell into confusion. The tribes grew suspicious of one another. Some tribes went to war; others scattered.

The river choked on its own silt and ran dry. The place became a desert. The tower crumbled and fell to ruins.

At the time language was confounded each man heard his neighbor say "Ba, ba, ba," and so the place was call Babel.

But God did not wish His act to become a curse. He gave each tribe's language a special sense and a special music — so that each loved its own language and was proud of its own mode of speech.

In the wars that followed Babel, the tribe of Nimrod vanquished the others and grew into a mighty nation. They spread northward from Shinar along the river — which was the Tigris — and built a vast walled city. The people called their city Babylon after the fallen tower, for they wanted to show that courage can turn failure into triumph.

The Babylonians prospered. Their armies marched north, east, and south, conquering everywhere. The nation became an empire.

In these years a branch of the tribe descended from Shem wandered into the great plain between the Tigris and Euphrates. The people settled in the hill country south of Babylon and built a city they called Ur.

And in Ur dwelt a stone carver named Terah, who was to be the father of Abraham.

THE PATRIARCHS

ABRAHAM

In Ur lived a man named Terah, who carved the stone idols that were worshipped by the people of that land. His sons helped him in his work, and his youngest son was named Abram.

One day, when Abram was twenty years old, Terah fell sick and left Abram to watch the shop.

A man came in and said to Abram, "I would buy this idol. Tell me the price."

Abram said: "I will tell you the price if you tell me your age."

"I am thirty years old."

"Thirty years old," said Abram. "And yet you would buy this idol, which I made this morning."

The man left the shop. Then Abram put a rope about the necks of two idols and dragged them into the street, crying, "See what you worship. It has a mouth but speaks nothing, eyes but sees nothing, feet but does not walk, ears but does not hear."

Terah was told what his son was doing and feared for his life. He rose from his bed and hurried to the shop. In the meantime Abram had smashed the idols with a mallet. Then, hearing his father come, he put the mallet in the hands of the largest idol, which stood unhurt.

Terah entered the shop, crying, "What have you done? You have broken the idols! Just so will the king destroy us!"

Abram said: "Father, I did not smash the idols. It was the largest idol who smashed the smaller ones. Let the king destroy him."

But the king heard that his stone gods had been smashed, and he ordered Abram to be burned alive.

A great multitude gathered to see this death. The executioner put a torch to the wood and made the flames leap in the fire that was to receive Abram. But a small rain came and put out the flames.

Another fire was lighted. Again rain fell from a cloudless sky and put out the flames, and the king was afraid.

Then Satan appeared to him and said: "I will build a roof over the flames to stop the rain, but you are to put Abram into a catapult and cast him swiftly into the flames."

Thereupon Abram was bound hand and foot and placed into the catapult and slung into the flames. The king shouted with joy, crying,

"Can your god save you now?"

And Abram said: "I trust in Him. He is the maker of heaven and earth and will rescue me."

Whereupon it was seen that the wood piled around Abram had burst into a bud, like the living tree from which it had been cut, and that the flames were red flowers growing, and Abram was unharmed.

When the king saw this he cried, "Witchcraft! Fire cannot harm you. You stand among the flames as in a garden."

But all the people who watched cried in a great voice, "No, King, it is not witchcraft, but the great God, God of Abram, the living God."

And many who watched that day followed Abram when he left the land of Ur.

Journey to Canaan

Abram's father, Terah, knew now that it was time to leave the country. He sold house and shop and stone-carving tools and bought a large herd of goats. He departed from Ur in the Chaldees. With him went his son Abram, and his grandson, Lot, son of Abram's dead brother, and his daughter-in-law, Sarai.

After a journey of many months they came to a city called Haran, and pastured their flock in the fields beyond the city, and raised tents and rested. But Terah never resumed the journey. He died in Haran.

Abram was now seventy-five years old, but he had no child. His wife was barren.

Then God spoke to Abram: "Leave this place. Leave your father's tents and come to a land that I shall show you. And I will make you a mighty nation. I will bless them that bless you, and curse him who curses you. And in you shall all the families of the earth be blessed."

Abram did as God had commanded. He took his wife, Sarai, and his nephew, Lot, and all their flocks and their servants and their goods, and journeyed out of Haran into Canaan. He passed through the land until he came to the plain of Moreh. There God appeared to him, casting a light more brilliant than the sun. Abram fell to the ground, hiding his eyes.

God said: "I give this land to your children and your children's children."

Abram raised an altar on the spot where the Lord had appeared in His

39

radiance. He traveled southward then, still dazzled by that strange light, and able to think only of God's voice and what it had said. He came to a mountain where he pitched his tent and built another altar. He stood upon that ground all night without sleep, gazing at the heavens and trying to think of ways to call to the Lord, for in him was the hunger to look again upon that radiance. And he called that place Beth-el, or "the house of God." He journeyed on, going southward.

He made his way across a vast stony plain, poor in grass. Most of his sheep died; his goats grew very thin. His followers drifted away. Finally there were only Abram and Sarai, his nephew, Lot, Lot's wife, their young daughters, and a few old herdsmen and servants. The sun stabbed at them; they were battered by sudden hail. Sandstorms blew up, and they had to cover their mouths and noses with cloth as they slogged on. They were filthy, exhausted, half-starved. No one seeing this wretched family inching across the plain would have believed they were destined to become a mighty nation. But the Lord has a way of concealing His intentions.

Abram spoke to God, saying, "We have come to the land you promised, and behold, we starve!"

God answered, "Fear not, Abram. I am your shield."

And God sent Abram a vision of sparkling streams and green pastures — and of the way to get there. Abram rose and roused the others, and they toiled into the wilderness again.

The servants complained, saying, "Our master wanders aimlessly. He has lost the way and we are all lost."

But Abram ignored their complaints and drove them on through sandstorms and pitiless heat. Finally he led them through a narrow mountain pass to a valley where a river ran, and the fields were green and lush. There they raised their ragged tents and pastured their herds.

Now came a time of increase. Abram's goats fed on the rich fields and grew fat. The herd multiplied. He kept sheep and cattle and donkeys. Abram lived at peace with his neighbors. He obeyed God and prospered. He became a man of wealth, with many servants.

But for all his wealth he felt poor, because he and Sarai were still childless. He spoke to God, saying, "Oh, Lord God, what can I do with what you give me, seeing that I am without child? Yes, I am childless and a cousin of Damascus must inherit my wealth. You have given me no seed, so what do you mean when you say that a son born in my house is to be my heir?"

Abram heard the voice of the Lord answering him, "This man of Damascus shall not be your heir. He that comes forth out of your own body shall be your heir. Look up, Abram. Look now toward heaven and count the stars, if you are able to count them. That is how many your seed shall be. For I am the Lord who brought you out of Ur in the Chaldees to give you this land as an inheritance. And your sons shall inherit."

Abram said: "Make me a sign, O Lord, that I may know it is your voice I hear and not the voice of a vain dream that I have conjured out of my sleep."

The Lord said: "Your visions also come from me. It is my voice, and this is my sign: Take a cow three years old, and a she-goat three years old, and a three-year-old ram, and a turtle dove and a young pigeon, and lay them upon my altar."

Abram did so. Eagles and hawks stooped, screaming, upon the carcasses, but Abram drove them away and stood in the heat of the sun, watching for a sign. The Lord made a deep sleep fall upon Abram. A great darkness fell upon him, and the darkness was full of fear.

In the depths of that fear Abram heard God's voice saying, "You must know surely that those who spring from your seed shall be strangers in a land that is not theirs, and shall serve those who dwell there. They shall be enslaved and afflicted for four hundred years. But that nation that has enslaved them shall be judged by me. And afterward the tribes that have sprung from the sons of your sons shall come out of that land with great wealth. But you, Abram, shall go to your fathers in peace when your time comes. But that time is not yet. For I have much for you to do."

Now Abram saw a smoking furnace, huge as a mountain, gushing fire. A torch was born of that fire and floated down past his face in the darkness. The torch hovered over the altar and passed between the bodies of the animals.

Again Abram heard the Lord say: "To your seed have I given this land. From the river of Egypt called the Nile to the great river Euphrates, all this shall belong to your sons."

Sarai said to Abram: "The Lord has promised you a son. I have borne you no son, nor a daughter. I am barren. Therefore you must have your son by another woman. Take my maid Hagar, the Egyptian. Make her your second wife. If you take her who has been my handmaid and who has served me well, then I shall own some portion of the son she bears you."

"You have always been the most beautiful of women," said Abram. "Now you show yourself the most understanding."

Hagar was slender as a gazelle with great dark, brimming eyes. She had adored Abram since she was a tiny girl, and was overjoyed now to become his second wife. And she scorned Sarai, secretly at first. But when she knew that her womb had been quickened by Abram's seed, she began to treat Sarai with great disdain.

Sarai said to Abram: "Your new wife, Hagar, has grown very proud. I know that she is young and fruitful, and that I am old and barren. But I have been your wife for seventy years and cannot bear to be treated like a servant."

Abram said: "You are my only true wife, from now until the end of our days. No one else means anything to me. Hagar is yours to do with as you please."

Sarai summoned Hagar to her and said: "You think you have taken my place in my husband's heart, but it is not so. He has told me to do what I please with you."

"I don't believe it," said Hagar.

"You will have reason to believe it," said Sarai. "You deserve death for the insult you have offered me. If I refrain from killing you now, it is only because you carry my husband's child. But walk softly. Cast your eyes to the ground when you pass me, and do not speak unless I speak to you first. Or I shall flog the flesh from your bones."

Hagar did not answer, but slipped out of Sarai's sight. She knew the depth of Sarai's nature, and feared for her life. She slid into Abram's tent and stayed out of sight in that fragrant dusk. When he returned, she helped him doff his dusty robes, then washed his feet and dried them with her long hair. He accepted her attentions, but did not smile.

"Master, master, are you displeased with me?"

"You have been a foolish girl. You have been sowing mischief in my household."

"Perhaps my wits have been addled by the glory to which you have raised me. Perhaps I have conducted myself unwisely. Does such a thing merit death?"

"Who speaks of death?"

"Sarai, your wife. She threatens to kill me. Will you let her kill me, my lord?"

"You have angered her."

Then Hagar knew that she was lost. Without another word, without stopping to provide herself with food and drink, she stole away from the tents of Abram and out into the wilderness, risking starvation and prowling beasts rather than the wrath of Sarai.

She found a fountain of water in the wilderness and stopped to drink. The tracks of great animals led to the fountain, and she knew it was where lions and bears and leopards came down to drink. And she was afraid.

An angel of the Lord appeared to her. He was huge; his wings were of brass and he carried a sword. He glittered terribly in the sunlight. The girl fell to her knees. She heard a voice full of enormous music, saying, "Hagar, servant of Sarai, where are you coming from?"

"From the tents of Abram."

"Where are you going?"

"I don't know. Anywhere I find myself. I am fleeing my mistress, Sarai."

"Return to her," said the angel.

"She will kill me."

"Submit yourself to her. She will not kill you."

"I do not fear for myself, but for the child I carry."

"Fear nothing. I serve Him who rules heaven and earth. I carry His message. Obedience to His will must banish fear."

"Tell me what to do."

"Return to Sarai. Walk softly before her. You shall bear your child in her tent; a son you shall bear. You shall call him Ishmael, which means 'God hears,' because God has heard your voice in the wilderness and has answered."

"Thank you for your mercy, God Most High. Thank you, bright messenger."

The angel spoke again. "Know this, Hagar. Your son will be a wild beast of a man, enemy to everyone, and seeing enmity everywhere. And his seed shall be a numberless multitude. He shall spawn nations who shall vex the sons of Sarai."

Hagar wept with joy, and raised her voice to the Lord: "O invisible one who sees everything, I thank you. I turn my eyes everywhere, but I do not see you though you are there. Merciful and mighty God, I love you and shall do your will."

Thereupon she returned to the tents of Abram and walked modestly before Sarai. And Sarai buried her wrath.

Hagar bore Abram a son, who was named Ishmael. Abram was eighty-six years old when Ishmael was born, and he rejoiced in the birth of his son. But he wished in his heart that Sarai had been the mother of his firstborn.

The Covenant

When Abram was ninety-nine years old, God appeared to him and said: "I am the Almighty God. Walk before me and be perfect in your obedience. And I shall make a covenant with you and with your sons, who shall be numberless."

Abram saw a radiance brighter than the sun and heard the voice he hungered to hear — a voice that spoke in thunderous syllables like storm, like whirlwind, like tidal wave, then sank to leaf fall, to birdsong, to the secret whisper of his own blood.

Abram fell to the ground, hiding his face from that enormous light. He heard God say, "My covenant is with you. You shall be the father of many nations. No longer shall your name be Abram; it shall be Abraham, 'father of nations.' For you shall be fruitful. You shall spawn nations. Kings shall come of you. This covenant shall not be broken. It binds me to your seed unto the last generation. They shall inherit this land of Canaan that I have given you, and it shall be theirs forever.

"And you shall cut a token of my promise into your flesh in a place that will be a sign to your seed at the moment of conception. A male child shall be circumcised when he is eight days old and wear the sign of my covenant forever. As for Sarai, your wife, her name, too, shall be changed. Her name shall be Sarah, 'the princess,' because she shall be the mother of nations, and kings shall be born of her."

Then Abraham laughed and said to himself: How can I father a child at my age? And my wife, Sarah, who is ninety years old, how can she bear a child?

And Abraham said to the Lord: "I have one son and am too old to have another. I beg you to bless my son, Ishmael."

God said: "Your wife, Sarah, shall indeed bear you a son, whom you shall name Isaac. It is Isaac who shall inherit the covenant; his sons shall inherit this land. But I will not forget Ishmael. Twelve princes shall he father, and they shall become a strong nation. But the great inheritance belongs to Isaac, whom Sarah shall bear in a year's time."

Abraham obeyed God's word and circumcised himself and all the men of his household, and his son, Ishmael, who was thirteen years old.

Now, Abraham was grazing his flocks on the plain of Mamre, and the Lord sent three angels there. They did not appear in their own bright form, but as three travelers. They came in the heat of the day, as Abraham sat in his tent door; they were dusty and stained with travel. But Abraham immediately recognized them as coming from the Lord.

"You are welcome," he said. "Rest yourselves in the shade of this tree. My servants will bring water to wash your feet, and a bit of bread, for you must be hungry."

He hurried to Sarah and said: "We have guests, very special guests. A mighty thing is happening, but I don't know what. Prepare a small feast as quickly as you can."

Sarah kneaded three measures of her finest wheat flour and baked cakes upon the hearth. She ordered a shepherd to kill a calf and dress it. It was a young one, fat and tender, and the savor of its smoke rose to the sky as it roasted over an open fire.

Abraham and Sarah served the guests with their own hands, bringing them the roasted calf, newly baked cakes, butter, and milk. The men ate. One of them said: "Do you know who we are?"

"You come from the Lord," said Abraham. "Do you bring a message?"

"He brings His own message. We are here to prepare His coming."

Abraham and Sarah knelt to the ground before the strangers and kissed the hem of their robes. Then they hastened to bathe themselves and put on fresh garments. They came out of the tent and heard the voice of the Lord: "Abraham, your wife Sarah shall bear a son, as I have promised."

Sarah laughed in her heart and said to herself: My husband and I are very old. Shall we return to such pleasures? And will I have a child as well?

One of the strangers said: "Why does Sarah laugh when the Lord tells her she will bear a child? Is anything too hard for the Lord?"

Sarah was afraid. She said: "I did not laugh."

"You did," said the stranger. "You laughed. Therefore, the son you bear next year shall be named Isaac, meaning 'laughter.' "

Abraham believed what God had promised. Sarah wished to believe, but still doubted.

Sodom
and Gomorrah

The Lord had assembled His angels for vengeance. He said: "The evil that is being done in Sodom and Gomorrah is a stench in my nostrils. These cities must be destroyed, their abominations rooted out. But I shall speak first to Abraham, for they are his neighbors. And Abraham is a righteous man who hears my words and teaches his household to obey my will."

The Lord spoke to Abraham, saying, "Hear me, O Abraham. My two messengers, my angels — those who visited you with great tidings — they go now to the cities of the plain to see if those who dwell there practice the evil that is reported. If I know them to do such evil, then I shall let my wrath fall upon these cities, and they will turn to ash."

Abraham said: "Will you destroy the righteous along with the wicked? Suppose there are fifty good men who live there, will not the cities be spared for their sake? It is not like you, O Lord, to punish those who do good. You are the judge of all the earth. Can your judgment be other than perfect?"

The Lord said: "If I find fifty good men in Sodom, then I shall spare the city for their sake."

But Abraham answered, "Do I dare to question Almighty God, I who am but dust? If I do it is because I am what you have made me, and I have learned righteousness from you. Suppose there are only forty-five good men there instead of fifty. Will you destroy the city because it lacks five good men?"

The Lord said: "If I find forty-five good men there, I shall not destroy it."

"Suppose there are only forty?"

"I shall spare the cities for the sake of the forty."

Abraham said: "Do not be angry with me, Lord that I love, but suppose you find only thirty good men?"

"Thirty will be sufficient."

"Twenty?"

"Twenty will be sufficient."

"Spare me your wrath, Almighty God, and forgive me for bearding you in this way, but suppose you find only ten good men in these wicked cities? Must the righteous be destroyed in the same fire that consumes the wicked?"

The Lord said: "From no other man on earth would I permit such harassment. But you have walked in my ways and done my will, and I may indeed have taught you more than I knew I was teaching. This is my answer then: If I find ten good men in these abominable cities, I shall withhold my vengeance."

Abraham went back to his tent, satisfied.

Now, as the sun sank, the two angels came to Sodom and were greeted by Abraham's nephew, Lot, who dwelt there. Lot rose to greet the angels, then bowed to the ground.

"Welcome, my lords," he said. "Enter my house, I pray you, and rest yourselves. You shall wash your feet, and eat a meal, and stay the night, if you wish."

"No," said the angels. "We will stay in the streets all night."

But Lot did not wish them to spend the night in the streets. He knew his neighbors well, and knew that they would rob the strangers, then enslave and abuse them.

"I beg you not to spend the night in the streets," he said. "Come into my house and rest there."

He urged them so warmly that they came into his house, and he served them a fine meal.

As he was settling to sleep Lot heard a great clamor in the streets and rushed to the window. Torches flared, lighting the wild, slobbering faces of the men of Sodom. He heard them shouting, "Lot! Lot! Where are your guests? Bring them out!"

"No," he said.

"Bring those tall young men out and give them to us. They are as beautiful as angels. Bring them out or we shall burn your house down."

Lot went out and faced the mob, closing the door behind him. He said: "Do not do this; it is evil."

"Bring them out! Give them to us."

"I have two daughters," said Lot, "lovely young virgins. They are dearer to me than anything in the world. I shall bring them out and give them to you to do with as you please, but do not molest these strangers.

47

They are my guests. Under God's law my life is pledged to their safety."

"You're a stranger yourself," they shouted. "How dare you sit in judgment on us? Now we shall take them, and you, too. And your wife and your daughters, and do with you according to our pleasure."

The mob surged forward. Cruel hands seized Lot, and began to batter down the door. By the wavering flare of the torches the mob saw the two young men come out. They bore flaming swords, brighter than the torches. Terrible was their strength. They pulled Lot away from his captors and went back into the house, closing the door. Then they came out again and stood before the door, facing the multitude. They slashed a pattern of flame in the night air, and the air took fire. All those who watched were struck blind on the spot. The strange flame seared their eyeballs, leaving empty sockets. But so wild was their lust that they kept groping for Lot's door in their blindness, until they grew weary and crept away.

The angels said to Lot: "Call your family together — sons, sons-in-law to be, wife, and daughters. Leave the house, and leave the city. Be gone before morning breaks. Because this is the last night of Sodom and of Gomorrah. They have angered the Lord, and He has sent us to destroy them."

Lot awakened his household and said: "We must leave this house. We must leave this city, for the Lord will destroy it. His angels told me."

But his sons-in-law to be jeered at him. "You have dreamed a dream, old man, full of flames and awful threats. Go back to sleep, and let us sleep."

They slept, and Lot did not wish to leave without them. But dawn was breaking now. The last day of the city had come, and the angels did not let him linger.

"Arise!" they said. "Take your wife and your two daughters, and leave this city now."

But Lot moved slowly. The angels seized him and his wife and his two young daughters, and carried them beyond the city gates.

"Do not linger upon this plain," they said. "Get up into the hills, for the two cities will burn, and all the land that lies between them. Go now. Don't stop to look back."

But Lot fell to the ground and prayed: "O, Lord," he cried, "if I have earned grace in your sight and such great mercy, allow me one mercy more. I am afraid of the mountain and its wilderness and the beasts that prowl. I am afraid. Therefore, I pray you, let me stop at that little city halfway up the hill and dwell there. And do not destroy that little city, for it is very small."

The Lord spoke, saying, "Go to the little city and dwell there. It will be spared for your sake."

And Lot hastened toward the city, which was called Zoar. It was full day now, and very hot, although the sun was hidden by black and purple clouds. The sky was like a great bruise. Lightning seared the clouds, terrible hooks of fire flashed from sky to earth. Then it began to rain — not water, but fire. Every raindrop was a flame; where they fell, great blossoms of fire grew. In Sodom and Gomorrah the houses burned. Men and women ran screaming into the streets, clothing on fire, hair on fire. Before an hour had passed, the cities of the plain were piles of smoldering ash. And the ashes of those who had dwelt there mixed with the ash of their houses.

Lot and his daughters climbed the hill toward Zoar. They felt the heat of the fire; they heard people screaming. They did not look back. But Lot's wife, who had been unwilling to leave her home, stopped and looked back — and was immediately scorched to a deathly dryness. She turned into a pillar of salt, then crumbled away.

That day Abraham went to the place where he had stood before the Lord, and looked down upon the plain. He saw Sodom and Gomorrah burning. He saw the plain become a furnace.

The Lord spoke like thunder out of the terrible sky: "Behold, my wrath has fallen upon the wicked cities. I have blotted out those men of twisted appetite and murderous intention. But I have spared Lot and his two daughters."

"Thank you, Lord, for your mercy," said Abraham, and left that place. He never saw Lot again.

The people of Zoar were unfriendly. They knew that Lot had dwelt in Sodom, but were ignorant of the favor God had shown him and feared that the curse of Sodom still clung to him. They said: "Leave this place or we will kill you."

Lot took his daughters and climbed into the mountain, and they dwelt in a cave. It was a wilderness, a place of bears and eagles. Even hunters

feared to go there. And Lot and his daughters saw only one another. One day the elder daughter led the younger from the cave and spoke to her. "God's fire will strike Zoar," she said. "It was spared only for our father's sake, and now we are driven out. Therefore the city will be destroyed, and the young men there, and we shall have no husbands."

The younger one said: "No one can find us in this cave. We shall have no husbands, and die childless."

"I will have a child," said the elder.

"Whose?"

"My father's. He is the only man left."

"It is a sin."

"To remain barren is a worse sin. God did not spare our lives and bring us to this ripeness that we might wither away without man and without child. I will lie with my father tonight."

"He will refuse."

"We will make him drunk."

"We cannot both lie with him. He is an old man."

"I am the eldest. I will go first."

That night they gave their father strong wine to drink, and made him drunk.

Lot dreamed that he was young again, and that his wife was not dead but was with him again, as beautiful as in the days of her youth. His withering heart swelled with happiness, and he embraced her.

The next night, his daughters again gave him wine to drink until he was drunk. And again that night he dreamed that his wife had returned to him — even younger this time, as upon their wedding night. He wept tears of joy and embraced her.

Lot never knew what had happened. After those two nights of wonderful dreams he missed his wife more than ever, and died of grief before his daughters grew big with child.

The elder daughter bore a son whom she named Moab. He became the father of a nation called the Moabites.

A son was born to the younger daughter, also. She named him Ben-Ammi, and he became the father of a nation called the Ammonites.

In days to come both these nations waged bloody war against the descendants of Abraham and were defeated after inflicting terrible losses. Some say that this slaughter was a sign of God's anger at the behavior of Lot and his daughters in the cave above Zoar, and of His further displeasure with Abraham for having persuaded Him to spare Lot from the rain of fire that consumed the cities of the plain.

There was a lake of blue waters whose shore touched the plain. On the Day of Wrath the ashes of Sodom and Gomorrah fell into the lake, poisoning its waters, killing all the fish that lived there. Since that day the waters have been too bitter for any creature to live in, and are called the Dead Sea.

Another story tells that the waters were made bitter by the tears of Lot's daughters, orphaned and widowed on the same day.

In another tale the Dead Sea takes its name from the deathly salt of Lot's wife, who fell into the lake and embittered its waters forever.

The Birth of Isaac

The Lord smiled upon Abraham, and the warmth of it was like the sun, which quickens old roots until they put forth green shoots. Abraham was filled with a springtime ardor, and Sarah was like a girl again. They embraced joyously, and Sarah knew that finally, after ninety barren years, she was to bear a child.

A son was born to Abraham and Sarah. And Sarah laughed again, for Abraham was a hundred years old, and she was ninety-one.

"It is time to laugh," she said. "That we, being old, are made young again. Therefore shall the name of our son mean laughter, as the Lord has said."

The babe was named Isaac, and Abraham cut the sign of the covenant into his flesh when he was eight days old.

Sarah used no wet nurse, but suckled the child herself like a young mother. And Hagar jeered. But not in Abraham's hearing, for she knew that the old man viewed his youngest son as God's special gift and doted on him.

Isaac grew and was weaned. Abraham made a great feast to mark that day. But in the midst of the rejoicing Ishmael, son of Hagar, looked wrathfully upon his little half-brother.

Sarah said to Abraham: "I have endured the sight of Hagar these fourteen years, although I loathe her. But now she must go. I do not wish to see her mocking face again. I do not wish her son to share with my son, and to have part of your inheritance."

Abraham grieved, for he loved Ishmael. And he asked God what to do.

God said: "Do not grieve about Ishmael or about his mother. You must do now as Sarah wishes. For her son, Isaac, shall inherit your special knowledge of me. I will bless him. And that blessing shall be the destiny of the mighty nation that he shall spawn."

Abraham arose early the next morning and went to Hagar. He gave her bread and a flask of water, and told her she must depart.

"You must never return," said Abraham. "You or the boy."

She wept and pleaded, but Abraham said: "It is God's will."

"It is Sarah's will!"

"In this they are the same. Go in peace now. And fear nothing. The Lord has promised to provide for you."

Hagar wandered in the wilderness near Beersheba. It was very hot and the flask of water was soon empty. She know that they could not live in the burning desert without water, and she did not wish to see the death of her child. She put Ishmael in the shade of a bush and said: "Stay here. Rest yourself, and your thirst will be less."

"Where are you going?"

"Just over there, a short way."

"Stay with me."

"I must go over there."

She began to walk away. She stopped. She turned to look at him. She could not bear for him to die alone, and walked back to him and sat close, weeping terribly.

An angel appeared to her as he had appeared once before. The brightness of him dazzled her eyes, and she fell to earth. She heard the angel say, "Why do you not trust the word of God? When you first were in the desert, fleeing Sarah, He promised that your unborn child would grow to be a man and king of men. Wherefore do you doubt?"

"We thirst to death."

"Arise!"

Hagar looked up. The angel was gone. But where he had stood, there gushed a fountain of sparkling water.

Hagar and Ishmael dwelt near the fountain, and all that the Lord had promised came to pass.

N ow, Abraham had obeyed God all his days and enjoyed his mighty favor. He had even dared challenge Him in the matter of Sodom and Gomorrah.

"He is the best man I have ever created," said the Lord to His angels. "The strongest and the wisest. But I shall test him once again. I shall test him to the utmost limits of his strength, so that I may know what those limits are. And it shall be a measure to me forever."

God appeared to Abraham and said: "Behold, I am here."

Abraham was in the fields. He bowed to earth and said: "I listen and obey."

God said: "Take your son, your only son, Isaac, whom you love, and go to the land of Moriah. There, upon a mountain, you shall build an altar, place your son upon the altar, kill him, and give him to me as a burnt offering."

Abraham did not answer. He arose and went back to his tent. There he sat all night, sleepless, and did not answer when Sarah called or when Isaac called. But all night the boy's face burned in the darkness — a narrow keen face with great dark eyes. Abraham could not weep; the horror went too deep for tears. Why is God doing this to me? he said to himself. How can I obey Him?

Early the next morning Abraham saddled his donkey and summoned two young men. He told them to chop wood and load it on the donkey and follow him on a journey. Then he mounted Isaac on the donkey and departed, still without a word to Sarah.

They traveled for two days, and on the third day reached the hills of Moriah. Abraham said to the two young men: "Stay here with the donkey. The lad and I will go up the hill to worship."

They climbed the hill, hand in hand. It was a barren place, all rock and sand, where no trees grew. But Isaac was happy to be journeying with his father — riding a donkey, seeing new places, and now helping his father carry wood up a hill. He laughed with joy as they climbed.

At the top of the hill Abraham raised an altar. He heaped wood upon it, and set the wood on fire.

"Father," said the boy.

"I am here, my son."

"I see the wood and the fire, but where is the lamb for a burnt offering?"

Abraham said: "My son . . . God Himself will provide a lamb for the burnt offering."

Then he bound Isaac's arms and legs with thongs, and laid him on the altar. Isaac smiled up at him. He thought his father was playing a game. And Abraham, seeing him smile, choked back his tears so that the lad should not be afraid. He drew his knife.

He heard a voice say, "Abraham . . . Abraham. . . ."

"Here I am," he whispered.

"Do not lay your hand upon the boy," said the voice from heaven. "Do not harm him in any way. For now I know that you love me enough to give me your son, your only son."

Abraham lifted his eyes and saw a ram caught in a thicket by its horns. He went to the ram and slit its throat, and placed it on the altar for a burnt offering to the Lord.

The voice spoke again. "Because you have not withheld your son from me, I will multiply your seed like the stars of heaven, like the sands upon the shore. They shall prevail against their enemies, and the whole world shall be blessed in them because you have obeyed my word."

Abraham and Isaac went down the mountain and journeyed back to their tents. But Abraham never told Sarah what had happened at Moriah, nor did Isaac.

ISAAC

Isaac was now a grown man. Sarah was dead, and Abraham was ready for death. But he had one more thing to do before he died. He called his servant, Eleazer, to him, and said: "You are my oldest and most faithful friend. You have lived in my tents all your life and shared my fortune, good and bad. You are my steward in all things, and keeper of my keys. Now I require one last service of you."

"Speak your wish."

"Put your hand under my thigh."

Eleazer placed his hand under the old man's thigh. This was a token that a mighty oath was to be sworn.

Abraham said: "I wish you to swear by the Lord God, maker of heaven and earth, that you will not allow my son Isaac to take a wife from among the daughters of Canaan."

"We have dwelt here many years," said Eleazer. "You are a great man among the Canaanites."

"Nevertheless," said Abraham, "I am not of their blood, nor is Isaac. And Isaac is the inheritor. It has been promised that he will father sons who will become a mighty nation, blessed of God. Therefore, I want him to take his wife from among the daughters of my kinsmen who dwell beyond these borders. You must journey there and choose a maiden strong and beautiful — like my beloved wife, Sarah — a daughter of our own people, to be the mother of nations."

Eleazer said: "Suppose the girl is unwilling to leave her family and come into a strange land. Shall I take Isaac back to her?"

"You shall not. Isaac is not to leave Canaan. God has promised him this land, and his sons after him. You shall journey to where I was born to find a wife for my son, and God will send his angel before you to clear the way. If the maiden does not follow you back to Canaan, then she is unfit to be my son's wife, and you must find another. Do you understand?"

"I understand."

"Do you swear?"

"I swear by the Almighty God to do as you wish."

Then Eleazer kissed Abraham's hand, but Abraham arose and embraced him, for he knew he would never see his servant again.

"Farewell," said Abraham. "Choose carefully. And do not grieve that I must leave you. The Lord has blessed me and blessed my seed. I am ripe for death and He harvests my soul. And I am glad, for where I go Sarah waits."

Eleazer packed bales of silk and samite, and gold and diamonds enough to load ten camels, and departed in a rich caravan. He journeyed to a land bordering Ur, where Abraham's brothers, the sons of Terah, dwelt, and their children and great-grandchildren. He did not enter the city but stopped before its gates, where there was a fountain of water and a deep well. It was evening, and women were coming through the gates to draw water. He made his camels kneel at the well, but did not allow them to drink.

Eleazer lifted his face to the sky and said: "Lord, show me the way, that I may serve your servant, Abraham, according to his wish. Show me a sign. I shall stand at the well as the daughters of the city come to draw water. And I shall ask certain of these maidens to give me a drink, choosing only those who seem graceful and strong, and fit to be Isaac's wife. And let this be the sign: The one who will say, 'Drink, and I will draw water for your camels, also,' that one I shall know to be the one you have chosen as Isaac's wife."

No sooner had he stopped speaking than he saw a girl come through the gates who was so beautiful that, old man though he was, he felt the sap rise in his limbs. She was slender as a gazelle, with great black eyes and long black hair bound in a silver fillet. He heard her laugh among the maidens, and her laughter was like music to him. He watched her as she came to the fountain, and filled a heavy copper pitcher and lifted it to her shoulder in one easy motion. He walked to her slowly, and she watched him come, modest before a stranger but unafraid. He said: "Give me, I pray you, a little water from your pitcher."

"Drink, my lord," she said, and swung the pitcher from her shoulder, tilting it for him to drink. Her fragrance was like the night-flowering jasmine.

Oh, God, let her be the one, said Eleazer in his heart. Let her say the words I want to hear.

He drank slowly to give her time. He drank until he thought he must burst. "Thank you, sweet maiden," he said.

"Are you a stranger, my lord?"

"I come from afar."

57

"Do those camels belong to you?"

"They do."

"May I draw water for them, also, and give them to drink?"

"They are many, and they are thirsty."

"I shall be swift," she said. She ran to the well and drew water, bucket after bucket, running back and forth with the heavy buckets until the camels had drunk their fill. And Eleazer stared in wonder.

When she had finished she returned to him and said: "Your camels have drunk. They were very thirsty."

"What is your name, gentle maiden?"

"Rebecca, my lord."

"You have been kind to a stranger, Rebecca. Will your father welcome us as well? Will he give us lodging in his house?"

"He will. And lodging for your servants and straw for your camels."

"What is your father's name?"

"Bethuel."

"And his father?"

"Nahor is his name."

"Nahor, son of Terah?"

"The same, my lord."

"Nahor, whose brother was Abram?"

"My grandfather tells us tales of his brother, who is called Abraham now and has become a mighty man in Canaan."

Eleazer bowed to the ground and said: "Blessed be the Lord who has showed me the way." He arose and gave Rebecca a heavy gold bracelet and earrings of ruby and gold.

"I cannot take such gifts from a stranger," she said.

"They are not from a stranger. They are from your grandfather's brother, Abraham, who is my master, and whose servant I am."

Rebecca ran home. "Mother, Mother!" she cried. "A guest is coming. He came all the way from Canaan — from the tents of Abraham, who is my grandfather's brother. Look what he gave me!"

Rebecca had a brother, Laban, who knew the ways of the world. When he heard his sister's words and saw the golden bracelet and the earrings of ruby and gold, he ran out of his house to the city gates and beyond them to the fountain. There he saw camels and many servants, and an old man with a long white beard.

"Why do you stand here at the gates, blessed guest?" he cried. "I am

Laban, brother of Rebecca, and I have come to show you the way to my father's house, which you will honor by your visit."

Laban led Eleazer and his caravan through the city to his father's house. He helped the drivers unpack the camels, feed them, and bed them down. Then he found food and quarters for those who had come with Eleazer. He led Eleazer into the house, where Rebecca and her mother were preparing a great feast.

Water was sent for, and Eleazer's feet were washed. All this time the old man said little, but sat observing the household and all in it. Food was set before him, and he said: "I will not eat until I have told my errand."

"Speak, honored guest," said Laban. "We listen."

"I am Abraham's servant," said Eleazer. "The Lord has blessed Abraham and made him a mighty man in Canaan. Great flocks of sheep graze upon his land, and herds of fat cattle. He is served by shepherds and herdsmen and tillers of the soil, by body-servants and handmaids. He has heaped up gold and silver and precious stones; caravans of camels and donkeys carry his bales to market. He is a mighty man, and mighty among the mighty, for all seek his counsel. His wisdom has been ripened in the service of the Lord.

"Now, Abraham has a son, Isaac, born of his wife Sarah when she was very old. This son will inherit all that his father has. The Lord also promises that the sons of Isaac shall, in their turn, inherit the entire land of Canaan."

All sat in the wavering torchlight listening to the words of the old man. Their food lay untouched before them.

"Therefore," said Eleazer, "my master said to me: 'I am about to die, and I must find a wife for Isaac. She must not be a daughter of the Canaanites, who follow other gods and other ways. You, Eleazer, must go to the land where I was born and find a wife for Isaac among my kindred, who are also Sarah's kindred. Only there will you find her who will be strong enough to bear God's heavy favor, and fit to be the mother of nations.

"I said farewell to my master and journeyed here from Canaan, and stood near the well beyond the gates of your city, and watched the women and maidens thronging through the gates to draw water. I was bewildered. How could I, a stranger, find a daughter of my master's kindred among such multitudes? I begged God for a sign, saying, 'I shall ask certain maidens for a drink, those who are comely and strong. And she who, giving me a drink, offers water also to my camels, that one I shall know has been chosen by you, O God of Abraham.'

"And, lo! I was answered! No sooner had I raised my voice to heaven than I saw this maiden coming through the gates, carrying a pitcher of beaten copper upon her shoulder, and shining like a torch among the women at the well. When I asked her for a drink, she answered in the words that God had put in her mouth as the sign of His choice. And when I asked her name and her parentage, she told me what I hungered to hear, that she was the granddaughter of Abraham's brother. Therefore I am here. O my hostess, wife to Bethuel, son of Nahor, Laban, son of Bethuel, son of Nahor who is brother to Abraham, son of Terah, and blessed of God, I ask for this maiden, Rebecca, on behalf of Abraham's son, Isaac."

"How far is Canaan?"

"Many days' journey."

"How can it be that Isaac is the sole inheritor?" said Laban. "He has an elder brother."

"That one, Ishmael, is not the son of Abraham's wife Sarah, but of Hagar, the Egyptian, Sarah's handmaid. He has long since left Abraham's tents and is disinherited. Do not doubt Abraham's wealth or Isaac's inheritance. Here are some small tokens."

He clapped his hands, summoning his servants, and told them to bring the camel packs from the stable. Bale upon bale of silk and samite were borne in and heaped about Rebecca and her mother.

"Enough!" said Rebecca.

"Treasure for treasure," said Eleazer. "What I give is less than what I take."

"Truly, your words are fraught with wisdom," said Laban.

Eleazer heaped up bars of gold and silver, and small leather pouches that spilled diamonds and sapphires and rubies, until Laban was bursting with joy.

"We may not tarry," said Eleazer. "I was instructed to return straightaway to Canaan with the girl who was chosen."

"So soon?" said Rebecca's mother. "I pray you, not so soon. She is my only daughter."

"She must leave you and go to her husband," said Eleazer.

"Canaan is so far. I do not know when I shall see her again. Stay ten days."

61

"Please, Mother," said Laban. "The man knows what he is doing."

"Only ten days!"

"Let us ask the girl," said Eleazer. He turned to Rebecca, who had been sitting there, silent. "Will you follow me now, or must I seek another to be Isaac's wife?"

"I am ready," said Rebecca.

Isaac was walking on the plain, and he was full of sorrow. His father had just died and had been buried in the cave at Hebron beside Sarah. Now Isaac was alone. He went to sit in the portals of Sarah's tent, which Abraham had never taken down, although she had been dead for many years. Sitting there, he seemed to see his mother again, and to hear her. He saw the brilliance of her eyes, felt her touch upon his hair, and heard her laughter. He bowed his head and wept.

Then he saw a boiling of dust on the plain, as of a caravan coming, and went to meet it. From afar he recognized his father's camels, which were his now. He saw the white beard of Eleazer and, riding a camel next to the old man, a maiden veiled against the dust. He stood watching.

The camels came near. The girl raised her hand and flung back the veil. There in the dust and fiery shadows he saw his mother, Sarah, alive again, but young, younger than he had ever known her, young as his father's memories and the tales of her beauty. For Rebecca's great black eyes, her floating hair, the brilliance of her smile were very like Sarah's, but also strange and for the first time.

Isaac knelt in the dust. "Thank you, God, for what you have sent me," he said. And he arose to claim his bride.

Isaac was rich, possessing flocks and herds, gold and silver and precious stones, caravans of camels and donkeys, and many servants to do his bidding. Nor did he busy himself to increase his wealth, for Eleazer was his steward in all things, his man of business. And there was no man shrewder than Eleazer. Rebecca was Isaac's sole occupation; he loved her beyond his own knowledge, and she returned his love. And they were all in all to each other — for they had no children.

Isaac raised his voice to heaven. "God Almighty, God of Abraham, the one God, maker of heaven and earth, I am not the man my father was, and do not hold easy converse with you. But my wife, Rebecca, is barren. She grieves because we are childless. I do not understand how this can be, for you made a covenant with my father that my sons would inherit this land. That sign was cut into my flesh when I was eight days old. Have I misunderstood your intention, O Lord? If so, I pray, enlighten your servant."

God spoke: "Your mother was barren until she was ninety. She knew how to wait. Your father knew how to wait. Rebecca is young."

"She grieves, being childless."

"Go to her tonight."

That night Isaac planted a seed in Rebecca's womb, and that seed quickened into life. She grew very big; her belly swelled to a size never seen, and she was in great pain.

"Twins," said the old midwife. "Perhaps more. And they are wrestling in there, causing you this pain."

Rebecca feared for her life and inquired of the Lord, who answered, "Two nations are in your womb, and two peoples shall be separated from your body. One people shall be stronger than the other. The elder shall serve the younger."

The struggling infants almost tore Rebecca apart, but she clenched her teeth and uttered few moans, for the Lord had told her she was to live, and she did not wish Isaac to know her pain. She labored a day and a night in great agony, and delivered twins. The first one came out with a pelt of red hair like a fox cub. And, holding onto his brother's heel in a way never before seen came the second twin, all clean and unmarked. They called the first child Esau and the second one Jacob. And from the first sight of him Rebecca loved Jacob best. She tried to hide her feeling, but the thing was known.

Esau grew into a hairy, merry young man, blazing with energy — a great hunter, a great meat eater, great in all his appetites. His brother, Jacob, was very different. Jacob was a quiet, reflective man, who tended his father's herds. He learned about cattle from a master herdsman hired by Eleazer — an islander of the Inner Sea who had been ship-wrecked on the shore of Canaan, a squat, sullen fellow who looked something like a bull himself and had knowledge beyond any man's of bull and kine. Working with him, Jacob learned how to cull the herd of weaker stock, and he learned secret tricks of breeding to make cows drop certain kinds of calves. He also learned the best ways of pasturing and watering the herds and keeping them in health.

Now, Isaac had become something of a glutton, and he loved Esau best because the lad brought him his kill, venison and wild boar. But Rebecca's love for Jacob was as fresh as when he was at her breast, sucking less greedily than Esau.

One evening Jacob was before his tent, boiling a pot of lentils over a fire of twigs. And Esau came in from the hunt, carrying a deer slung over his shoulders. He was ravenous, for it had been a long chase. Too hungry to wait until he had roasted the venison, he snatched the pot from the fire. But Jacob snatched it back and said: "It is mine."

"Brother, I want it," cried Esau. "Let me eat the pottage, the red pottage, before I die of hunger!"

"What will you give me for it?"

"What do you want?"

"Your birthright."

Now, birthright in those days meant all that the eldest son would inherit from his father by sole virtue of being firstborn. Its advantages were almost sacred. In rich families the firstborn son inherited wealth beyond the wealth of any of his brothers, not only flocks and herds, gold and silver, but possession of any high office the father held, and of the father's interest in lease and treaty.

Jacob had long chafed at the idea that he, born two seconds after his brother, would inherit less. Now he saw his chance.

"If you want my pot of lentils you must sell me your birthright."

"Take it! Give me the pottage. What good is a birthright if I starve to death?"

"Not so fast," said Jacob. "Swear first."

"I swear, I swear," said Esau, seizing the pot and swallowing the red lentils in one gulp. Then he ate a loaf of bread, drank some wine, and went away.

Beersheba

There was famine in the land, and Isaac prepared to go down into Egypt, where there was food. He inquired of the Lord concerning this.

God answered, "Do not leave this land, for I have given it to you and your sons forever."

64

"The land is stricken, O Lord," said Isaac. "My flocks are wasted because no grass grows. The grass has perished because no rain falls, and the wells are dry."

"Do not go into Egypt," said the Lord. "Your son's sons will go into Egypt and abide there in bitter servitude, and come forth again — but the time is not yet. Send your men to dig."

"My men dig deep into the earth and find no water," said Isaac.

"Send your men to dig again where they have dug. Let them return to the southern plain, to the dry wells, and dig again. I am the Lord. My footfall is thunder, my frown is famine. Shall not fountains gush at my pleasure?"

Isaac sent his herdsmen south. They grumbled, saying, "The earth is dry as stone there. Our master grows old, and his wits are enfeebled."

But Isaac rode with them, harrying them day and night, until they reached the dry wells. "Dig here," said Isaac.

"To what purpose?" said the chief herdsman. "Hearken. I drop a stone and you hear it rattling against the stones at the bottom."

"Here you shall dig," said Isaac. "The Lord has promised that we will find water in the dry wells."

"Our bones will whiten on these sands before we find water."

"Then whiten they must. Shall not He who hung the sun and lit the stars and made man from a handful of dust — shall not He, the Almighty God, squeeze water from a rock if He wishes? Dispute me no more. Dig or die!"

The men began working without hope. Their shovels struck rock. The sun beat down on their heads, and they grew very weary. But Isaac stood above them, arms raised to the sky, beard bristling, eyes glittering, and made them dig without rest.

Deep in the hole, deeper than a well had ever been dug before, a man was digging. His shovel struck rock. And with his last strength, with all the rage of his thirst, and his hatred of Isaac, he struck again — and felt his burning head laved, as a fountain of living water sprang from the rock.

The men raised a great shout of joy and scooped up water in their hands, drinking and splashing and laughing. They dug a trough, which filled with cool water, and the cattle rushed to drink.

"Thank you, God," said Isaac. And he named the place Beersheba, meaning "well of the vow."

The Lord was pleased with Isaac, and famine was lifted from the land. Rain fell, grass grew, the flocks fed. Isaac prospered in all things. His herds increased. And he became a man of greater wealth than his father, Abraham.

Esau was forty years old and took two wives. Both of them were daughters of the Hittites, who followed other gods and other ways. And these ways offended Isaac and Rebecca, whose hearts were filled with bitterness.

But Isaac still preferred the red-headed hunter, Esau, who brought him fresh meat for his table. Rebecca still loved best her other son, the quiet smooth Jacob. Now, Isaac had grown very old; he was feeble and almost blind. He called Esau to him and said: "I am grown old, Esau. The day of my death is coming swiftly, when I do not know. But before I die I want to eat once more of the savory venison you have always brought me — that I may feel nourished by your abundant love, O son of my heart. So take your bow and your quiver of sharp arrows and hunt. Kill me a deer and roast its haunch. I will feast upon it, and bless you."

Now, Rebecca had been on her way to Isaac's tent and heard voices inside. She stopped at the portal and listened. When she heard what Isaac said, she turned and hurried away. She went swiftly to Jacob's tent and said: "Your father has sent Esau into the forest to hunt. When he returns with a deer and roasts it, he will be blessed by your father and receive his inheritance."

"My father loves him best," said Jacob.

"I love you best," said Rebecca.

"I must be content with that," said Jacob. "My father is the bestower of blessings and legacies."

"It must not be!"

"It will be."

"No, I say! No! The inheritance must be yours. That hairy glutton despised his birthright and sold it to you for a meal. He cannot regain it now. And he shall not, if you obey me."

"What do you want me to do?"

"Go among the flocks. Select two kids, the fattest and tenderest, and bring them to me. I shall roast them to a perfect savor, basting them in their own fat and spicing them with pepper and marjoram and wild thyme the way he loves. And you shall bring your father this meal and receive his blessing before Esau returns."

"He will wait for what Esau brings."

"He will get hungry, waiting, and the smell of the roasted meat will fuddle his wits. He will think you are Esau bringing venison."

"His sight fails, but not his touch. He will caress me, thinking me Esau. But I am smooth and Esau is hairy, and so my father will know what is being done. He will not bless but curse me."

"Let the curse fall on me," said Rebecca. "Just do what I say and you will inherit."

Jacob went into a field where goats were cropping grass and caught two fat kids. He cut their throats and brought them to his mother, who skinned and dressed them, then roasted them on a spit over an open fire, basting them in their own fat and spicing them with marjoram and wild thyme. She built her cooking fire upwind of Isaac's tent so that the savory smoke drifted down to him. He was frantic with hunger by the time the meat was roasted.

While the meal was being cooked, Jacob went to Esau's tent, and, as Rebecca had bidden, took Esau's garments from a chest and dressed himself in his brother's clothes. Then Rebecca took the hairy goatskins and covered Jacob's arms and the backs of his hands, and wrapped one about his smooth neck. She gave him a platter of smoking meat and said: "Go to him, and do as I have told you."

Isaac was sitting in his tent, seeking its cool shadows against the heat of the day as he waited for Esau to return. He knew it was too soon for Esau to have caught a deer, but his hunger made him impatient. Then he heard someone coming. He heard the portals of his tent being drawn aside. He heard a voice say, "Father. . . ."

"Here I am. Who are you?"

"I am Esau, your eldest son."

"Are you Esau?"

"I have brought you what you wanted, a haunch of fresh-roasted venison. Come and eat . . . and bless me."

"You killed quickly, very quickly."

"He was a young buck, fair and prime, and very fleet of foot. But I knew how hungry you were, and God guided my arm. I felled him with my first arrow. . . . Why do you not eat? Are you not hungry?"

"Starved . . . and confused, my son. My eyes are dim, and I cannot see. Come close that I may touch you."

Jacob came to his father and knelt before him. The old man strained his eyes; all he could see was a blur. But he smelled the odor of Esau's garments, a special fragrance to him — of horse and woodsmoke, sunshine and crushed grass. His fingers groped slowly over the young man's face and neck, down his arms. He grasped Jacob's wrist and stroked the back of his hand.

"The voice is the voice of Jacob," he said. "But the hands are the hands of Esau."

"Shall I serve the meat, Father?"

"Are you truly the son of my heart?" he murmured. "Are you he, my brave one, my bowman, of red rage and golden laughter, master of the chase? Are you my son, my furry one, fragrant of woodsmoke, the wild red Esau?"

"I am he," said Jacob.

"Bring me the meat," said Isaac. "I shall eat. And when I have eaten I shall bless you."

"Here is meat, Father. And wine. Eat, I pray you, and drink."

Isaac ate heavily, and drank up the flagon of wine. "Come here and kiss me," he said.

Jacob came and kissed him. Isaac touched the back of his hands again, stroking the hairy goatskin.

"I bless you, firstborn," he said. "And bequeath to you the special favor that the Lord showed to my father, Abraham, and to me afterward. Keeper of the covenant you shall be, inheritor of this land and father of nations."

"Do you bless me, Father?" murmured Jacob. "Do you bless him who kneels before you now?"

"I bless the son who kneels before me now. For the smell of him is the smell of a field that the Lord has blessed. May God give you of the dew of heaven and the fatness of earth, and plenty of corn and wine. People shall serve you and nations bow down to you. You shall be lord over your brothers, and your mother's sons shall bow down to you. Cursed be the one who curses you, and blessed be he who blesses you."

"Thank you, Father," said Jacob.

He arose, took platter and flagon, left the tent, and went to his mother.

Isaac fell asleep but slept uneasily and dreamed. In his dream he

69

heard the sound of a huntsman returning, the clamor of hounds, and the jingle of harness. It seemed to him that he heard the bawling, laughing voice of his son, Esau, shouting, "I am here, Father! Arise and eat!"

Isaac's soul quaked within him, and he tried to sink deeper into sleep and change his dream. But the shouting came closer, "Father! Father!" It was Esau's laughing voice. Isaac heard running footsteps, and the latchets of his tent being thrust aside, and a voice crying, "Father!" He leaped from his couch and stood trembling, knowing it was no dream but Esau returned from the hunt.

"Father," said the voice, "I am home from the hunt. I killed you a buck, fat and fine. Here is his haunch all roasted and hot. And a flagon of cool wine."

"Who are you?" whispered Isaac.

"Who am I? I am Esau; who else could I be? Esau, your firstborn."

"Are you Esau?" said Isaac. "Then who was it who brought me roasted meat and served it to me and poured out wine — and waited until I had eaten and drunk, and knelt before me and received my blessing? Who was it?"

"Not I," said Esau. "I am just home from the wood."

"Who was it?" cried Isaac angrily. "Who came wearing your clothes and feeling like you to the touch but speaking with Jacob's voice? Who dared?"

"It was Jacob," shouted Esau. "He tricked you."

"Then I curse him!" cried Isaac. "No! I cannot! I blessed him before heaven, and swore the great oath, and bound him to God's covenant. It is God's own special favor, not bestowed by me, but passing through me. I cannot retract the blessing. Only God can do that. I have been deceived, Esau. And you have been tricked out of your inheritance."

Esau beat himself upon the head and cried a loud and bitter cry. "Bless me, Father! Bless me, too!"

"How can I? Your brother came and took the blessing meant for you."

"He has tricked me twice," said Esau. "He took my birthright, and now he takes my blessing."

"We both sold ourselves for a meal," said Isaac. "Our appetite was his profit."

"Did you give him all your blessing, Father? Did you keep nothing for me?"

"Behold," said Isaac, "I have made him your master and have appointed his brothers to serve him. I have given him first call upon the rain of heaven and the crops of earth, grain for bread and grapes for wine. What shall I give you, Esau, beloved son?"

"Have you only one blessing, Father? Bless me! Bless me, too, for I cannot live without it." And Esau wept.

Isaac said:"The wild places of earth shall be your dwelling, and the great spaces. Horses shall be yours, and swift camels, and a warrior's heart and a hunter's joy. You shall live by the sword, serving your brothers. But, one day, you shall break free and shake off the yoke. This is all I can give you now. Take it, Esau, and my entire love."

The old man bowed his head and wept. Esau took him into his arms and they embraced. Isaac stood wrapped in the fragrance of horse and woodsmoke and sunshine and crushed grass, and wept bitterly for all that was lost.

JACOB

Now Esau's laughter was heard no more among the tents. He looked wrathfully upon Jacob and turned his face from his mother. It was reported to Rebecca that he had said: "Jacob shall not live to enjoy his inheritance. I will kill him with my own hands."

Whereupon Rebecca sent for Jacob and said: "You must leave this place. Flee the land."

"Why, Mother?"

"Esau has promised to kill you. And he is a man of his word. Go to my brother, Laban, and dwell in Haran."

"How long must I stay?"

"Until your brother's wrath has cooled. His rage is terrible, but he forgets. I shall send for you as soon as he has forgotten his grievance. But leave now, today!"

Then Rebecca went to Isaac and said: "I am sickened by the sight of those Hittite wives of Esau. If Jacob takes a daughter of Canaan, I shall want to die."

"He must marry," said Isaac.

"Let him do as you did. Let him go to Haran for his wife. My brother, Laban, has daughters."

Isaac sent for Jacob, and said: "I do not wish you to take a wife from among the daughters of Canaan. Go to Haran, to the house of Laban, and take a wife there."

"I shall do so," said Jacob.

"God Almighty bless you and make you fruitful," said Isaac. "May your seed multiply and inherit this land that was promised to Abraham."

Jacob mounted his camel and departed. Rebecca watched him ride away across the sandy plain. She watched until he disappeared. She did not weep; her face was like stone.

Word came to Esau that his brother had gone north to find a wife among Rebecca's kindred. Esau said to himself: "It is by my choice of wives that I have displeased my mother. Now I know how to please her. I, too, shall find a wife from among my kindred."

He went into the desert, to a wild place, to the tents of Ishmael, who was Isaac's brother, Abraham's son by Hagar. Ishmael was a warrior, a rider of swift horses, a raider of caravans. There was love between the outlaw, Ishmael, and the wild red Esau. And Esau took one of Ishmael's daughters to be his wife. But his parents were displeased by this, also.

Jacob went northward from Beersheba toward Haran. The sun was setting. There were no trees; it was a barren place. He chose a stone to be his pillow and lay down to sleep. He dreamed. A ladder of fire was flung across the blackness; it reached from earth to sky. Its sidepieces were fire, its rungs were bars of fire, and it was taller than a mountain. A throng of bright angels were on the ladder, going up and down.

A voice spoke out of the sky: "I am the Lord, God of Abraham, and God of Isaac. The land you lie on I give to you and to your seed. And your seed shall be as the dust of the earth; you shall spread abroad to the west and to the east, and to the north and to the south, and in you and in your seed all the families of earth shall be blessed. Behold, I am with you, and will go with you and guard your way. And I will bring you again into this land, and will not leave you until I have done what I have said."

Jacob awakened and was filled with fear. "Was it God's own ladder, and God's own voice, or all just a dream?" he said to himself. "How do I know? How can I tell?" And he muttered to himself, "This is a dreadful place. Can this be God's own house? Are these the gates of heaven?"

He took the stone he had used as a pillow and raised it upon its end, making it an altar. He poured oil on the altar stone.

"I will call this place Beth-el, 'the house of God,' " he said. "And perhaps it is. The voice in the night promised many things. . . .We shall see. If God will go with me and guard my way, and give me food to eat and clothes to wear; if He will bring me back to my father's house in safety, then I will take this God as my God. I will come back to this place and build a temple where the stone now stands. And a tenth, yes, a tenth part of all that God gives me, I will give back to him."

Jacob mounted his camel and journeyed eastward into Haran.

Jacob rode eastward until he reached a grassy plain where cattle grazed. There was a well there; its mouth was covered by a large rock. Jacob spoke to the herdsmen: "Of what place are you?"

"We are of Haran."

"Who is your master?"

"Laban is his name. This is his herd, and we are his herdsmen."

Laban's Daughters

"Does he not have sheep, as well?"

"He has a flock. His daughter drives it. She brings it here each day at noon. Rachel is her name. And who are you, young stranger, who come with questions?"

"I am Jacob, Laban's kinsman from Canaan."

Jacob waited in the field for Rachel. At last he saw a mass of jostling sheep being driven by a tall maiden brandishing a staff, whistling to the dogs. His heart turned over. For she was tall like the daughters of Terah, tall and free-striding and beautiful as the old tales of Sarah, beautiful as his first memory of Rebecca. When she came closer he saw that her eyes were not black like Rebecca's, but the color of the gem called chrysoprase, which is a strange green, a living green, its blue flecking with yellow lights as you watch. And he was as delighted with the difference as with the resemblance.

He stood before her and said: "You are Rachel, daughter of Laban. I am Jacob, son of Isaac. My mother is Rebecca, your father's sister."

She laughed with pleasure and embraced him, crying, "We are kindred. Our house is yours." And Jacob wept for joy.

He rolled the stone off the well and drew water for the sheep. Rachel worked with him, spilling the water into the trough that the animals might drink. Jacob saw that she was as graceful as a young tree and as strong as a shepherd lad. His mouth was parched and he drank deeply from the well. Still he felt a burning thirst. He knew that water could not quench his thirst; he burned for the girl.

Rachel ran home to tell her father the news, and he came out to meet Jacob. Laban embraced the young man and said: "You are my sister's son, of my bone and my flesh. Enter, I pray you, and dwell in my house."

Now, Laban had two daughters. Rachel was the younger; her sister was named Leah. And Leah, the elder sister, was less comely. She had squinted eyes and a timid manner. She looked upon Jacob secretly, and blushed and stammered when he spoke to her. But Jacob thought only of Rachel.

Jacob dwelt in Laban's house for a month. He went to the fields each day to tend the herds, for he saw that they were slackly managed. Rachel went each day to the field at noon, driving her sheep, attended by dogs. Flock and herd grazed the same field under the burning sun, and Jacob and Rachel worked together, drawing water from the well and spilling it into the trough. Each day he fell more and more in love with the tall maiden. And she returned his love.

Jacob took great pains with Laban's cattle, calling upon all his special lore to improve the herd. After a month's time the cattle had lost their scrawniness and grown sleek and fine — all of which Laban observed.

One day Jacob said to him: "I love Rachel. I want her for my wife."

"She is my treasure," said Laban. "And her beauty has not escaped notice, I assure you. Rich merchants have offered for her, and princes of the land. Gold and silver have they offered, and more besides. What can you offer?"

"My father is a prince in Canaan, and a man of great wealth. And I shall inherit."

"You have an elder brother, do you not?"

"We are twins. In matters of twinship there is some dispute about who is firstborn. My father has decided in my favor. I shall inherit."

"But your father is alive, and we all want God to grant him years."

"We do," said Jacob. "And He did. My father is a very old man, as you know. However, I can offer you wealth in another form — my skill with cattle, which you have observed. I will serve you seven years for Rachel, and increase your stock twentyfold."

Laban looked at him silently; his eyes gleamed through folds of skin like a turtle's. "There are things more important than money," he said in his grating voice that was like a key turning in a lock. "Kinship is one. I accept your offer, Jacob, because you are my sister's son, and have become like a son to me. Did you say seven years?"

"Seven. . . Father."

"So be it. At the end of seven years Rachel is yours. Do you think I should hire that field east of the well?"

"You will need it," said Jacob. And he ran out of the room to look for Rachel.

For seven years Jacob served Laban as master herdsman, and there was great increase among the cattle. They grew sleek and fat and fetched high prices at the market. Each day Rachel went to the fields, driving her sheep, and they grazed their flocks together. The seven years passed like a week of days because Jacob was so much in love.

At the end of seven years, Jacob went to Laban and said: "It is seven years. I claim my bride."

"So be it," said Laban.

Laban prepared a great feast for Rachel's wedding. All the wealthiest men of Haran were invited, and their wives and grown children. Calves and oxen were roasted whole in great pits, and lambs and fat young goats. Strong wine was served by the barrel. There was music of harp and psaltery, and as they gorged on the rich food, the guests watched jugglers and acrobats and dancing girls. Such feasting and revelry had never before been seen in Haran. All day the guests caroused and far into the night. Then Jacob looked at Laban, who nodded, smiling. Jacob slipped away from the feast and went to his chamber.

It was the custom at that time for the bride to be led to the groom by her father, to be taken to the wedding chamber in utter darkness, and be given into her husband's bed. After the feast, Jacob entered the chamber, snuffed the candle, and waited upon the bed in utter darkness. He heard the heavy footsteps of Laban and the quick light steps of a maiden. Then he heard the door close, and the heavy footsteps going away, and the rustle of garments falling on the floor.

"Rachel," he whispered.

She answered nothing, but he smelled the fragrance of her hair. A hand touched his face. He took his bride in his arms.

When he awoke, he looked at the face next to his in the gray light. And it was not the face of Rachel, but of Leah.

He sprang to his feet, roaring in anger. Leah clutched at him, but he pulled away, flung on a single garment, and stormed out of the room, seeking Laban. He searched through the house and found Laban in the counting room, counting money. He seized Laban by the beard, crying, "Liar! Cheat! Where is Rachel?"

Laban was a very strong man. He thrust aside Jacob's hands and said: "Peace, my son. I do not mean to cheat you."

"Do you do it without meaning to? Did you not bring Leah to my chamber in the darkness, and usher her into my bed that I might give her what I owe my bride? And in the morning, who do I see lying next to me? Not my beloved Rachel, but that blinking simpleton, Leah."

"Do not speak so of your wife," said Laban.

"She is not my wife, coming like a thief in the night with another's garments and another's scent. She stole from her sister in the cheating darkness."

"Even as you stole from your brother," said Laban. "I have heard the tale of the inheritance."

"This shall be a darker tale when I finish telling it," said Jacob. "All men shall know you for a liar and a cheat. Your sister, Rebecca, shall curse you."

"No," said Laban.

"Did you not promise me Rachel? Did I not work seven years for her?"

"And you shall have her. But you must take Leah first."

"Never!"

"It is our custom," said Laban. "The younger sister cannot wed before her elder sister. Be kind, Jacob. Take pity on the woman. She is past her ripeness and pining for a child. Without one she will wither and die. Give her a week's husbandly service, then take Rachel. And cherish Rachel, and be merciful to Leah."

"Two for the price of one?" said Jacob. "Or perhaps you want me to work another seven years?"

"Why not?" said Laban. "I am a man of wealth. Of flocks and herds and wide grazing lands. Gold and silver have I laid up, also. And what is mine may be yours."

"You were not so prosperous before I came," said Jacob. "Twentyfold have I increased your flocks, and you know it."

"I know it," said Laban. "God smiles upon your labors. Why else would I want you as my son and the husband of my daughters? Take thought, Jacob. You will be as my eldest son and inherit everything here — with no one to dispute your claim. Incidentally, I hear that Esau still bears his grievance."

"So be it," said Jacob. "A week with Leah, then I want Rachel — and no more tricks!"

"And you will stay another seven years?"

"It seems to be God's will," said Jacob. "He also works in darkness."

In a week's time Jacob took Rachel to his chamber and sent Leah away. He loved Rachel with all the love that was in him. But she did not conceive. The Lord saw that Leah was despised and pitied her. Jacob wanted a son and visited Leah, and God opened her womb. But Rachel remained barren.

Leah bore a child and cried, "Behold, a son!" She said: "The Lord has seen my suffering and made my husband love me." She named the child Reuben, meaning "Behold, a son."

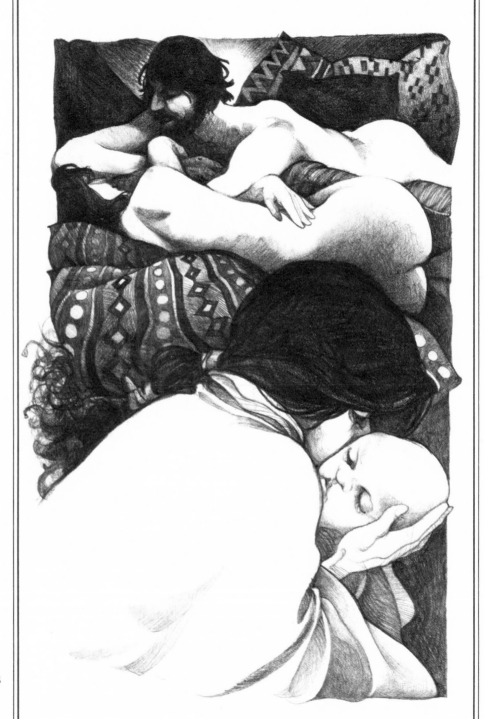

But Jacob did not change. He loved only Rachel, and visited Leah rarely. Yet the next year she bore another son and said: "The Lord has heard me." She named this one Simeon, meaning "to hear."

Jacob loved Rachel with a great love, but Leah gave him sons. In the third year she bore a third son whom she named Levi, meaning "joined," for she hoped that her fruitfulness would make her husband love her and join his life to hers.

But Jacob could not love Leah; he loved Rachel alone, and visited her sister only when God goaded him to get sons. Leah ripened again under God's pity and bore a fourth son. When she saw him she said: "Praise God who makes me fruitful!" And she named him Judah, meaning "praise."

Now, Jacob was torn in two. God was leading him on a dark and twisted journey, and he was following His light without understanding His purpose. Jacob did not know that he had been brought to Haran to beget sons. He welcomed these sons, but he could not love them as he wanted to, because they were not Rachel's.

Rachel knew that Jacob was torn and felt herself being ripped apart. She said to him: "They say birth pains are the worst pains a woman can suffer, but I tell you, this barren agony is worse. Give me a child, or I shall die."

"What else can I do?" cried Jacob in a rage. "Am I God Almighty who opens wombs or closes them at his pleasure?"

"Listen, my beloved," said Rachel. "There is a way. Not the best way, but a thing that has been done. Your grandmother, Sarah, did it when she was barren. She sent Abraham to her handmaiden, Hagar, who gave him the son he wanted."

"That son was Ishmael," said Jacob, "the outlaw Ishmael, driven into the desert by Sarah, along with his mother. I know that tale well. It is full of jealousy, rage, and vengeance."

"The case is different," said Rachel. "Sarah changed after she bore a son herself. But I am barren and may remain so. And I want a child so badly that I shall enact the ancient rite of foster mothering. Go to Bilhah, my handmaiden. Plant your seed in her. When her time comes I shall be with her and imitate her labor and feel her pains. She will bear the child on my knees. I shall feel a part of this birth, and it will save me from grieving myself to death. Go tonight."

"So be it," said Jacob.

79

He visited the chamber of Bilhah, who was a spirited wench, healthy as a heifer, and very willing to please both husband and wife in this matter. She conceived and bore a son. Rachel imitated her labor and shared her pain, and she bore her child on Rachel's knees.

Rachel said: "God has judged me and has given me a son." She named him Dan, meaning "judgment."

Now Jacob stopped visiting Leah altogether, and Rachel rejoiced. She knew that if he could beget sons elsewhere, he would neglect Leah completely. Therefore she urged him to visit Bilhah again. He did so. Bilhah conceived, and bore another son the same way.

Rachel said: "I have wrestled with my sister and prevailed." She named the child Naphtali, or "wrestling."

Then Leah said to Jacob: "How can I bear sons if you do not come to me?"

"You have borne four sons," said Jacob.

"Your neglect has left me half-dead," said Leah. "Don't kill me altogether. Embrace my handmaid, Zilpah, if you cannot embrace me. And I shall know that I am of some use, and have the courage to go on."

Jacob visited Zilpah, and she bore a son. Leah said: "Another son! A troop!" She named him Gad, meaning "troop."

Now, Gad was a very sturdy boy, and Jacob knew that he would need warrior sons, also. So he visited Zilpah again, and she bore him another son. Leah cried: "A son again! I am happy!" She named him Asher, meaning "happy."

Rachel hungered for a child of her own and sought out old wives, asking them for charms and potions. One old woman told her of the magic plant, mandrake, which has roots like little arms and legs and, when pulled out of the earth, makes a sound like a child crying. This plant, the old wife told her, made young wives fruitful — but it was very hard to find.

Rachel spent long hours in the fields searching for the mandrake, but she did not find it.

Now, Leah knew what her sister was doing and told Reuben to go to the field for mandrake.

"Mandrake, Mother?" cried Reuben, laughing, for he was a merry lad. "Do you wish to be more fruitful than you are? How many brothers must I have?"

"Do not jest," said Leah. "Go."

The men were harvesting wheat. Reuben went with them as they harvested, and searched the ground where they had passed. Reuben was red-headed like Esau, and, like Esau, had a hunter's eye. He spotted two mandrakes and pulled them, screaming thinly, from the ground. He took them home to his mother.

Then Leah said to Zilpah, her handmaid: "Gossip with my sister's maid, Bilhah. Let it drop that Reuben has found a mandrake."

Zilpah did so, and Bilhah ran to Rachel, crying, "Mistress, mistress, Reuben has found a mandrake!"

Rachel went to Leah and said: "I have never asked you for anything, but I do now. Give me, I pray, the mandrake that your son has found."

"You do not ask," said Leah. "You take. You took my husband. You shall not have my mandrake."

"Please."

"Beg and plead all you like. You shall not have it."

"I must have it. I'll give you something you want."

"You have nothing I want."

"I have everything you want. I have Jacob. He is entirely mine, but I will let you have him for a little while if you give me the mandrake."

This was a bitter thing for Leah to hear. But she wanted Jacob so much that she listened.

"Well," said Rachel, "make up your mind. Your mandrake will hire my husband for three nights."

Two desires wrestled in Leah: to have Jacob, and to deny Rachel. But a thought came to her: "When he visits me, I conceive. If I bear thrice more — and she remains barren despite the mandrake — then he will know that no charm can make her ripe and may begin to love me, the mother of sons."

"Take the mandrake," said Leah. "And see to it that you keep your part of the bargain."

Leah was visited by her husband that night, and she conceived. She bore a son and named him Issachar, meaning "hire." Rachel remained barren.

Jacob visited Leah again, according to agreement; again she conceived. And again she bore a son. "I am a despised bride," she said. "But God has given me a rich dowry. Jacob will surely dwell with me now that I have given him six sons." She named this one Zebulun, meaning "dwell."

81

Jacob visited Leah again on the third of the appointed nights. She conceived. The child she bore this time was a girl. Leah did not love this one; not because it was a girl but because it was beautiful and reminded her of Rachel. "God has judged me for bribing Rachel with the mandrake," she said to herself. She named the girl Dinah, meaning "judged."

But Jacob's love never swerved from Rachel, though she bore him no child. They cherished each other as in their first days together.

Then God pitied Rachel and opened her womb. In wonder and joy she told Jacob that she had conceived, and he wept for happiness. She labored and bore a son — a beautiful child with skin like a sun-warmed apricot and his mother's gem-green eyes. And Jacob who had sired ten sons now knew for the first time the wild protective strength of true fatherhood. His ten sons together counted for less to him than this last son who was Rachel's.

"God has taken away my reproach," said Rachel. "A son of our own has been added to our love by our love." She called the boy Joseph, meaning "added."

By this time Jacob had served Laban for fourteen years. He went to Laban and said: "It is time to leave. I will take my wives and children and go back to Canaan."

"So soon?"

"Soon? Fourteen years?"

"Too soon," said Laban. "I still need your labor, and you need my wage. If you leave now you shall take nothing — except two wives, two handmaids, eleven sons, and a daughter, all of whom will have to be fed on the long journey. How will you feed them?"

"Do you mean that after fourteen years you will pay me nothing out of that flock that I have increased fiftyfold?"

"You have had your wage," said Laban. "Leah was your wage for the first seven years, Rachel for the next seven years. That was the agreement. I promised nothing else."

"My children are your grandchildren," said Jacob. "Would you let them starve?"

"If their father chooses to leave them in need, what is a grandfather to do? A father's will prevails. Come now, be sensible. You have worked off your bride fees. Now work for a wage. I will pay you generously."

"Forgive me, Laban, but I do not trust your generosity. If you wish me to work for you one day more, we must have an exact and binding agreement."

"Speak, then. What do you want?"

"With God's help I will increase your flocks and herds as I have before. Give me half the increase."

"Half? Equal shares? Impossible."

"A third."

"Out of the question. How about one in every hundred of the increase? If you work diligently and stay lucky, you can leave here after some years with a nice little flock of your own."

"Laban, farewell," said Jacob. "Tomorrow I take my wives and children and leave for Canaan. God brought me here and will take us back."

The old man fixed Jacob with his tortoise eyes. Jacob looked back at him. They stood in the field among the goats staring at each other. Finally Jacob spoke: "Here is my last offer. It means a certain risk for both of us, but much more for me. Go with your men among your sheep, your goats, and your cattle. Separate all those that are spotted or speckled or striped or parti-colored, leaving me only those of solid color, and these are the flocks I shall tend. Now, when the time comes for me to go I shall take as my wage only those of the increase that are spotted or speckled or streaked or parti-colored."

Laban pondered this, head bent. He was a merchant, a man of the counting house. His herds and flocks had always been tended by others. But it seemed to him that Jacob was making a very bad bargain for himself. For the young of animals, even more than those of humans, resemble their parents.

Laban smiled. "So be it," he said. "I am being less than prudent, I know. But I am simply unable to control these impulses of generosity, when confronted by the demands of kinship."

He called his men, and they went through the flocks of sheep and goats and the herds of cattle, cutting out those who were speckled or spotted or streaked or parti-colored, and drove them off, leaving Jacob only with those of solid color.

What Jacob knew and Laban did not was that the mating of solid-colored stock will usually produce parti-colored offspring if sire and dam are of different colors. So Jacob took the white bulls to serve black cows, and black bulls to serve the brown cows, and black rams to serve white ewes, and bred the goats in the same fashion. More than that, Jacob took great pains to cull herd and flock of weaker stock. Even though it meant a loss in numbers at first, he knew that the stronger animals would be more fruitful and their offspring much more likely to survive.

In the fourth year it was reported to Laban that Jacob's cattle had become a wonder to the countryside. "Sheep and goats and kine, sleek and fat and fine. And many of them, master — oh, many — are speckled and striped."

Laban sent men to spy upon Jacob, who was expecting this and performed certain acts just for them. He peeled willow wands so that they were striped green and white and stuck them in the gutters of the watering troughs. He marched the freshening sheep and cows and she-goats past the wands, as if the sight of these peeled sticks would stripe the offspring inside the womb. The men ran back to Laban telling what they had seen.

"A trick!" raged Laban. "A foul piece of magic to cheat the laws of breeding. It is not in the bargain!" But then he thought further and said: "This trick of peeled wands may explain the striping of the young. But how about the rate of increase among his stock — and their size and strength? There is something more that he does. Go spy again."

Jacob spoke to Rachel. She let drop among the women that each morning she would take the little wooden idols from the house and sit them on the fence to watch over the cattle and bless their couplings.

This, too, was reported to Laban, who thereupon took all his household idols and had his men place them on the pasture fence. The idols sat on the fence staring woodenly at the animals. But Laban's herds did not prosper.

"I do have a magic," said Jacob to Rachel. "But it is the kind of thing no spy will discover, nor can it be understood by anyone who tries to get something for nothing. Diligence and care and some knowledge of animal ways, these are the sorcery. And, of course, each morning before I go to the field I ask the Lord to bless my labors. And this God is no little puppet but the one God Almighty, maker of heaven and earth, who is everywhere at all times."

Now six years had passed, and Laban saw that Jacob could claim as wage hundreds of speckled and spotted, striped and parti-colored animals — that, according to agreement, he could leave with great flocks and herds, more than Laban himself owned. And the old man did not feel kindly toward Jacob.

The Lord spoke to Jacob, saying, "It is time to leave this place. Return to the land of your fathers, and I will go with you."

Jacob called Leah and Rachel to him and said: "Your father begins to hate me, because my flocks increase and I shall be able to claim a great part of that increase as my wage. Therefore I wish to return to Canaan, taking you and the children. Will you go with me or stay home with your father?"

Leah said: "He is no longer our father. He has disinherited us. You have increased his flocks a hundredfold, and that was our bride price, but he has never given us our share. He has sold us like servants. Anything you take from him now is only what he owes you, and to us, and to the children."

"It is so," said Rachel. This was the first time since Jacob's coming that the sisters had agreed about anything.

"So be it," said Jacob. "We leave tomorrow."

He gathered his sheep and goats and cattle, and camels and donkeys. He mounted the women and children on camels, but rode a horse himself so that he could drive the cattle. And they left their tents, which were outside the city, and set off for Canaan.

The night before, Rachel had gone back to Laban's house and taken certain wooden idols, called teraphim, that had been in her room. She had known them all her life and cherished them. She believed they had eased her pains during the birth of Joseph. Since she was with child again, she did not wish to leave the idols behind. She hid them in the saddlebags of her camel.

It was a large company that struck tents in the chilly dawn — Jacob, Leah, Rachel, the two handmaids, Bilhah and Zilpah, their eleven sons, and Dinah, the one daughter. When Laban heard that they had left, taking the flocks and herds that were Jacob's wage, he decided to kill Jacob. He called his men together and set out in pursuit. Seven days he pursued them. He overtook them on a plain before a mountain called Gilead. There Laban encamped, meaning to attack in the morning.

That night God appeared to him in a dream and said: "I am the God of Jacob, God of Abraham and Isaac. You do not know me, but I know you, Laban. And I say to you, do not harm Jacob in any way."

Laban did not believe in dreams, but he was not a man to take chances. He left his men encamped on the plain and rode alone to Jacob's tent. Jacob came to meet him.

"Why did you leave in that unfriendly way?" cried Laban. "Why did you carry off my daughters as though they were captives taken by the sword?"

"They are not captives."

"Why did you flee without a word to me? Why did you not tell me that you wanted to go? I would have feasted you as becomes my son-in-law, and sent you on your way with mirth and song, with the music of the taboret and harp."

"Let us say that, knowing your lavish nature, I wished to spare you the expense of hiring musicians," said Jacob.

"I wasn't even able to kiss my daughters good-bye. Or my grandchildren. You should not have done this, Jacob. I have men with me. I could punish you for your treachery."

"I have no troops," said Jacob. "My God guards me on this journey. He does not make a show of weapons, but do not take Him lightly."

"Certainly not," said Laban. "I respect all gods, even those I cannot see. I suppose you think these flocks and herds you have driven off from Haran are your just wage?"

"I do. And you know it to be so."

"And the kindly idols made of wood that were stolen out of my house — were they part of your wage?"

"I know nothing about any idols."

"They were stolen on the night that you departed. Someone here took them. I want them back."

"Why would I need wooden images?" cried Jacob. "Or anyone here? Search for them. Search my tents, every one. If any of my family or any of my servants has indeed stolen them, I say that person shall not live!"

Of course Jacob did not know that Rachel had taken her father's household idols.

Laban strode off and searched all the tents; he found nothing. He went into Rachel's tent. She knew he was coming and was sitting on the saddlebags in which she had hidden the idols.

"Pardon me for not rising, dear Father," she said. "I am stiff from the journey."

Laban grunted and searched the rest of the tent, then stamped out.

"Have you found them?" said Jacob.

"I have found nothing," said Laban.

"Before you go, let me say this, O father-in-law. You complain about the great herds and flocks of speckled animals that I have taken as my wage. But cast your mind back over the twenty years that I have served you. Seven years of it was a straight cheat — as you know — because you shuffled daughters on my wedding night. During those twenty years that I labored among your flocks, increasing them a hundredfold, I took all the losses myself as if I were the owner, not the herdsman. Those lost to drought, and calves and lambs born dead, all those I subtracted from my share. All those lost to wild beasts, those, also, have I tallied to your favor. Look upon me, Laban. You will never meet an honest man. For you cannot recognize honesty."

"It may be so," said Laban. "But be kind. You have what you want, for all that I did or meant to do. You go to Canaan with a large family; I return to an empty house. You are protected by a god I cannot begin to understand, but whose power I have felt. My gods are little wooden dolls, and most of them are chipped, and some of them are stolen."

"It is true," said Jacob.

"For all that I have done and not done I beg your forgiveness," said Laban. "Now let me kiss my grandchildren farewell."

And Jacob and Laban swore peace between them forevermore. The old man went to his daughters and his grandchildren, and kissed them all farewell, and blessed them, and departed.

Now Jacob had but one more river to cross before going into Canaan, and he knew that he must at last meet his brother, Esau. He tried to prepare the way. He sent messengers over the river, bidding them seek out Esau. "Say these words to Esau: 'Your brother Jacob has sojourned with Laban these twenty years. Now he has come home with oxen and donkeys and flocks of sheep, and goats and herds of cattle, and menservants and women servants. More than this, he comes with wives who are the daughters of Laban, and with eleven sons and a daughter. He comes home a man of wealth, but his one wish is to be your servant and to beseech your forgiveness for all that he has done.'"

Jacob waited on the eastern bank of the river for the messengers to return. They came the next day, saying, "Esau comes with four hundred horsemen. They come like the wind, raising dust before them. And all men shrink before their coming."

Jacob raised his face to heaven and said: "Oh, Lord, you bade me return to Canaan, and here I am. Here, too, is my brother Esau, who comes to smite me. Deliver me, I pray you, from the hand of my brother, from the hand of Esau."

No voice answered, and Jacob took steps for himself. He divided his company in two, saying, "He can attack only one encampment at a time; this will give the other one a chance to escape." Then he called his herdsmen and prepared a rich gift for Esau: two hundred she-goats, twenty he-goats; two hundred ewes and twenty rams; thirty milk camels with their colts; forty cows and ten bulls; twenty donkeys and ten foals. He had his herdsmen divide the stock, drove by drove, bidding them ford the river with their stock, and travel toward Esau.

"When you meet my brother," he said, "say this: 'These belong to your servant, Jacob, who gives them to his brother Esau.' "

That night Jacob left his tent and slept alone in a field, for he knew what the next day might bring, and he wanted to be ready if God wished to speak to him. He had noticed that God preferred to show Himself outdoors. It was a hot night and a rocky field. Overhead hung a great chandelier of stars. Their white fire burned into his marrow, and even in the depths of his fear he wondered at God's handiwork. Wondering, he fell asleep. Light struck his eyeballs. Heat touched his face. He leaped to his feet. There in the blackness of the night he saw one striding toward him terrible and bright. "Who are you?" he cried.

The stranger did not answer but strode toward him. "It is Esau," Jacob said to himself, "Esau grown more terrible, brilliant with rage, and primed for murder." His heart shuddered; his breath caught in his throat, and his legs trembled. The stranger was very close now. "I die," said Jacob. Then he thought, not of his own death, but of the way of the victor among the vanquished. Of women raped and put to the sword, of children taken by the legs and their brains dashed out against the stones. He thought of Rachel being forced to the ground. He thought of Joseph, his beloved little Joseph, lifted suddenly by the ankles in those brutal red-furred hands. He heard a sound he did not recognize. It was himself growling in his throat like a sheepdog when a wolf nears his flock.

Jacob flung himself on the stranger and seized him. All thought of self was gone. He was only a pair of hands to hold back the attacker of Rachel and Joseph, a pair of hands to hold, to punch, to gouge. A pair of legs to

88

thresh and kick, a head to butt, teeth to bite. He grappled the stranger close.

The one who had come in the night had a terrible easy strength, like the spate of a river in flood. Jacob was shaken and buffeted. But his fingers had become rods of steel. He grasped the enemy and would not let him go.

Now the blows from that huge heavy fist seemed to be falling from a great distance. The pull of the stranger's arms as he strove with Jacob seemed to be coming from the very center of the earth. Still Jacob clung. A swoon was stealing over his senses; he knew he could not hold out much longer.

And now with the tip of one finger the other touched Jacob in the hollow of his thigh. Jacob's leg locked. The sinew of his thigh shrank under the uncanny touch; his leg dangled useless. But Jacob planted his good leg and held on, although in agony. A mist passed over him. The foeman held Jacob so he could not move. "What is your name?" Jacob heard a voice say.

"You know my name. I am Jacob. Are you not Esau?"

"You are no longer Jacob," said the voice. "Your name is Israel now."

And Jacob was filled with awe. For the name Israel in that language meant "he who wrestles God."

"Who are you?" Jacob whispered.

"You may not utter my name," said the voice. "Do not ask it. . . . But you are still holding me. Let me go."

"I have wrestled with you all night long, whoever you are, bright stranger," cried Jacob. "I will not let you go unless you bless me."

The stranger smiled, and his smile had the beauty of the dawn. "I bless you, Israel," he said.

He vanished. And Jacob sank to the ground again, and slept. When he awoke, he thought it had all been a dream. But he was lame.

The next morning Jacob crossed the river and waited there for Esau. He no longer feared him. After wrestling the angel, he feared no man. Nevertheless, he was careful; he had his family to protect. He had separated his family into three parts, putting the handmaids, Bilhah and Zilpah, in front with their sons. Behind them he had placed Leah and her sons. Last he had put the little Joseph and Rachel, who was big with another child. Jacob stood before all of them, awaiting his brother.

Esau came like the wind, with four hundred horsemen. Their horses

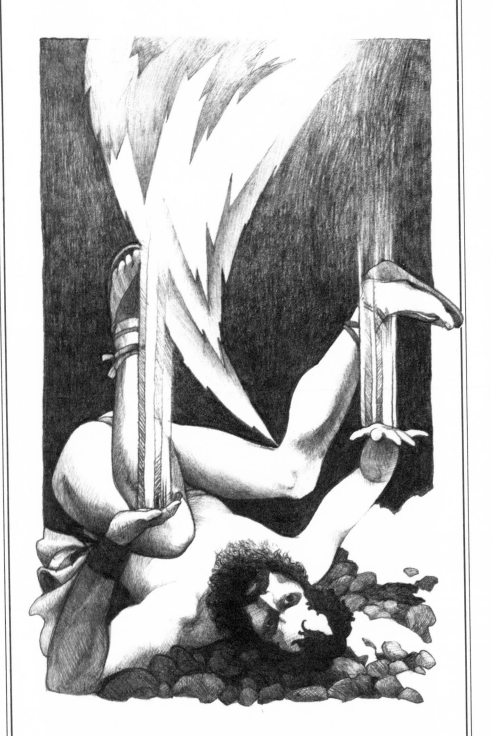

were swift, their spirits like eagles. Their swords flashed in the sun.

Esau reined up his horse, pulling it back onto its hind legs so that it stood very tall over Jacob, snorting and foaming. Looking down from this height, Esau watched his brother bowing to the ground. Seven times Jacob bowed to the ground. Esau leaped off his horse, pulled Jacob to his feet, and swept him into his embrace. They held each other in their arms and kissed each other's face, and both wept.

Esau saw the hordes of women and children and said to Jacob: "Who are they?"

"The children that God has given me," said Jacob, and beckoned. Bilhah and Zilpah came near, bringing their sons, and they bowed to Esau. Leah came near with her six sons, and all bowed to Esau. Then came Rachel, smiling, leading one beautiful child by the hand and thrusting out her big belly with great pride.

Esau watched her with admiration, for she was a beautiful woman. Rachel bowed to the ground; Joseph bowed. Esau raised them, and embraced them, and kissed them both.

Then he said to Jacob: "Coming here I met drove after drove of fine cattle, and the men tried to give them to me. What did they mean?"

"The cattle are yours," Jacob said. "Cows and bulls, sheep, goats, she-camels with their foals, and donkeys. All yours. They are my gift to you."

"I have enough, brother," said Esau. "Keep what is yours."

"No," said Jacob. "If I have found grace in your sight, if you have forgiven what I did to you, O brother, please show your forgiveness by accepting this small gift. God has dealt graciously with me, and I have great herds and flocks, more than enough."

"I thank you," said Esau. "And know this: My old rage is forgotten, and the youthful trick that caused it. And what is not forgotten is forgiven. All I feel now is love for my brother, my twin, who departed this land twenty years ago, and has come again."

The brothers stood looking at each other, trying to see beyond the courtesies into each other's heart. The twenty years had barely touched Esau. He had thickened and coarsened somewhat, but his face was as red as his hair, which was as red as in his youth. And his beard sprang like flame from his face. He was a stallion of a man, flashing with rage and laughter. Jacob marveled at his youthfulness.

Esau, looking at Jacob, could scarcely believe how his brother had aged. Hair and beard had gone quite gray. Jacob was very thin, and he limped. But his eyes, which had been so small and prudent, now glared out of bony sockets with a wild visionary light. Esau felt those eyes looking through him and beyond him, and knew that within his brother's meekness dwelt a weird power. And Esau shuddered as if a cold wind had touched him on this hot noon. He was not afraid; he had never known fear. But he was confused. For his twin brother, Jacob, had grown beyond his knowledge.

Esau said: "Between us, brother, we own too many cattle for this country to feed. I shall drive my herds to the southeast, crossing the river again, even into the red hills of Edom. And you stay here in Canaan. Graze your herds and flocks here in this land that our father gave you."

And Jacob knew that his brother spoke wisely; that their newfound friendship would flourish best if there was distance between them. "So be it," he said.

They embraced again. Esau's men gathered the gift of cattle into one herd, and the brothers parted.

Jacob journeyed westward from the river to a wide grazing land. There he built a house and made booths of leafy branches to shelter his cattle against the sun. Thereafter the place was called Succoth, or "booths."

He journeyed onward and encamped before a city called Shalem, which was the chief city of Hamor, king of a powerful tribe called the Hivites. Hamor's eldest son was a tall youth named Shechem, and he was a prince in Canaan.

Dinah, Leah's youngest child, and Jacob's only daughter, met Shechem in the field beyond the city gates. Now, Dinah was just budding into womanhood. She was more like Rachel than like her mother. She was supple as a young willow, fleet-footed, and of quick laughter. She helped her brothers drive the sheep. She delighted to follow the flock, carrying a staff and attended by dogs. Being the only girl among eleven boys, she had grown willful as a princess. And when she met the young prince Shechem in the field in the purple light of dusk, they came together as naturally as two young trees bending toward each other in a gale of wind. They lay together there in the spring furrows, and their love was like a spring torrent.

The next morning Shechem went to his father and said: "Father, I love a daughter of those strangers from the east who have pitched their tents beyond our gates. I want her and no other as my wife. Please go to her father and get her for me."

Hamor, king of the Hivites, went to Jacob and spoke to him, telling him of the prince's love for Dinah. Jacob called Dinah to him and spoke to her privately. He understood from her answers that she had already lain with this man in the field. Jacob was angered. But he spoke to Hamor courteously, saying that first he would speak with his sons concerning this marriage, and then he would return his answer. Hamor departed.

Then Jacob called Dinah's elder brothers from the field, those sons of Leah who were old enough to consult. They were Reuben, Simeon, Levi, and Judah. Now, Simeon and Levi were angered by this tale, and Simeon said: "Levi and I are nearest to Dinah in spirit, and know her ways best. She drives the sheep with us, and spends her days with us, and we love her. Therefore, Father, let us be your spokesmen in this matter, and do what has to be done. We will stand in your stead and do as you would wish in all things."

Reuben and Judah agreed, and Simeon and Levi went to seek their sister's lover. These brothers were fierce-hearted young men, full of Damascus pride, who looked upon the Canaanites as savages. They were bitterly displeased by what their sister had done, but they showed nothing. They found Shechem walking in the field with Dinah. "Go to your mother," said Simeon. "We would speak with this young man concerning your marriage, and we must speak with him alone."

Dinah laughed with joy and embraced her brothers, and ran off. Then Levi said to Shechem: "Do you wish to marry our sister?"

"I do," said Shechem.

"Even though she is not a virgin?" said Simeon. "Or do you not count that a virtue among the Hivites?"

"Your words call for swords," said Shechem. "But we are to be brothers and must not fight. Your sister is a virgin to all the world but me, who shall be her husband, and shall be the only man who will know her. Let us arrange this matter without anger."

"Truly spoken," said Levi. "We offer no dowry. Do you offer a bride price?"

"I do. My father is king. I am his prince and shall be king. Dinah will be my queen and share all that I have."

"Your reign lies in the future, which only God can read," said Levi. "What do you offer now?"

Shechem raised his head proudly. "Please yourself about the details. My father's treasury is open to you. And his herds and his flocks. Take the price you want. Your sister is a treasure beyond price."

"Truly spoken," said Levi.

"Arrange matters as you wish," said Shechem. "I leave it all to you. But let the marriage be soon."

"Not quite so soon," said Simeon. "We follow a God you do not know, and have our own customs. We cannot give our sister to one who is uncircumcised."

"What does that mean?"

"We sons of Abraham pledge ourselves to our God in a certain way, by cutting the mark of his covenant into our flesh. You must do that, too, and your father and all the men of the Hivites, before we can give our sister into your hands."

"It shall be done," said Shechem.

"You had better understand what you are agreeing to," said Levi. "It is a bloody pledge, and painful. Among us it is done when the infant is eight days old. For grown men it is a more serious matter. We cut the mark of that covenant into the very fountain of our manhood, even our foreskins, which are cut away."

Shechem stared at them, amazed. "A savage custom," he whispered.

"Pardon me, prince," said Simeon. "I do not mean to give you the lie, but we view this as the mark of a blood oath between us and God. And our God is all-powerful, maker of heaven and earth — not a stone idol squatting on its pedestal. To us this mark cut in our flesh is a caste mark, separating us from savages and idolators. If you hold other views, you cannot have our sister."

"So be it," said Shechem. "I am a man of the sword, a man of the chase. I have no special insight into the ways of this god or that. But I have met a goddess, and her name is Dinah. And I would cut off my left arm for her, and shall surely submit to the small carving you propose."

Simeon's face and neck were swollen with blood. His fingers itched so for the hilt of his sword that his arm trembled. But he clenched his lips and said nothing. Levi, knowing that his brother could not speak for rage, said: "It is well. Go to your father and tell him what is to be done. And let each male of your tribe, every one from your oldest man to your youngest infant, be circumcised according to our custom."

Shechem nodded and strode off. "Keep a rein on yourself," said Levi to Simeon, "or you will show your intention and they will escape our vengeance."

"You do the talking, then," said Simeon. "And I shall stand by. For when I come close to him, I want only to take my sword and lop his pretty head off."

"It may be that you will have the chance," said Levi. "But not yet."

Shechem went to his father and told him what had been demanded. "Must this be?" said Hamor. "It is a sore thing."

"We must do it," said Shechem, "or I cannot have her. We must do it, or I must attack them and take her by force. And we shall lose more blood through sword-cuts than through the small knives of their rite. Besides, they are a peaceable people. Skilled herdsmen, people of wealth. It will do us no harm to exchange daughters with them. It may improve our stock. They are full of a strange fire and see things that we do not."

"You see things that I do not," said Hamor. "I loathe these Israelites. I should like nothing better than to summon our horsemen and smite them in their tents and quench these strange fires once and for all."

"Do not hate them," said Shechem. "I am to marry their daughter. . . . But first we must circumcise ourselves, as they have instructed."

"You must explain it to all the men," said Hamor. "I am their king, their captain, master of revels, rainmaker. I cannot go to them with an edict concerning foreskins. You must speak for me and tell them what to do, and it shall be done."

Shechem did so. Then he circumcised himself, and Hamor circumcised himself, and Shechem made sure that every man of the tribe, and every male child, was circumcised. And he sent word to Jacob that this had been done.

Now the men of the Hivites were weak from loss of blood, and in pain. Simeon and Levi watched at the gates until they saw that every man had been circumcised. Then they called a band of armed herdsmen, which they had posted at a nearby grove. Each man took his sword and entered the gates of the city, and went into each house and fell on the helpless men and slew them. Simeon and Levi stormed the palace where Hamor and Shechem lay on their couches in pain. Before the king and the prince could rise to defend themselves, Levi passed his sword through

Hamor's body. Simeon swept his blade like a scythe and cut off Shechem's head.

They called together their men and left the city. Then the other sons of Jacob came with their herdsmen and sacked the city. They looted each house, put chains on the women and children, and took all the gold and silver and precious things that were in the city. The herds and the flocks they took, also, and drove them off. Then Levi and Simeon went in to tell Jacob what had been done.

"You have defiled our name!" cried Jacob. "You have made it stink throughout the land. You have acted like murderers and thieves. You promised to go in my stead and act as my spokesmen, and stand for me in all things. Is this what I have taught you — lies and treachery and murder? And have you used the sacred rite of circumcision for your foul ends? Will not that Hivite blood given in pledge to God call out to God for vengeance?"

"He treated our sister like a harlot," said Simeon. "He had to die."

"And his father? And all the men of the Hivites?"

"They would have been our enemies when we killed their prince. So they had to die, too, or they would have killed us."

"We shall have more enemies than you can count," said Jacob, "when the tale of this deed is spread throughout the land. For they are many and we are few. They will band together and wipe us out. Get out of my sight, you fools! Go to the altar I have built and beg God to show you how to erase your crime."

The two young men left the tent, and Jacob was alone. Then he went out into the night and raised his face to the sky, and said: "Forgive them, Lord, for they were but the tools of my unuttered wish. They read my wrath and did what I myself could not have done. Forgive them, and forgive me. But I could not bear the thought of my daughter coupling in the field like an animal."

And God answered, saying, "Arise. Go to Beth-el and dwell there. And build there an altar unto me."

Jacob called his sons to him, and all his household, and said: "Put away the strange gods that are among you. Cleanse yourselves and change your garments. For the marks of this bloody deed must be washed off our bodies and out of our souls. We will go to Beth-el. There I will raise an altar to God and we will pray to Him for forgiveness. Now, if any among you has kept wooden idols from Haran or has adopted any of the stone idols of this land, give them to me. Also, the jewelry you wear, for we must face the Lord unadorned."

They gave to Jacob all the wooden idols and the stone idols and their rings and earrings and necklaces. And Jacob buried them under an oak tree that grew in the field near the city. But Rachel kept back the wooden idols that she had taken from her father's house. The time of her labor was almost upon her, and she wanted them for luck. She hid them among the saddle bags of her camel, and took them with her as she rode toward Beth-el.

They came to Beth-el and Jacob raised an altar to the Lord. The Lord appeared to him and said: "Your name was Jacob and shall be Israel, for you wrestled with my angel. Be fruitful and multiply. A nation shall come out of your body; kings shall issue from your loins. The land which I gave to Abraham and Isaac I give to you and your seed after you."

Now this place had become a most holy place. Jacob raised high altars there. Upon these altars he poured drink offerings of wine, and he anointed the stone pillars with oil.

Simeon and Levi prostrated themselves before the Lord and begged forgiveness for the slaughter of the Hivites. And their brothers did likewise. As for Dinah, she had not come to Beth-el. She had vanished on the night of blood and was never seen again.

They journeyed from Beth-el and neared a place called Ephrath, and Rachel knew that her time was upon her. She labored in great agony. The child had turned in the womb and was coming out arm first, tearing his mother as he came. Waiting outside the tent, Jacob heard his wife screaming like a lamb being torn by a wolf.

"Help her, O merciful God," he whispered. "Spare her this pain."

Her screams sank to a gurgling moan. Jacob raced to the tent and burst in. Rachel lay on her couch; her legs were bathed in blood. A circle of wooden idols grinned down at her. A naked baby gleamed in the midwife's hands.

"The blood!" cried Jacob. "Stop the blood!"

"She was torn," said the midwife. "She is stuffed with bandages, and still she bleeds."

Jacob snatched up a handful of wrappings and fell on his knees beside the couch. He pressed the cloth against her thighs, trying to stop the terrible flow. The clean rags were immediately soaked. He heard her whispering and bent to her face.

Her voice was a thread. "He is Ben-oni." This means "son of sorrow."

"Do not leave me," said Jacob. "Please . . . stay with me."

She did not answer. Her eyes opened and looked into his; their green light pierced his soul. Then their light went out. Very gently he closed her eyes. Now she lay as if asleep. He gazed down at her as he had done so many times when, waking first, he would raise himself on his elbow and study that beloved face, the blue lids and long, black lashes. Once she had told him, "When I was a little girl, I tried to sleep with my eyes open to see where the dreams come from."

"Now perhaps you will," he muttered.

He kissed her face for the last time. Then he spoke to the midwife. "Find a wetnurse," he said. He gathered up the wooden idols and carried them from the tent. He built a fire and fed the idols to it one by one, and stood watching the flames until they fell to ash. Then he went back to the tent.

He allowed no one to touch her body. He bathed her himself, wrapped her in a white shroud, then dug the hole with his own hands, and buried her where she had borne a son and died. He raised a stone over the grave. The children wept. Bilhah and Zilpah wept. And Leah wept, too. Jacob did not weep. He walked away over the plain, head weaving, striding crazily — for he was going back to Beth-el to break down the altar he had built.

A voice spoke out of the sky: "Stop!"

Jacob raised his face and said: "Why did you take her?"

"You ask what all men ask and no one answers."

"I am asking you."

"You wished me to ease her suffering."

"Not by killing her."

"I gave her to you. She is mine to reclaim."

"But why her? Why not another? She was young. I loved her. Why, O God, why?"

"I am the Lord. My ways are my own and not to be challenged. I am the Lord of all things seen and unseen. I shed light and quench the sun. I bestow life and quench that strange little flame, also. I am beyond questions."

"And beyond belief," said Jacob.

Fire hooked out of the blue sky. The voice spoke in thunder. "Say you so? Dare you to say so?"

"Maker of heaven and earth," cried Jacob, "you also made me, such as I am. I have heard your word and followed your way. I have been tempered in your fire. I am your handiwork. It was you who lodged the question deep in my being, where it must burn and burn until quenched by your answer. God that I have loved, who gave me the woman I loved, why did you take her away? Why?"

Jacob sank to earth, sobbing. Now the voice lost its thunder and spoke like the wind through the trees.

"Know this, O wrestler, son of the dutiful one, grandson of the idol smasher, I who wield life and death am also master of reunions."

"Shall I see her again? Shall I be with her somewhere? Where is she? What happens after death?"

"In you, Israel, the question demands an answer so that it can breed other questions."

"Where is she now? What is she? Shall we meet again?"

"Wherever she is, whatever she is, she waits for you."

Jacob beat his head on the ground, laughing and sobbing. "Forgive me, Lord. O merciful God, who gives and takes only to give again, forgive me."

"Go watch over your sons. Instruct them. Bear with them in their triumphs and crimes and do not abandon them in any travail, for you are their father and they are your sons. Caring for them, you may, perchance, learn a little of those things that trouble God who has no one to question."

The voice ceased. Jacob wept. But he no longer despaired, for God had told him that he would meet Rachel again.

JOSEPH

Call him Ben-oni, "son of sorrow," Rachel had whispered before dying. But Jacob could not saddle his youngest son with so unlucky a name. He named him Benjamin, meaning "son of my right hand." Benjamin, the youngest son was called, and his father was tender to him, but he could not love him as he loved Joseph. Twelve sons he had, and they all jostled anonymously in his mind when he thought of Joseph.

Rachel's firstborn was seventeen now, graceful as a dolphin and very beautiful, with his apricot skin and gem-green eyes. But he seemed unaware of his own beauty. He was modest in his bearing and courteous to his brothers, who hated him nevertheless. Jacob could not bear to be parted from the lad and did not send him out with his brothers, but kept him close.

Jacob had raised his boys to be shepherds, and now in his old age they did all the work of flock and herd. But he had kept his special touch with the stock and still took upon himself the task of restoring sick animals to health. Since he kept Joseph at his side, he was able to teach the boy the animal lore he had learned so long ago from the Cretan bullman and had polished to a wizardry among Laban's cattle. And the old man was amazed and delighted at the way Joseph devoured information. He snapped up his father's words like a sheepdog taking chunks of meat. Nor did he keep this knowledge only in his head. It flowed down into his hands and made them instruments of healing. Ewes in labor, cows with milk fever, rams with blood ticks — he moved among them and brought them to health.

And Jacob was well pleased, and made Joseph a coat of many colors. He sent his elder sons among the speckled flocks to pick out those with the most curiously marked fleece. Then he bade them shear these sheep of rare markings and had the most skillful of his servants weave a coat. The white parts were dipped in dyes, according to his wish. This was his gift to Joseph, a coat of many colors such as had never been seen. And his other sons hated Joseph more than ever.

Then Joseph dreamed a dream and told it to his brothers, because it was a wonder to him and he wanted to share it. He wanted them to stop hating him.

"Hear my dream, I pray you," he said. "Behold, we were in the wheat

field binding sheaves, and, lo, my sheaf stood upright and your sheaves stood round about and bowed to my sheaf."

"Shall you indeed reign over us?" said Simeon. "Shall you be our master?"

"I do not say so," said Joseph.

"Your dream says so," said Levi. "It is an arrogant and hateful dream."

Then he dreamed another dream and told them this one, also. "I was a star in the sky and you were eleven stars circling me. And the sun and the moon and the eleven stars bowed to me."

"You hope to master not only us," said Dan, "but our father and his wife, as well. Your dreams grow more ambitious nightly."

The brothers told their father, hoping he would be displeased. He was displeased, but not altogether. He rebuked Joseph mildly, saying, "What is this dream? Shall I and my wife and your brothers all pay homage to you? Try to dream more modestly, my son."

This second dream angered his brothers more than ever. Judah said to his father: "He is puffed up because you keep him here in idleness. He has nothing to do but dream vain dreams. Why not send him to us, and we shall teach him to tend the flocks."

"Who shall teach whom?" said Jacob. "He knows more about the stock now than any of you will ever learn."

"Then we need his knowledge. It is the best of your cattle we drive to the grazing grounds. There will be plenty of work for him to do out there. And perchance he may pick up a trick or two of day-to-day shepherding even from us."

These words made Jacob thoughtful. For he meant to leave Joseph the bulk of his wealth, and the boy could learn much from his brothers that would serve him well when he became master of vast herds.

"It is well," said Jacob. "He will go to the grazing grounds with you."

The brothers were ready to drive their flocks off, but Jacob could not bear to part with Joseph, and he said to them: "Go. He will follow."

Some days passed and Joseph said: "I think, Father, it would be seemly for me to help my brothers in their labor."

Jacob knew it had to be. "Go, then," he said. "And God go with you." But he was fearful, and he embraced the lad and wept at his departure.

Now, the brothers were grazing their flocks on the empty fields near the ruined city of Shalem, where they had slaughtered the Hivites. Judah, who watched everything, saw his brother Simeon prowling like a tiger, as if he smelled the blood of the enemy he had killed. And Levi's ferocity was kindled by the place, also, and he was restless.

Then they drove their flocks to Dothan, where the grass was thicker, and waited there.

Joseph went to the city of Shalem, seeking his brothers, and was told by a man of the place that they had gone to Dothan. He followed them there.

The sun was veiled by sickly clouds, and the air was not hot but hard to breathe. For this was the season of the sirocco, an ill wind that blows out of Africa and is the parched fatal breath of the desert itself. When it blows, tame dogs bite and men run mad.

The brothers loitered about, speaking of their flocks and of other flocks and herds belonging to their father, and of the camels he owned and the donkeys. Reuben, usually merry-hearted, felt himself being flayed by the south wind. And he felt something gripping his entrails, but it was not of the body. He said: "I shall see nothing of this great wealth. I have offended my father by lying with Bilhah, who has given me sons, also. I am the firstborn but shall not inherit."

Simeon said: "My father's wrath was kindled against me when I slew Shechem. I shall not inherit."

"I share your guilt in the slaughter of the Hivites," said Levi. "And share our father's displeasure. I shall not inherit."

Judah listened to the others speak but said nothing. His habit was to speak less than he thought. When he did speak, his words had great force.

The next eldest, Dan and Naphtali, the sons of Bilhah, also said nothing. They, too, were envious of Joseph and had been angered by his dreams, but now they were made sullen by Reuben's words about their mother.

"O my brothers," said Issachar, "it counts little how you offended our father, by this deed or that. The fact is, he has never loved any of us who are Leah's sons. For he despises our mother."

"Truly spoken, brother," said Zebulun. "The sons of Leah are not esteemed. Nor are the sons of Bilhah or Zilpah, whom our father never considered to be his wives but only servants performing a service."

Gad said: "If our father does not love the sons of Leah or of Bilhah or of Zilpah, why, that leaves only the sons of Rachel to possess his entire love."

"One son — Joseph," said Asher. "It is Joseph he made the coat for, Joseph he dotes on."

103

Reuben was silent. He was sorry he had started the discussion. His brothers' wrath was spreading like a bushfire, and he knew what they might do in their wrath, especially Simeon and Levi.

"He will inherit!" cried Simeon. "He will get all; we shall get nothing. It is unjust!"

Levi said: "You are silent, Judah. Will you not give us the benefit of your wisdom?"

"Do you seek wisdom?" said Judah. "Has all this talk not led you straight back to the same idea you had when you began talking?"

Levi leaped to his feet and shouted, "And you, sitting there silent, drinking it all in, not deigning to let a precious word drop — what is your opinion? Do you have an opinion or only contempt for our poor efforts? Speak!"

Judah said: "I am not to be bullied, Levi. You should know that."

"Perhaps you disagree with us?" said Simeon softly. "Perhaps you esteem your brother, Joseph, and will become his friend, and he will throw you a few bones from our father's legacy?"

"And perhaps your wits are poisoned by your spite," said Judah. "I am no friend of Joseph. But I have always known there will be those who displease me in life. I cannot draw my sword upon them all."

"Who speaks of swords?" said Simeon. And his words were no more than a whisper.

"Your fingers fidgeting at your hilt are more eloquent than words, O brother."

Levi said: "He gets under my skin, the father's pet. He festers in my soul, and there is no balm. It is a deep abscess, and only the blade can heal it."

"Well spoken, brother of my heart!" cried Simeon. "He threatens us all, the meek one. His dreams are coming true even as he tells them. When he inherits, he will be a man of great wealth. And we, we shall have only a few paltry flocks. We shall be poor shepherds always on the move, searching out grassy lands for our flocks to graze on, at the mercy of wolf, bandit, weather. And if a famine falls on the land, then we shall have to go to him, to Joseph, the inheritor, the young prince, and beg him for bread —"

"And have to sell ourselves, perhaps," said Levi, "and work as bondsmen to get bread for ourselves and our children. If he inherits."

"He will surely inherit," said Gad.

"If he lives . . ." said Simeon.

Naphtali spoke: "He comes now! I see him far off. I see the colors of his coat."

"Behold, the dreamer comes!" cried Asher.

"He comes," said Levi. "Will he go again? Shall we permit it?"

Simeon stood tall and raised his staff. "I say he shall not! What say you, my brothers? Are we of one mind? We must stand together before our father in this. I shall perform the execution if you wish, but I need your agreement."

They raised their voices in a wild yell of approval, all but Reuben, who was trying to think of a way to prevent an actual murder. Nor did Judah agree. He, also, wished to save Joseph's life, but he bided his time, knowing he could persuade his brothers only by misdirection.

"So be it, brothers," said Simeon. "You have spoken your wish. You shall be the hand, and I will be the sword."

Zebulun said: "I have always thought that coat needed one more color, the color of blood."

Then many spoke at once, their words crossing and mixing: "When he is dead we shall cast him in a pit —"

"Dip his coat in his own blood and return to our father, saying that his lamb was torn by a wolf, or some other evil beast —"

"And we shall see what happens to dreams. What happens to dreams after death, brothers?"

"We shall see. . . ."

Joseph suspected nothing, riding on his donkey to Dothan. His father had given him a rare saddle donkey for his own, the best of the string. She was mist-gray, very alert, and sweet-tempered, with a gait so even you could fall asleep riding her. Now Joseph, bundled up in his coat of many colors against the harsh wind, jogging along to meet his brothers, was half asleep as he rode, and pleasant scenes drifted through his head. He would take his place among his brothers as a man among men. He would work hard tending the sheep, and drive his flock to where the grass grew thickest and water flowed. He would whistle clear signals to the dogs and be vigilant against wolves. And his brothers would observe him, and look at one another and smile grudgingly as if to say, "He is a good lad, after all. He has not been spoiled by our father's favor. He is our brother, one of ourselves."

Joseph was passing among speckled sheep now and knew that his

105

brothers must be near. Beyond the milling sheep on a low hill, he glimpsed tall, cloaked figures holding staffs. Now the sun swam out from behind the clouds. He was riding west and the sun was kneeling low over the western rim of the sky, glaring straight into his eyes, and he saw nothing but blood-red light.

So he did not see Simeon and Levi walking out to meet him. And did not know that he was among others, until his donkey was pulled back on her haunches, braying in surprise, and an iron hand grasped his arm, hurling him out of the saddle with great violence. His head hit the ground, and a darkness passed over him. But he struggled to his feet, believing he had been attacked by bandits, and he drew a great breath so that he might shout to his brothers, who were on the hill. The dust cleared and he saw that he stood within a circle of men, tall, cloaked men with bristling beards and stony eyes, and he knew pure terror as he saw that the strangers were his brothers.

A voice said: "You won't need this now." And a pair of hands tore his coat from his body.

"Brothers," he cried, "it is I, Joseph. I have come to be with you."

"You are not our brother," said a voice. "You are a thief come to steal what is ours. But we have caught you, thief, and you shall be punished."

"No!" he shrieked. "No! No! Don't kill me!"

His cries were choked, as Simeon grasped him by the throat and forced him to his knees.

Joseph saw a blade flashing above him. He bowed his head and closed his eyes, whispering, "Help me, O Lord," and waited for the blade to fall. It did not fall. "He torments me by making me wait for my death stroke," said Joseph to himself. "But he shall not hear me plead again." Then he heard Levi's voice.

"You shall not take the blood guilt upon yourself, Simeon. Let us cast lots." Joseph opened his eyes and saw Levi standing above him, holding Simeon's sword arm, and Levi's own sword was drawn.

"If we cast lots," said Dan, "whoever kills him will take the blood guilt. But we must share that guilt, all of us. We must each take a stave and beat him to death. We must form a circle and all strike at the same time, and keep striking until he is dead, and no one will know who struck the fatal blow."

"The Lord will know," said Reuben. "He can unravel your feeble tricks, Dan. The only way to escape guilt is for no fatal blow to be struck. Let us throw him into a pit and leave him there. He will have no food, no water, and must surely perish. Or perchance a lion will come this way and feast himself, and the tale we tell our father will have come true."

"He may escape," said Simeon. "He has a lucky look about him."

"Escape?" said Reuben. "Out of a pit with his arms and legs bound fast? How?"

"I shall find the pit," said Levi, "and make sure it is deep."

"And I shall bind him," said Simeon. "And make sure the bonds are fast."

Simeon bound the lad, pulling the thongs so tight they cut into his flesh. Joseph moaned with pain, and Simeon struck him brutally across the face; his nose bled, and his mouth.

"Not a sound, little pet!" cried Simeon. "Or I'll break every bone in that pretty face."

Levi led them to the pit he had found, a dry waterhole, and they threw Joseph in. It was almost dark now, and they departed. And Reuben was content because he meant to return alone and free the lad. He felt something touch his shoulder and whirled about. It was Judah.

"No," whispered Judah. "They will be watching you. There is only one way. After we have eaten and all their hungers have been dulled, I shall make a suggestion. Drop your own plan and support mine. It is the only way we can prevent murder."

They left Joseph in the pit and gathered their flocks and moved away. They slaughtered a lamb for their meal and ate and drank. Now Judah rose to his feet and said: "Hear me, I pray. We have bound our brother hand and foot and thrown him into a pit, where he must die. That death will stain us with blood guilt as surely as if we had cut him to pieces with our swords or broken his body with our staves. And we shall all share equally in this guilt — which will not lessen, being divided by ten, but will be multiplied greatly, because we are many against one, because we are grown men against a boy, and because, worst of all, the blood that will cry out for vengeance is a brother's blood. Yes, brethren, each of us will stand before God's awful eye. He will brand the mark of Cain on our foreheads. And all men's hands will be turned against us. No tree will offer its shade, nor will night bring repose."

"Speak your whole meaning," growled Simeon. "Shall we pull him out of the pit and embrace him and feed him and send him back to our father to inherit everything and leave us nothing? Is that your purpose? If so, I will go to the pit alone, leaving you all here proclaiming your innocence. Down into the pit I will go, and cut his throat like a sheep and take the guilt on myself."

"I want no part of such innocence!" cried Levi. "Where you go, I go. Where you strike, I strike!"

"I am not proposing that we release him," said Judah. "I am proposing that we do not murder him."

"If he lives, he inherits," said Zebulun.

"Not so," said Judah. "Suppose he vanishes and is never seen again?"

"It is death you describe," said Dan.

"No," said Judah. "There is another way. Let him stay in the pit overnight. He will not perish in one night, and perchance his dreams will be humbled. In the morning we shall draw him forth and sell him to one of the merchant bands that cross this way. Midianite caravans go down into Egypt to buy and sell, and slaves fetch large prices. We will sell him to the Midianites for silver. They will take him down into Egypt and resell him. And from the slave pens of the Pharaoh there is no return."

"I say yes!" shouted Reuben. He leaped to his feet and pulled out his sword. "And I back my opinion with my blade. It's Judah's way or fight!"

"Fight!" said Simeon, smiling. "Personally, I never avoid a fight. What say you, Levi?"

"No!" Levi's voice rang clear. He sprang to Simeon's side and grasped his brother's wrist. "For once I refuse to go your way, Simeon. We do not fight Reuben. We do not kill two brothers."

"Three," said Judah, drawing his sword. "I am not quick to unsheathe my blade, as you know, but I will stand with Reuben if it comes to the folly of fighting."

"They are right," said Dan. "Put up your sword, Simeon, and think of this. That arrogant princeling will be punished more sorely by long servitude than by dying young. And he will die finally under the taskmaster's lash. And we shall incur no blood guilt."

"So be it," said Simeon. "But I insist he be sold tomorrow. I want to see money pass. I want to see him wear the copper collar and be driven off with the slave string."

The wind blew. It was striped with cold airs now and freighted with sand. The brothers drew up their robes, muffling eyes and mouths, and sank to sleep where they stood. The flocks moved restlessly. Dogs barked, circling. A camel bawled, a donkey brayed. Simeon uttered a strangled cry in his sleep. But they all slept.

Joseph did not sleep. He lay like a heap of rags at the bottom of the pit. The thongs cut into his flesh, and his arms and legs were numb. And he was very cold. He realized how long it was since he had been out in the cold without his beautiful fleecy coat. He drove the thought of the coat out of his mind and threshed about, trying to make himself warm. His face was swollen from Simeon's blows and very painful.

Why am I trying to keep alive? he said to himself. I must surely die here; the sooner I do, the less I shall suffer. He lay still, trying to make his mind go blank, trying to summon the final darkness. But he was looking straight up. A star glittered coldly in the black sky and seemed to shine straight into the pit. It cast a silvery-blue light, giving the rocks hard-edged shadows. And Joseph, for all his pain, felt himself very much alive, perhaps more alive than he had ever felt before. And he knew that he was not capable of such surrender, but that he was doomed to live until life was taken from him. Is it the peril? he said to himself. Is this why that beast Simeon likes to fight? Not only to kill but to challenge death, to find this excitement?

The desire to live surged up in him, and he fought his bonds. They cut into him, and he knew how helpless he was. He wept from pain and rage. Then a thought came. I dreamed this once.... This is not unfamiliar, this pit, these bonds. I must have dreamed the very thing and forgot the dream because it was too terrible to remember. But why, why must they hate me so? Because they think I have injured them, stolen their father's love? I did not steal his love; it was given. He is my father, also, my father more, for he loves me more. And who knows the ways of love? There are no reasons; it makes its own reasons. But I am innocent of theft. Nevertheless, I am accused of theft, condemned of theft, and sentenced to death. And so I must die because of my father's love. How can this be? Is not love a good thing? It must be a good thing, or life itself would be without sense or form or meaning. Can evil come of good? Assuredly. The old tales tell us that God Himself repented of His handiwork and sent a flood, and then repented of the flood. If evil can come of good, then good can come of evil.... Is that a lion growling, or is it the wind? Be merciful, God....

Suddenly Joseph fell asleep and slept without dreaming.

Morning light struck him. He opened his eyes to see Judah sliding down a rope. He tried to speak to his brother, but his tongue was too swollen. He groaned. Judah gave him water to drink but did not look at Joseph or speak to him. Judah tied the rope about him and shouted. Joseph felt himself being pulled up. Sunlight hit his eyes like a blow. He shut them. Now, indeed, he was able to sink into a darkness. And he did not try to come out of his swoon. Many times he had dreamed an ugly dream and had escaped the final terror by knowing he would awake. But now he did not wish to awaken, because he knew this was not a dream. Then unfamiliar voices beat about him and the familiar ones went away.

He felt himself being handled, not cruelly, but with skillful force, as a donkey is handled. He felt a copper collar being locked onto his neck. He felt himself goaded into a line with other bodies. And the docility of these shuffling bodies entered him; he felt himself changing, becoming cattle. It was the utmost anguish he had ever known. Now he opened his eyes, but saw nothing because he was blinded by tears.

And it was in this way that Judah and Simeon saw the last of their brother, his head bent and weeping, shuffling along in a file of slaves. And then the caravan disappeared in its own dust as it headed south.

Judah and Simeon rejoined their brothers and shared out the silver that was the price paid for Joseph. Twenty pieces of silver. Thirty pieces was the price for a grown man, twenty pieces for a boy.

Simeon dipped Joseph's coat into the blood of the lamb they had slaughtered for their meal, and the brothers returned to Jacob — all except Reuben, who dared not face his father. "The child is not," cried Reuben. "And I, where can I go now?" And he did not return to his father but stayed with the flocks.

When Jacob saw his sons, he said: "Where is Joseph?"

"He did not come to us," said Judah. "But we found this in the plain before Dothan."

Jacob uttered a terrible shriek and clawed at his own face. "It is the coat, the coat of many colors I made for him. A wild beast has torn him. He is dead. . . ."

He fell to the floor, sobbing and rending his clothes. Leah came to him, and the other women of the house, and tried to comfort him. And Jacob's sons gathered about him and wept with him, but he was not comforted.

"Be merciful, God," he said. "Take this life that has become an empty thing and let me go where Rachel waits. For Joseph is there, also. . . ."

Each collar had a ring in it. Every night a chain was passed through the rings, linking the slaves to one another, and making it impossible to escape. But the collars galled the necks. The galls became sores, which became abscesses, and these were attacked by sand flies and putrified. Slaves dropped as they walked, and died where they dropped. Their collars were removed, and they were left for the vultures that followed the caravan.

Joseph moved in a tunnel of despair. Its darkness shut off thought and, he was dimly aware, spared him the final suffering. Worse than bodily pain, worse than fatigue or nausea, was the idea of himself as cattle. And he knew that it was this idea that must finally kill him. One night he resolved to die. A wind had sprung up, and the linked slaves shuddered and clanked in their stinking rags. Joseph lay on his back, looking straight up. There above him blazed the great chandelier of stars, God's own crystal handiwork, which, in the old tales, had scorched his great grandfather Abraham to the overwhelming recognition that there was but one God, the Almighty One, maker of heaven and earth, and that all idols had to be smashed. And Joseph, looking at the high jewelry of the desert night, was stricken by an agony worse than any that had come before. These were the stars that had looked upon his enchanted boyhood. Now, indifferently, they looked upon his ordeal. "Yes," he whispered. "God has forgotten me. And I know what to do."

He planned how to do it. In the first hours of the march, he thought, I shall drop as I walk and lie still. They will kick me for a while, and when I do not arise they will leave me for the vultures. And I shall continue to lie there and submit to the death birds, who will make my feigning real.

Now all the stars were running together in one huge blur of light, and he thought he must be seeing them through his tears. But his eyes were dry. Now the sky was one great star, unbearably bright, but the night kept its darkness. Now the sky spoke: "Joseph. . . ."

"I am here."

"Know this: Who pities himself leaves no space for my pity."

Joseph sprang to his feet. There was a loud clanking as the slaves on each side of him were pulled to their knees. They snarled and groaned and flung themselves down again, dragging him to his knees. He turned and looked up into the sky. The huge light was gone; it had divided into its many stars. But an arrow of it had pierced the boy's heart, flooding him with unearthly light, muting pain, easing fatigue, filling him with a burning mandate — to live.

"Thank you, Lord," he whispered. "Give me the wit to understand and the strength to obey."

There were always slaves who could not arise in the morning. If they could not be flogged to their feet, they were left to the vultures. The caravan chief himself took charge of this morning round. If he did not, the drovers would take the food for the dead slaves and eat it themselves. This morning the caravan chief was hailed by Joseph. "I would speak to you, Master."

The man gaped in astonishment and lifted the butt of his whip to strike the boy down.

"Gently, good sir," said Joseph. "Do you not notice that I speak your tongue?"

The man said nothing, but lowered his whip.

"My God taught me your language in the watches of the night. He wishes me to speak to you on a matter of importance."

"Speak, but quickly! I am not in the habit of conversing with my stock."

"You are unthrifty, Master."

"What?"

"Before I came into your hands, I was a shepherd. My father was master of vast herds. Our animals multiplied, our wealth multiplied; we did not let our cattle sicken and die. Now we slaves are your stock, as you say. Your flocks and herds, your wealth. By killing us on this march you filch money from your own pocket."

The man spoke: "I have been driving slaves to market for twenty years. There is no way to prevent loss."

"You have already lost three out of every ten slaves you have taken. By the time you get to Egypt, you will have lost seven out of ten, at least. Put me in charge of them, and I shall keep them all alive. Not only alive, but in such fettle as to fetch a large price at the market. Look at them, skin and bones, ulcerated, unfit for labor. Under my care they will grow sleek and fine. You have nothing to lose but loss. Let me try."

"Did that god of yours tell you all this?"

"He gave me eyes to see, wit to understand."

"You Hebrews are always prating about this god of yours that nobody sees. If he is so great, why did he let you fall into our hands?"

"He moves in mysterious ways. Perhaps He has decided to make you wealthy, O Syrian, and has sent me to guard you from your own wastefulness. The first thing you must do is remove these collars."

"Are you mad?"

"The collars are madness. Their weight exhausts us. Their metal galls us. They are the chief killer. They rob you of your merchandise."

"I see your idea. You want to escape."

"Where to? Without water we would drop in an hour, and an hour later would be vulture bait."

"So be it. The collars come off. But hearken to me. If this is some plan to cheat me of what is mine, you had better keep praying to your god. For I will pull out your clever tongue with hot pincers."

Joseph bowed. The man bellowed orders. The collars were taken off. That day, during the march, Joseph searched about, picking certain herbs. They work on cattle, he said to himself. They should work on men who have become cattle. That night he boiled his herbs into a broth and dipped clean rags into it, making poultices. And he passed among the slaves, bandaging their sores.

When the Syrian saw that the men were gaining strength and that their sores were healing, he accepted more and more of Joseph's advice. He shortened the hours of the march. He allowed the slaves more food and water. He bade his men ease up on the routine floggings. By the time the camel train had crossed into Egypt, he was driving the sleekest string of slaves he had ever taken to market. Not one had died under Joseph's care, and none had fled.

He did not put Joseph on the block and auction him off with the others, but took him to Potiphar, who was Pharaoh's chief officer in that part of Egypt. Joseph saw a tall, bald, hawk-faced man clad in a brocade skirt and wearing armlets of beaten gold — a very courteous man, who listened quietly to what the merchant had to say. But Joseph saw that Potiphar's eyes gleamed like a falcon's from under hooded lids, and knew that for all his smoothness he could be a cruel and dangerous man.

"Prime stock, O Potency," said the merchant. "His physique speaks for itself, but it is his intellect that is the true marvel."

"Intellect? What can you possibly mean?"

"Knows every variety of medicinal herb. Sets bones, cuts out tumors. And picks up languages overnight. His god sends an angel to tutor him."

"He has a pleasing appearance. Have you enjoyed him on the journey?"

"You must be jesting, Master. Don't you know what they say about Hebrews?"

"I am not in *their* confidence, whoever *they* may be. What is said?"

"It is worth one's life to molest a Hebrew in that way. Their god carves his initials on their private parts, and the molester is struck by lightning or blasted by the plague."

"Interesting," murmured Potiphar. "There is an old tale about one of our Pharaohs, who suffered misadventure with a Hebrew girl. How much do you want for him?"

"I pray you, Excellency, accept him as a gift."

"I thank you, Syrian, but accepting gifts can get very expensive. Put a fair price on him."

And so Joseph was sold to Potiphar, who put him in charge of the household slaves. Now, Egypt was the most powerful country in the world at that time and very prosperous. Merchants from every land drove their camel trains to Egyptian markets and sold slaves and gold and ivory, amber, musk, and gems. The great wood and papyrus ships put out from both coasts of Egypt and sailed to every port on every known sea. And ships from every port visited the Egyptian coast cities to unload their rich cargoes.

Potiphar was Pharaoh's chief officer in the western part of the realm. Much business passed through his hands, and he was always on the lookout for bright young men to help him. And the brightest and the most capable was the young Hebrew in his own household. By this time Joseph had picked up many languages, could do large sums in his head faster than any abacus, and was an expert healer of man and beast. Five years after his purchase Joseph was handling all Potiphar's affairs and had become a man of power in the western realm.

The Syrian had praised Joseph's brains and beauty, and for once had spoken no more than the truth. But it was a double-edged truth. Joseph's brains brought him prosperity among the Egyptians; his beauty brought disaster.

For Potiphar had a wife. She was much younger than her husband, and the men who came to the house looked upon her with lust. But they feared Potiphar and did not declare themselves. And she was quick with the whip, and the servants of the household walked in terror. Joseph had always avoided her, and few words had passed between them.

Now, the Egyptian gods were honored by great festivals at which the ancient legends were acted out. In these dramas, Pharaoh always played the chief god, Horus. Princes and captains and noblemen and their wives impersonated lesser gods and goddesses. In the fifth year of Joseph's sojourn in Egypt, Potiphar's wife was chosen to impersonate Edju, the cobra goddess, at the midwinter festival.

She summoned Joseph and appeared to him as Edju. A live cobra was about her waist as a belt, and another cobra twined up her leg. And the heads of the two cobras shuttled close, as if they were conversing. Her garment was mottled black and green with full sleeves, and when she locked her hands behind her head she was undulant, with a taut silken hood like a great cobra.

He heard her speak. "Do not cast your eyes upon the ground, young man. Look at me."

He looked at her and said nothing. "Well," she said, "do I resemble Edju?"

"I am not acquainted with anyone of that name, my lady."

"Edju, the cobra goddess. Very beautiful, very deadly."

"I am a Hebrew, my lady. We recognize only one God, and acknowledge no others."

"I did not ask for a lecture on theology."

Her voice rose in anger and she stepped toward him, clenching her hands. The snakes swerved their heads and looked at him out of lidless eyes.

Joseph did not flinch. He spoke to them in soft, hissing tones; the snakes lowered their heads and slept.

"How did you do that?" cried Potiphar's wife.

"I know about animals, my lady. It is my particular skill."

"Pity you don't know anything about women."

"I was about to say, before you lost patience, that if the Edju of your fables is described as beautiful, then it is most fitting for you to impersonate her."

"So you are capable of pretty speeches?"

"I speak but the truth, my lady. And let me say this. Those cobras are

dangerous. They should be curled in a ball under the earth, sleeping the braided sleep of winter serpents. If handled out of season and made to do strange things in strange places, they may strike at you. And their bite is fatal."

She smiled and stretched her long arms. "They will not attack their goddess."

"They are only snakes. They may not know your fables."

"Then you shall simply have to cure me of snakebite, shall you not?" She smiled and moved closer to him.

"The best cure for snakebite," he said, "is to render the bite harmless."

"That would not please me."

"I can remove their venom. It is not difficult."

"The cobras are Edju's living girdle. They are the very sinews of peril. Who can worship something that is harmless? . . . But we will speak of this again, little Hebrew."

She turned away. The snakes stirred. And Joseph was very uneasy.

Potiphar summoned him and said: "My wife impersonates Edju at the winter festival."

"I have seen her in costume," said Joseph.

"Have you? Impressive, isn't it? A bit too realistic for my taste. Some years ago a woman was stung to death by her ceremonial serpents. I shouldn't like that to happen this time. Can't you drug them so that they sleep during the ritual?"

"They may not awake," said Joseph. "Such creatures do not take kindly to drugs."

"They must not die!" cried Potiphar. "It would be regarded as a sign of high disfavor and the worst omen possible."

"The only way is to remove their venom."

"Very well, do it."

"I suggested this to your wife, sire, and she said no."

"I don't like to cross her in these matters," said Potiphar. "She is a priestess of that cult, after all. I may be tampering with matters beyond my ken."

"If I may comment," said Joseph, "there is no possible way she could know that they were rendered harmless — unless they bit her. And if they do and she lives, she will not quarrel with the result."

"As usual, you are full of sense," said Potiphar. "Disarm the serpents. Do it yourself and do not let the matter be known."

Joseph went to the cobras' cage that night and milked them of their venom, handling them so deftly that they did not comprehend their loss. And husband and wife departed for the palace of Pharaoh, where the midwinter festival was to be held.

They returned, and she called Joseph to her. She smiled, and he trembled at her smile. "Your fears were groundless," she said. "The snakes did not bite me."

"I am delighted, my lady."

"But I was never in much danger, was I?" He said nothing. She said: "That night after the ceremony I bade my handmaid tease the cobras until they struck. She almost died of fright but took no other harm. You disobeyed me, did you not?"

"I obeyed your husband."

"You defied my express command and mutilated the sacred serpents, nullifying them, transforming them from lords of the hidden way into earthworms."

Joseph bowed. "Forgive me, my lady."

"Forgive you? Is it possible? I dreamed a dream. I was flogging you and you knelt bleeding before me. And, lo, the whip became a snake that turned and bit me. I felt its venom running through my blood, but it did not kill me. It was a sweet venom, kindling my blood. And I burned. Belly, breasts, thighs, I burned. And you arose and put your hand on me. And your touch was like ice, quenching the fire. Read the dream, barbarian."

"Alas, I cannot."

"No? You read the dreams of all my slaves. Do you refuse to read mine? Shall I indeed flog you to death with my own hands?"

"I am in your power."

"Your eyes are like those gems called chrysoprase. Lie with me."

"I may not."

"You mean, you will not."

"Your husband has exalted me, trusted me. Can I steal that which he values most?"

"Your scruples are praiseworthy. Lie with me."

"Alas, my lady — "

"I have a brooch of chrysoprase, but its gems are not quite the green of your eyes. It has a long copper pin, that brooch, good for gouging eyes out of heads. I can do that, too, you know."

"I know, my lady. Your husband has looked upon me with favor, and I have prospered. But never for a moment have I forgotten that

I am a slave in Egypt."

"Slaves must do as they are told. Lie with me."

"How can I do this great wickedness?"

"I will protect you from his wrath."

"Who shall protect me from the wrath of God?"

"Forget that disagreeable god of yours. He has certainly forgotten you. Come, little serpent, I am Edju, your princess, your holy nest, your cave of delight. Come lie with me, and we shall sleep the sweet, braided sleep of winter."

She seized his garment and tried to pull him into her embrace. When he did not come to her, she ripped it off his body. He fled. She called to the sentries, who rushed to her chamber. She said: "See, my husband has brought a Hebrew to us to mock us. He came to my chamber to lie with me, and I cried out with a loud voice. When he heard me cry out, he fled, leaving his garment in my hand."

When Potiphar came home, she showed him Joseph's garment and said: "That Hebrew of yours, the little favorite, the trusted one, came in to mock me, saying, 'Your husband has put all that he has into my hands, and that includes you. Let us lie together, for you are young and I am young, and he is old.' And when I raised my voice and called out to the men, he fled, leaving his garment in my hand."

Potiphar listened to his wife's tale, then said: "You have handled matters with your customary skill, my dear. Now I will take care of the rest."

"What will you do?"

"I have not decided. But you can be certain that he will not trouble you again."

Potiphar summoned Joseph to him and said: "You know of what my wife accuses you."

"Master, I am innocent."

"Of what?"

"Of whatever she accuses me."

"I know who tried to rape whom," said Potiphar. "But that makes your crime even more intolerable."

"What crime, Excellency?"

"Why, the crime of being more attractive to your master's wife than your master is. She would never dream of tearing off *my* clothes, not in a thousand years. Which, incidentally, is the age you make me feel."

"I am innocent."

"You are guilty. You have dared to be more richly endowed than I am in a most vital area. My household is a small but highly placed social structure. You have turned it upside down. In this sphere you are a revolutionary. And you know the punishment for fomenting social disorder."

"You would impale me?"

"That is the punishment demanded by law."

"If I have done you any service, O Potiphar, grant me a painless death."

"I can't quite bring myself to do that," said Potiphar. "But, in recognition of your remarkable services, I grant you a painful life. Painful, filthy, confining. The alternative to impalement is imprisonment."

"Thank you, Master."

"You may be choosing unwisely. Impalement is uncomfortable but lasts only a few hours. You may rot in prison for forty or fifty years."

Joseph bowed. Potiphar smiled. And Joseph was cast into prison.

He was taken to a dungeon made of stone, standing at the desert's edge under the roasting sun. It was one great room without windows, and its door was a slab of rock. Iron rings were set into the wall, and men were shackled to these rings by their ankles. They lay on dirty straw and waited to be fed. Food was shoved through the door, and it was wormy and foul. But they fell on it like wild animals, devouring it and shrieking for more. And they sank back upon the straw and waited for the next day's meal.

Joseph called upon his God, who answered, saying, "Joseph ... are you brought low?"

"I never rose very high, O Lord. A slave exalted is still a slave. O God of my fathers, help me again. You who brought me up out of the pit, who saved me from the taskmaster's lash, help me now in this vile place."

"Do you remember the words I spoke when you wore a copper collar and called to me out of the camel train?"

"I have remembered your words, O Lord, and do not indulge in self-pity."

"Look about you. Here are others who suffer exceedingly. They need your help. I am the All-Father and my children call unto me, and I shed my mercy upon the merciful."

Joseph sent a message to the keeper. "I have been sent to change your fortune. Put out your hand, and I will fill it with gold."

The keeper sent his guards, and Joseph was brought before him. "Impudent slave!" he cried. "How dare you offer me a bribe when you have no money. You were searched when you came here and have nothing."

Joseph tapped his head and said: "Behold my treasure house, O keeper. In it now is an idea that will fill your coffers many times over. And it will cost you nothing but a little patience, as I explain."

"Speak."

"You receive a fixed sum of money for the keep of each prisoner. You pocket most of the money; with the rest you provide starvation rations — until your prisoners die. All wrong, my lord. You should not be feeding the prisoners at all. They should be feeding you."

"Your words have no meaning for me."

"They will. They will. You have heard of me. You know that I was Potiphar's chief man of business and that his affairs prospered under my management. So I am a man of capacity, not a fool or idle chatterer. Hear, O keeper. Treat your prisoners like men, not like beasts. Unshackle them. Feed them decent food. Allow them exercise in the open air. And — put them to work. Many of them are able men. Farmers, fishermen, makers of tools and weapons, artificers of all kinds. You will sell what they make, and your return will be many times what you can keep out of their food allowance."

"I propose a bargain," said the keeper. "I will put you in charge of the prisoners. If you can make a skilled work force out of these stinking skeletons, then I will permit you to oversee their labors and market their wares. But if at the end of three months' time you do not show a handsome profit, then you shall suffer most painfully. Do you agree?"

"You will never regret this bargain."

"If I do, you will regret it even more."

The keeper put Joseph over the prisoners and allowed him to order things as he wished. And it all happened just as Joseph had promised. The prisoners became healthy men, working in the open air and confined only to the prison grounds. They worked hard at their different trades under Joseph's eye, and he sold what they made and gave the money to the keeper, who was very content.

It came to pass that the butler and baker who served Pharaoh fell into disfavor and were cast into prison. Joseph saw that they were able men and put the butler in charge of wine making and the baker in charge of cooking and baking. And it happened that they both dreamed a dream on the same night. When Joseph saw them the next morning, he said: "Why do you look so sad?"

"I have dreamed a dream," said the baker. "And he has, also. We do not know what our dreams mean — but they are full of foreboding."

"God sends dreams," said Joseph. "He sometimes allows their meaning to be revealed and sometimes does not. Tell me your dreams."

The chief butler said: "I saw a vine with three branches. The vine was budding, and blossoms shot forth and became clusters of grapes. Pharaoh's cup was in my hand, and I took the grapes and pressed them into his cup, and gave the cup into his hand."

"This is the interpretation," said Joseph. "The three branches are three days. In three days Pharaoh shall lift you up again and restore you to your place. And you shall give the royal cup into his hand as you did before. . . . I pray you think of me when you are restored to your place. And do me this kindness. Mention me to Pharaoh so that he may deliver me from prison. For, believe me, I have done nothing to deserve imprisonment."

"Tell me what my dream means," cried the baker. "Lo, I stood with three white baskets on my head. In the top basket were all manner of cakes and loaves that I had baked for Pharaoh. Then birds swooped down and ate the cakes and loaves right out of the basket. What does it mean? Shall I be restored to my place, also?"

"The three baskets are three days," said Joseph. "In three days Pharaoh shall cut your head off and hang you on a tree, and the birds shall eat the flesh from your bones."

The baker fell to his knees, gibbering with fear. "How do you know you're right?" he cried.

"Let us hope I am wrong," said Joseph. And he went to select another man to do the baking.

Three days passed, and it was Pharaoh's birthday. A great feast was held. To mark his birthday, he pardoned his chief butler and ordered him released from prison and restored to his place. The man was Pharaoh's cupbearer again and poured wine into the royal cup. And Pharaoh ordered his baker to be hanged, as Joseph had foretold. But the butler did not remember Joseph and did not speak his name to Pharaoh.

One night Pharaoh dreamed a dream. He was standing at the river's edge; out of the river came seven fat cows and grazed on the meadow.

Then he saw seven other cows in the reeds, but these were ugly and bony. They leaped out of the reeds like wolves and attacked the fat cows and ate them up. Pharaoh awoke and tried to fathom the dream but could not, and slept again. He dreamed again. He was in a field. Before his eyes seven ears of corn sprouted out on one stalk; they were ripe and full of kernels. Then, as he watched, seven thin ears of corn sprouted, and they were mean and dry, blasted by the east wind. They crawled off their stalks like great green insects and seized the seven fat ears of corn and devoured them.

Pharaoh awoke and could not sleep again. In the morning he called for all the magicians and wise men of Egypt, for he could not forget the two dreams and was troubled in spirit. He told his dreams. The magicians listened, and the wise men. They listened and pondered, but no one could tell him what the dreams meant. And Pharaoh was angry, and all men trembled.

Then the chief butler spoke: "O King, forgive me for speaking. But when I was in prison with the baker, we each dreamed a dream on the same night and we did not know what our dreams meant. But in that prison was a young man, a Hebrew, who was the keeper's chief man and did all the business of the place. We told him our dreams and he interpreted them, reading the events according to his wisdom. He told me that I would be restored to my place in three days, and he told the baker that in three days he would lose his head. And it all came to pass."

Pharaoh heard the words of the butler and ordered Joseph to be taken from prison and brought to the court. When the keeper heard the news, he shot orders in all directions and told Joseph to shave himself and bathe himself, and gave Joseph fresh garments to wear out of his own wardrobe. And Joseph went to court.

Pharaoh received him in private and said: "I dreamed twice last night, and the dreams trouble me. I do not know what they mean, but they vex my spirit. I have told them to all the magicians and all the wise men of my court, and no one can interpret them. But I hear that you have a special understanding of those sleep visions that men call dreams."

"O great Pharaoh," said Joseph, "I am honored to serve you. But it is God who sends us dreams. Sometimes He allows their meaning to be revealed, other times He does not. Be gracious enough to relate to me what you beheld in your sleep, and I shall attempt to read it."

Pharaoh told Joseph what he had dreamed — how the seven lean cows had devoured the seven fat cows, and how the seven blasted ears of corn had eaten the seven fat ears. Joseph said: "Pharaoh, your two dreams are one. God has spoken twice in a single night to warn you of His intention. I can read that intention, if you wish."

"Speak," said Pharaoh.

"The seven fat cows are seven years, and the seven fat stalks of corn are seven years. The dreams are one. The seven thin and wolfish cows are seven years, and the seven wind-blasted stalks are seven years, and these are years of famine. And this is God's intention, which He has announced to you in the watches of the night. The next seven years shall be years of great plenty throughout all the land of Egypt. Good crops you shall have; your cattle shall graze and grow fat. And the land shall prosper. But after that seven years of plenty shall come seven years of famine. No rain shall fall. The east wind shall blow, withering the corn in the ear. The grass shall fail and cattle die. There shall be hunger in the land. The famine shall be so terrible that the years of plenty shall be forgotten."

"You speak dire things, Hebrew. Are you certain of what you say?"

"Very certain. God doubled the dream for you to show you that He meant all this to begin at once. This year shall be the first year of plenty. You have seven years of plenty in which to prepare for the famine that will follow."

"But can I believe you? Or are these vain words and empty boasting?"

"Consult yourself, O Pharaoh," said Joseph. "It was in your own slumbering imagination that God planted the seeds of these prophetic visions. Out of your own head came these night pictures. Ask yourself if the meaning I have given your dreams does not echo your inward feelings."

"Does your god have anything else to tell me?"

"These dreams are warnings. He warns you to guard your people against the great famine. This is what I advise: Select a man discreet and wise, and set him over the land of Egypt to speak for you and act for you in the matter of provisioning. Let this man of yours appoint officers for different districts to do his bidding. And this is what he must do in your name. He must send men to each farm and take one fifth of each food crop; this food must be put into separate granaries and stored there and not eaten. Thus for the grain. Also a fifth part of every herd and flock of kine and goats and sheep must be separated out and kept in special places and not slaughtered until the years of famine come. Thus, with God's help, you will be able to put aside enough food during these years of plenty to feed your people during the time of famine, and they will not perish. It is God's wish that you do this. That is why he sent you the double dream."

Pharaoh called his wise men and magicians to him and told them how Joseph had interpreted his dreams. And Pharaoh cried: "I will do as he says. I will appoint a chief officer. But where will I find a man discreet and wise to do this great work? A man through whom the spirit of god speaks, uttering words of wisdom."

There was silence. No one answered. And Pharaoh said: "Behold the man! It is he himself, the man who has spoken the meaning of my dreams after my wise men and magicians failed. He has been sent to do this work himself, and it is him I choose."

Then he said to Joseph: "Since your god has shown you his intention, I believe he has selected you for me. So I will put you over my house, and my people shall be ruled according to your word. And only I on my throne shall be greater than you are. Joseph, Hebrew, reader of dreams, I put you over all the land of Egypt. Here is my ring. Wear it, and rule."

Pharaoh took a ring off his finger and put it on Joseph, and put a gold chain about his neck, and ordered the royal tailor to make him garments of fine linen. He gave him a golden chariot, and gave him men to run before him, crying, "Bend the knee!" And Joseph was second only to Pharaoh in Egypt and ruled the land.

Pharaoh esteemed Joseph beyond all men and gave him an Egyptian name, Zaphenathpaneah, meaning "revealer of secret things." And Joseph took to wife the daughter of the head priest. Her name was Asenath and she was beautiful. He was thirty years old when he began to govern. He went to every corner of the land, instructing the people how to put aside a part of their harvest in the years of plenty and save it against the years of famine. He gathered up all the food that was saved during these seven years and laid it up in granaries near the cities. And he built great storehouses for the enormous quantity of wheat and barley.

During these years, Asenath bore Joseph two sons. He named the firstborn Manasseh, which means "forgetting," because the Lord's bounty had made him forget his past suffering. His second son he named Ephraim, meaning "fruitful." "Because," said Joseph, "God has made me fruitful in the land of my affliction."

The seven years ended, the years of plenty, in which Joseph had taken of this plenty and saved grain against the years of famine. Now the time of want began. No rain fell; crops withered in the field. No grass grew, and the cattle starved. But Joseph had laid up grain in the storehouses and food for the cattle, as well. And when famine lay on the land and the people cried out unto Pharaoh for bread, he said: "Go to Joseph and do whatever he tells you." The people went to Joseph, who opened the storehouses and sold them enough grain to keep off hunger.

Famine lay on all the lands in that part of the world, on the lands bordering the Inner Sea and as far inland as the Chaldees. But there had been no food saved in those lands, and the people were starving. They came to Egypt to buy corn.

There was famine in Canaan, also. People died in the cities and dropped in the fields. Jacob and his sons had great flocks and herds, but the grass had withered on the meadows and there was nothing to feed them. The sheep were dying, and the goats and the cattle. Jacob and his sons killed the beasts for food, but they needed grain for themselves and for the stock. And Jacob said to his sons: "We are in want, but you do nothing. You stand here staring. What do you expect to read in one another's foolish faces?"

"What would you have us do?" said Judah.

"Get you down to Egypt. Their granaries are full of corn, and they are selling it. I have heard this. Take money and go, all ten of you. I shall keep Benjamin here with me."

Benjamin was the youngest, the last son of Rachel. And Jacob feared that some terrible thing might happen to this lad, also, if he went down into Egypt.

The sons of Jacob, the ten brothers of Joseph, journeyed southward from Canaan and crossed into Egypt. They came to buy food and they brought gold with them. But when they sought to buy, they were told they would have to see one called Zaphenathpaneah, who was Pharaoh's governor, and who kept all business in his hands. "Go to see him," they were told. "He alone can sell you corn."

Now, Joseph was master of all Egypt and had ruled in Pharaoh's name for many years. He was looked upon as a savior, for the people knew that it was he who had taught them to put aside grain against the famine. He lived in a great palace, second only to Pharaoh's, and was attended by servants. Fountains played in the courtyard. The air was cool and scented by flowers.

The weary, travel-worn brothers were awed by such pomp, and were uneasy as they waited for the great man to appear. His word was life or death to them. If he refused to sell to them and they had to return to Canaan without corn, then, they knew, it was only a matter of time before they must starve, they and their families.

Trumpets blared. Armed men marched into the courtyard, clanking their weapons, and formed a double row of spears. Through the aisle of spears came a man. He was clad in gorgeous robes. His face was shaved. A ring shaped like a great golden beetle glittered on his finger. On his arms were bands of beaten gold. He walked toward the brothers. And they knew that they were in the presence of the mighty one, the governor of the land of Egypt. They bowed very low before him.

Joseph, walking into the courtyard, saw the ten men bowing before him. Time turned inside out. He was back in his youth, back in that first dream that had offended his brothers. And, lo, the dream had engulfed them. Here they were in Egypt, bowing before him even as their sheaves of wheat had bowed to his. He knew them immediately. But they did not know him. They had last seen him as a boy, and now he was a man, in the flower of his years, clad in power. He wished to hide his knowledge of Hebrew, and spoke through an interpreter. "Where do you come from?"

"From the land of Canaan," said Reuben. "To buy food."

Joseph looked at them closely to see if he could name each one. Twenty years had passed, but he knew them as surely as when they had bound him and flung him into the pit. He looked at Simeon and his voice grew very stern. "You are spies," he said. "You have come into Egypt to spy out the nakedness of the land. And you will return to Canaan and gather men, perchance, and seek to attack us."

When the brothers heard this, they were stricken with great fear. This man was all-powerful. If he believed them to be spies, he could order them imprisoned, tortured, beheaded, anything he wished.

"No, my lord!" cried Judah. "We are not spies. We are shepherds. We have come to buy corn. For there is hunger in Canaan."

"It is a simple matter for spies to pass themselves off as shepherds," said Joseph.

"Please, my lord," said Judah. "Please hear our tale. We are brothers, the son of one man."

127

"That man — your father — is he alive?"

"He lives, my lord."

"He must be quite old."

"Very old, master. But vigorous."

"And he had ten sons?"

"Twelve sons, my lord."

"I count but ten."

"Twelve brothers are we," said Judah. "But one is dead, and the youngest son is at home with his father. And we have come into Egypt to buy food. For our cattle starve today, and our families starve tomorrow."

"I have heard that tale before," said Joseph. "And spies have come before, and have not returned to their own lands. For we did not permit it, but made them suffer grievously for their spying."

"We are your servants," said Judah. "And you are our master. How can we prove to you that we are not spies?"

"Hear me. You shall not go out of Egypt unless you pledge to bring back your youngest brother and leave him with me as bond for your lives. One of you may go into Canaan to fetch him. The rest of you shall be kept here in prison until your words be proved. And if your youngest brother does not come, then I shall know that you are all spies, and your heads shall be lifted from your bodies."

He raised his arm. The soldiers advanced and surrounded the brothers. Joseph spoke, and they were taken off to prison. They were kept in prison three days, and they despaired for their lives. But on the third day Joseph ordered them released.

They were ushered into his presence. They bowed low and waited for his words. "Rise," he said. "My God has bidden me be merciful. I shall release you, all except one, who will stand bond for the rest. Nine of you shall return to Canaan, and I shall give you grain to feed your families and your flocks. But I require you to return from Canaan with your youngest brother to redeem the brother who has been left here. If you do not return, the life of him you leave in Egypt is forfeit."

The brothers conferred, and Judah cried out, "This is God's vengeance! It falls upon us because we sold Joseph into slavery. We heard his cries, we saw his tears, we knew the anguish of his soul when he begged us not to do what we were doing. We sold him for twenty pieces of silver and watched him being marched off under the lash. Therefore we have come to this pass."

128

Reuben said: "Did I not warn you? Do not sin against the child, I said. But we did. Now we see that we have incurred blood guilt and must pay."

They spoke in Hebrew and did not know that Joseph could understand, for he had always addressed them through an interpreter. And when Joseph heard what his brothers were saying, he turned and wept. Then he went back to them with his soldiers, who took Simeon from among the brothers and bound him with thongs.

Simeon did not utter a word, but stood there, head flung back, eyes stony with despair. For the first time in twenty years he felt the blood guilt descend upon him, thick and deadly. He knew that of all the brothers he had sinned most sorely against Joseph. He spoke to his brothers again, saying, "Do not return with Benjamin. Let me be killed for what I have done. Do not return, or he will kill all of you. He hates us, and is the instrument of the Lord's vengeance."

Then Simeon was taken to prison, and Joseph bade his men fill the strangers' sacks with corn, and bade his steward return every man's payment and put the gold secretly in the sacks with the corn. He spoke no more to the brothers.

They loaded their donkeys with the sacks of grain and departed. They stopped for a meal on the way. Asher opened his sack to get grain for his donkey and saw a pouch of gold in the sack's mouth. "My money is restored," he said to his brothers. "It is in the sack." Each man looked in his sack and found his gold there. And they were again stricken with fear, for they thought they would be accused of stealing back what they had paid and would be pursued by the Egyptians and imprisoned. But no one pursued them. They continued on their way and crossed over into Canaan. They went to the tents of Jacob and told their story.

"Simeon in prison!" he cried. "What manner of brothers are you? You do not preserve one another. Once you departed and returned, and Joseph was not among you. You brought me back only his bloody coat. Now you return without Simeon, the stalwart Simeon, and leave him to rot in an Egyptian dungeon."

"Do not reproach us," said Reuben. "We shall return for Simeon and bring him up out of Egypt. It is part of the bargain."

"What bargain?" said Jacob.

"The governor keeps Simeon only as bond," said Judah. "He thought we were spies. If we return with Benjamin we can redeem Simeon."

"You shall not return with Benjamin," said Jacob. "You shall not give your youngest brother to the Egyptians. You have bereft me of my children. Joseph is gone. Simeon is gone. Now you would take Benjamin. Never!"

Reuben said: "I shall leave my two sons with you. If we do not return with Benjamin, you may slay them. They are my bond."

"I do not wish to slay your sons," said Jacob. "And I do not wish to lose my sons. Benjamin shall not go with you. Joseph is gone, and I have no other son of Rachel. If anything happens to Benjamin, then you will finally bring down my gray hairs in sorrow to the grave."

The brothers saw that their father would not allow Benjamin to depart and said no more. And famine lay on the land and people starved. Soon all the grain that the brothers had brought back from Egypt was eaten up, and Jacob said to them: "Go back to Egypt. Buy more corn."

Judah took Jacob aside and spoke to him alone. "All grain is in the hands of the governor. And he gave us his solemn word that we would never again go into his presence unless we took Benjamin with us."

"Why?" cried Jacob. "Why must he have Benjamin?"

"That I do not know," said Judah. "I have thought about it, and there is no answer. But this I know: We cannot return to Egypt without Benjamin. And if we do not return we must surely starve."

Jacob said: "Why did you do me this terrible injury? Why did you tell the man you had a younger brother at home?"

Judah said: "The man inquired very closely into our family affairs and about our kindred, saying, 'Is your father still alive? Do you have another brother?' And we told him the truth. How could we know that he would say, 'Bring your brother to me'?"

"I do not understand," said Jacob.

Judah said: "Send the lad with me. We shall go down into Egypt. Otherwise we must all starve. We shall starve and you will starve, and our wives and children."

"I cannot allow you to take Benjamin," said Jacob.

"I shall be bond for him," said Judah. "If I do not bring him back to you, then the guilt is mine."

"How will your guilt comfort me if Benjamin is taken? . . . Very well. I see it must be. You must do what the Egyptian bade you. Take Benjamin and depart. But do this, also. Take the best of the fruits in our orchard, the golden oranges, the figs, the dates, and the olives as a gift to the man. Take him balm and honey, spices and myrrh, nuts and almonds. And take much gold, double the price of the grain you would buy. Also, take back to him the money that you found in your sack, the price that you did not pay the first time. Take him all this, the fruits and the spice, and the sweetmeats and the gold — and Benjamin. Judah, my son, pray to the Almighty God to instill that man with mercy so that he may release Simeon and restore Benjamin to me. For if I am bereaved of my children, then I must surely die."

Judah spoke to his brothers, and they did all that their father had said. They took fruits and spices and sweetmeats and much gold. And they took Benjamin, also. He rode a white donkey. He was clad in his finest garments and was a very handsome lad. He glowed with the excitement of the journey, for he was not afraid.

They journeyed into Egypt and to the palace of Joseph. When Joseph was told that the brothers had returned, bringing another, he said to his steward: "Kill a fat calf. These men will dine with me today."

The brothers were not admitted to Joseph's presence but were led out of the courtyard and into the house. And they were afraid. They had not been told that they would dine with Joseph; they thought they were being led to prison. At the door of the house, Dan spoke to the steward: "O sir, we came indeed into Egypt the first time to buy food. It was sold to us, and we paid for it. But it came to pass that when we stopped for a meal and opened our sacks to feed our donkeys, behold, every man's money was in the mouth of his sack, our money in full weight. But we do not know how it got there and we have brought it back again."

"Fear not," said the steward. "You are not suspected of theft. And here is your brother, also."

The steward brought Simeon to them. He had been released from his cell, and had bathed himself and been given fresh garments. The steward took the men into Joseph's house and gave them water to wash their feet, and stabled their donkeys. The brothers gathered their gifts in a great heap and waited for Joseph.

When Joseph came in, they bowed themselves to earth again and Judah said: "Greetings, O lord. Accept, I pray, this small gift of fruits and spices and sundry delicacies from the land of Canaan where we dwell."

Joseph turned away to fight back the tears again and said: "Is your father well? That old man you spoke of — is he alive?"

"He is alive," said Reuben. "He is in good health. God may yet grant him many years. It was he who prepared this gift for you, for he seeks your favor. He sends his thanks, too, for selling us food."

All the brothers bowed again, very low. When they arose they saw that

Joseph was looking steadily at Benjamin. "Is this your youngest brother?" he said.

"It is," said Levi.

Joseph looked upon Benjamin, the handsome young Benjamin, his only full brother, his father's youngest son, and Rachel's. He felt the cords of his body loosening with love. His guts yearned toward the lad. He left the room hastily and went off by himself to weep where no one could see him. Then he washed his face and returned to his brothers, and bade the steward serve the meal.

They all sat at a long table, and Joseph sat with them. Now, Egyptians of the high caste did not eat with Hebrews. Breaking bread with anyone not descended from the falcon god, Horus, was an abomination to them. And the brothers thought Joseph a prince of Egypt, and they wondered that he ate with them.

Joseph not only dined at their table but honored them exceedingly. He sat them in order around the table: Reuben, the firstborn, sat next to Joseph in the place of honor, and Simeon next, and Levi, then Judah, and so on according to their age, down to Benjamin, who was last. And the brothers wondered that he knew their ages so surely. From time to time during the meal he ordered the butler to take special delicacies from his plate, as the custom was then, and sent them to one guest and then another. But he sent Benjamin five times as much as any of the others. Benjamin wondered at the favor that was being shown him, and Judah watched his host narrowly, for he did not understand what was happening. The food was lavish and the wine was strong, and the brothers ate and drank and were merry at the table.

After the meal Joseph spoke to the brothers: "I see that you are not spies and I release you from your bond. Take your youngest brother with you — also, the brother I have released from prison — and return to your father. And take with you as much corn as you can carry."

The brothers prostrated themselves before Joseph and thanked him for his kindness. He still pretended not to understand their language, and spoke through an interpreter. Before they departed Joseph took his steward aside and said: "Do as you did before. Return each man's gold to him but do not let him know. Put it secretly in his sack with the corn. And do this, also: Take my silver cup and put it in the sack of the youngest."

The brothers slept overnight in Joseph's house and departed in the first light of the morning. They saddled their donkeys and loaded them with heavy sacks of grain and rode off. Then Joseph said to his steward: "Pursue the Hebrews. Bind them and bring them back."

The steward took a troop of men and followed the brothers on swift horses and overtook them on the road. The brothers were surrounded by armed men. Simeon and Levi seized their swords and prepared to fight. Simeon was wild to fight for he had been galled by his imprisonment. But Judah struck down their swords with his staff, crying, "Hold! Sheathe your swords! It is death to fight!" Reuben and Dan joined him and they forced Simeon and Levi to put up their blades. And the brothers submitted to being bound and taken back to Joseph's house.

Joseph spoke to them through his interpreter: "You stand accused. You have stolen back what you paid for the corn and put it into your sacks. Worse than that, there is one among you who has stolen my silver cup, the cup from which I drink and in whose lees I divine what is to come. My silver cup is stolen, and you are all thieves!"

Judah said: "God forbid that your servants should do this thing. Behold, we brought back to you the gold that we found in our sacks the first time we left Egypt. Why should we steal it again? As for your silver cup, no one here would think of taking it. Search us. Search our sacks. If the cup be found on anyone here, then let him die and let the rest of us be taken into slavery."

Joseph said: "I shall not be so severe. If any of you has taken my cup, then I will keep him as my servant. The others shall be held blameless and permitted to return to Canaan."

There in Joseph's courtyard, under the eyes of the armed men, each brother took the sack off his donkey and opened it. They opened their sacks in the order of age, Reuben first. And when Reuben saw the gold in his sack, he was afraid. But Joseph said: "It is well. I do not care about the gold. I seek only my cup."

Then Simeon opened his sack, then Levi, and Judah, and each in order of age through Zebulun. And no cup was found. Then Benjamin opened his sack and a great groan went up from all the brothers. Reuben tore his beard. There in the mouth of the sack, gleaming like a fallen star, was the silver cup.

"What have you done?" cried Joseph. "What manner of men are you to return evil for good?"

Judah said: "What shall we say to you? How shall we speak? How shall

133

we clear ourselves? I know that my brother did not steal your cup. But God has searched out another evil that we have done and is punishing us for it. So we are all your slaves. Our youngest brother in whose sack you found your cup and we, also, his elder brothers, we will enter servitude with him."

"God forbid," said Joseph. "I shall not take you all into servitude, only the youngest one, only the lad who stole the cup. As for the rest of you, go in peace, and return to your father."

Judah came closer and said: "O my lord, let me speak a word just for your own ears and do not let your anger burn against me. For I am nothing and you are as high as Pharaoh."

"Speak," said Joseph through his interpreter.

Judah said: "When we first came into Egypt you questioned us, saying, 'Have you a father, a brother?' And we answered, saying, 'We have a father, an old man. And we have another brother, the child of his old age, who is young. He is the son of my father's younger wife, the one most dear to him, who died. And she had an elder son who is also dead. So that our youngest brother is the only son of his mother, Rachel, and his father loves him beyond all others.' Thus we answered, my lord, in reply to your questions. And you said to us: 'Bring that youngest son down to me.' And we said: 'He cannot leave his father, for his father will die.' And you said: 'If you do not bring him you shall see my face no more, and shall not be able to purchase food in Egypt.'

"When we returned to Canaan we told all this to our father. And he refused to send his youngest son to Egypt. We urged him and he refused and kept refusing until hunger was heavy upon us. Then he said to us: 'Go down into Egypt and buy food. Take my son Benjamin with you, since that is the way it must be. But remember this. Rachel bore two sons. Joseph was torn to pieces by a wild beast and Benjamin alone is left of her sons. If you take him from me and mischief befalls him, then you will bring down my gray hairs in sorrow to the grave.' Now, my lord, how can we return to our father without our youngest brother? His life is bound up with the lad's life. If he sees us returning without Benjamin, he will surely die. I pray you, O governor, O mighty one, be merciful. Take me into servitude instead of Benjamin. Let me be punished for my brother's crime. Let me take his guilt upon myself. Let Benjamin return to Canaan so that his father may live."

Joseph could not hold himself back any longer. He cried out to his men. "Depart! Leave me alone with these Hebrews!" The soldiers departed, and the servants, and Joseph cried out in his own tongue, "Behold! I am Joseph!"

The brothers were struck dumb. They could not answer him. They were mute with guilt and fear. Joseph spoke softly, his voice running with tears: "Come to me, I pray."

They approached very timidly, and he said: "I am Joseph, your brother, whom you sold into Egypt. Now listen to me carefully. Do not be grieved at yourselves. Do not be enraged at your own deed. When you sold me, you did God's errand. God wished me to go before you to preserve you and your children upon the earth, and to deliver you from starvation. He sent me to find a place for your generations, who are precious to the Lord. So forgive yourselves, my brothers. It was not you who sent me here but God; you were only His hands. Blind brutal hands perhaps, but only hands. And God made me counselor to Pharaoh, and lord of all his house, and ruler through all the land of Egypt.

"Now you must hasten from this place. Go up into Canaan and say to my father that Joseph lives, that God has preserved his son and made him lord of all Egypt. And take this message: 'Beloved Father, Jacob named Israel, come down to me in Egypt and do not tarry. Come down to me, Father, and you shall dwell in the land of Goshen and be near to me, you and your children and your children's children and all the people of your house. And I will keep you here in Goshen and see that you do not want.' "

"Is it true?" whispered Judah. "Are you Joseph, our brother, who returns such good for such evil?"

"Your eyes see me," said Joseph. "The eyes of our brother Benjamin see me. You hear the words of my mouth. And you shall tell my father of all my glory in Egypt, of all that you have seen. So hurry, and bring him here."

He fell upon Benjamin's neck and wept. And Benjamin embraced him and wept. Then Joseph went from brother to brother. He embraced each of them, and kissed each one. The brothers wept. Even the iron Simeon wept. Levi wept most bitterly, for his guilt was keen upon him and he could not forgive himself. Shame burned in him at Joseph's goodness. Joseph went to him privately and said: "Do not weep so. Forgive me my compassion as I forgive you your transgression." And Levi felt a load lifting from his heart. He bowed low to Joseph and said: "Assuredly you are the wisest of men. You read men's hearts as you read dreams."

Then Joseph went to Pharaoh and told him all that had happened. Pharaoh marveled greatly at the tale, and was well pleased. He said to Joseph: "Say this to your brothers: 'Load your beasts and go. Return to Canaan. Take your father and your households and come back to Egypt. I will give you the good of the land and you shall eat the fat of the land. For Pharaoh is pleased.' "

Joseph thanked Pharaoh and went back to his brothers and told them what Pharaoh had said. He gave them wagons and provisions. To each man he gave fine garments. To Benjamin he gave three hundred pieces of silver and many fine garments. And he gave them a gift for Jacob: ten donkeys loaded with corn and bread and meat, and the best fruits of the orchard and honey of the hive. The brothers departed with their donkeys and their wagon train. They went out of the land of Egypt and into Canaan and to the tents of Jacob.

Jacob rejoiced exceedingly when he saw them returning with Benjamin. Then Reuben said to him: "Joseph lives. He is governor of all the land of Egypt."

Jacob almost swooned. He could not believe what he was hearing. Then each brother spoke, telling him all the words of Joseph. For he insisted on hearing every word that had been said. And when they told him all that had been said, and described what Joseph had done and the way he had done it — and when he saw the wagons loaded with Joseph's gifts, then he felt himself filled with a great joy and with renewed strength.

He said: "It is enough. Joseph, my son, is alive. I will go and see him before I die."

They journeyed out of Canaan. The men rode donkeys; the women and children rode in wagons. And those of Jacob's household and his children and children's children numbered sixty-seven souls, who went out of Canaan into Egypt. Judah rode before to guide them on their way, and they crossed into Egypt.

Joseph rode forth in his golden chariot to meet his father. Jacob saw him coming. The years fell away and he did not see a man in his prime, the governor of Egypt in court robes, but a slender youth, riding sheaves of light and clad in many colors. Jacob's heart fainted with joy and he fell into Joseph's arms and wept tears of rapture. Joseph embraced his father and let him go, only to embrace him again and kiss his face and neck. And they laughed and wept and clung to each other.

Jacob raised his wet face and cried: "O Master of Reunions who crowns loss with gain, I thank you! I thank you for bringing my son out of the darkness, clad in robes of glory. I thank you, Almighty God, and beg your forgiveness for being unable to discern the good that resides in evil."

Now Joseph led forth his little sons, Manasseh and Ephraim, to meet their grandfather. Jacob said: "Beloved boy, I had not thought to see your face again, and now I see your sons. Praise the Merciful One!"

Joseph took his father and his brothers to the palace and led them into the presence of Pharaoh. Pharaoh looked at them in wonder. He looked upon Jacob and thought: This man, born a shepherd, is prouder than I, son of a thousand kings. Behold him standing there in his desert robes, face gouged by thought, eyes blazing with the sight of what cannot be seen. Behold the man! This ancient nomad, spinning ladders of fire out of his wizard beard, siring a wolf litter of mighty sons. The sight of him makes me believe the alien fables — that he has been strangely maimed into power, lamed by his god's touch as he wrestled an angel. And his sons, also, maimed into power. For has not the gentlest of them climbed out of the dungeon to sit next to me on the throne? He spoke then to Jacob: "How old are you?"

Jacob answered: "My pilgrimage upon this earth has lasted a hundred and thirty years. Few and evil have been the days of my life. My fathers were better men; their years were many and fruitful."

"In my eyes you have been fruitful enough," said Pharaoh. "I am honored that you have come to sojourn in my land. Joseph, I bid you take your brothers to Goshen and give them the best of the land, even of the rich land of the Rameses, and let them graze the royal herds, also, as they graze their cattle."

"I thank you, O Pharaoh," said Jacob.

"I thank you, Prince Israel. I thank you for your son Joseph, who has been the savior of Egypt. And I thank you for your other mighty sons, who will add to my strength and my honor. Now bless me and depart."

Jacob blessed Pharaoh and departed. He and his sons went to Goshen and dwelt there, and grazed their flocks, and begat many children, even during the years of famine.

Jacob was one hundred and forty-seven years old and knew that he was about to die. He called his sons to him and said: "Gather about my bed that I may tell you what shall befall in the last days."

The twelve sons came about him to listen. His eyes were full of prophetic fire. Though he was feeble, his voice was strong and seemed to be coming from a long way off. They did not say a word or stir from their places as they listened to him tell the shape of things to come. He told them many things, very little of which they understood. But they listened to him hungrily; they knew these were the last words of his they would hear.

One by one Jacob called his sons to him, and kissed them and bade them farewell — Reuben first, Benjamin last. Then he sent them out of the room, but kept Joseph and Judah at his bed. He spoke first to Judah: "You are the chosen one. Chosen not by me but by God, the God of mysteries, whose intention can be read but not his reasons. The power passes to you, Judah. In the long scroll of years that unfolds before my eyes, I see God's heavy burden falling upon your tribe. Hear me now, O Judah, chosen of God. The scepter shall not depart from you, nor the staff of power."

His voice failed for a moment. Then he said: "Go now, son, and let me speak to Joseph." Weeping, Judah kissed his father and left the room. Joseph knelt at the bed and took his father's hand. Jacob said: "You, Joseph, beloved son, what can I give you now who have been all in all to me? May the God of your father bless you always. May He bless you with the blessings of heaven above, blessings of the deep that lies under, blessings of the breast and of the womb. O son of Rachel, my blessings gather strength from the blessings of my fathers unto the utmost bounds of the everlasting hills. And these blessings shall be upon your head, Joseph, on the crown of your head, O Prince, who have been separated from your brothers."

He fell silent. His head dropped. Joseph lifted his head and put a cup to his lips and gave him wine to drink. Jacob spoke again: "Farewell, my son. Bury me with my fathers in the cave purchased by Abraham. Bury me in the land of Canaan where Abraham is buried, and Sarah and Isaac and Rebecca, and Leah, also. Do not bury me in Egypt."

What Jacob had asked was done. His sons bore him to Canaan and buried him in the tomb of his fathers.

And the grain that Joseph had stored in the years of plenty saved Egypt from starvation. Pharaoh put all power into Joseph's hands. Joseph governed the land, and his brothers dwelt in Goshen.

But there were men of high counsel in Egypt, priests and magicians and officers of the crown, who feared that Joseph had grown too powerful. They hated him, and they loathed his kindred, whom he had brought into the land and who were growing rich in flocks and herds — whose cattle were fatter than other cattle, whose fields yielded better crops, and who worshipped an invisible god. They hated Joseph and his kindred, these men of high station, but they could do nothing because Pharaoh esteemed Joseph beyond all others and extended his favor to the Israelites. So the priests waited.

Joseph lived to be a hundred and ten years old. On his deathbed he said to his sons: "Make me an oath that will be passed on to your sons and to your sons' sons, even unto the generation of departure. The oath will be that they will remember me and take my bones from their vault and carry them up out of Egypt when they return to the land that God has given them."

They swore this oath. Joseph died. He was embalmed and put in a coffin in Egypt.

FLIGHT FROM EGYPT

MOSES

The children of Israel dwelt in Goshen, and prospered in that fertile land. They lived separately and followed their own ways and were very fruitful. About two hundred years had passed since Joseph had brought his brothers down into Egypt, and now they were a mighty horde, a nation within a nation. And the Egyptians began to fear that the Israelites would grow mightier yet, and take their country away from them.

A young Pharaoh was on the throne, and he hated and feared the Israelites. He spoke to his captains, saying, "That Hebrew of the old tale bewitched Pharaoh and stole his throne, and he took crops and cattle and sold them back to the people in the time of famine at an enormous profit. Yea, that Hebrew, that foul enchanter did bring all his kinsmen down from Canaan into our land, where they occupy the best acres and breed like rats and consume the harvest. We must master these Israelites or we perish. For two hundred years now, they have lived off the fat of the land. Yes, truly, they have eaten us down to the very bone. Now we will make them disgorge what they have eaten. We will take what they have and leave them nothing but their bodies, which we will use in our service."

The captains were joyous. They raised their swords and shouted: "Pharaoh! Pharaoh! It shall be done, mighty King!"

It was done. Egyptian troops went into Goshen and robbed the Israelites of their herds and flocks and their plowed land. And took away their fine houses and gave them to Egyptians, and built huts for the Hebrews, hardly better than cattle stalls. They set taskmasters over the Hebrews and enslaved them and forced them to do all the heavy work in Egypt, and all the menial work. They made the lives of the Hebrews bitter, and delighted in their suffering. They made them field serfs and house serfs, and treated them like animals, but more harshly than animals were treated. And the Hebrews built the treasure cities of Pithom and Rameses, built roads and tombs and monuments for the Pharaoh.

But the Pharaoh was not content. He still feared the Hebrews, although they were enslaved. For they did not die under the yoke. They lived and bred and their numbers increased. It was most strange. Although the Hebrews were weaponless and enslaved and crushed under their burden, still the Pharaoh feared they would rise again, and throw off their chains, and vanquish their masters. And the Pharaoh feared the god of the Hebrews, of whom such tremendous tales had been told, but who had fallen silent. He feared that the god who had lifted Joseph out of the dungeon and set him to rule over Egypt would speak again and call his people to rise. And the Pharaoh determined to make an end to the Hebrews forever. He called the Hebrew midwives together and told them, "You who aid birth do my bidding. You shall attend the women's labors as before, and help them deliver their children. But if a son is born, you must strangle him immediately. If a daughter is born, she shall live."

But the words that God had spoken to Abraham at Moriah had become a law to the Israelites. They were not permitted to slay children. And the midwives feared God and did not do as the king of Egypt had commanded, but saved the male children. The Pharaoh called again upon the midwives and said: "Why have you done this thing? Why have you saved the male children?"

The midwives answered, "We have not disobeyed you, O lord. We have been unable to do what you said. The Hebrew women are not like the Egyptian women. They are lively during the birth pangs. They labor swiftly, and their children are born before we come to them."

The Pharaoh dismissed the midwives and pondered. He did not wish to slaughter the Israelites, because they were useful as slaves, but he wished them to die out as a people by being deprived of male children. So he did nothing. And the Hebrews worked as slaves. But they were more fruitful than ever; their numbers multiplied and they were a mighty horde.

The Pharaoh instructed his captains again, saying, "Send a man to attend each Hebrew birth. Every son that is born alive you shall cast into the river; the daughters may live."

Now, some years before this, a man named Amram, of the tribe of Levi, married his aunt, whose name was Jochebed. The man worked in the field making bricks; his wife was a slave in the house of the Pharaoh's daughter. Their firstborn was a son, whom they named Aaron; three years later they had a daughter, and the daughter was named Miriam. Then, after five years, Jochebed conceived again, and was terrified — for now the Pharaoh's word had gone out: "Kill the newborn males."

She wore loose garments to hide her pregnancy, and toiled as hard as before, so that no one would know that she was with child. When her time was upon her, she stole away and bore her child in secret. It was a boy, as she had known it would be. She hid him in a small cave for three months, and went to the cave to suckle him.

But then he grew too big to hide, and she was afraid. She cast about for a way to save her child. She thought of her mistress, the Pharaoh's daughter. This daughter was a beautiful young princess, and her husband was a prince, but they had no children. Each morning the princess came down to the river to bathe, and her maidens attended her. Thinking of this, Jochebed hit upon a desperate scheme.

She awoke her daughter at dawn and they went to the river's edge. They picked reeds called bulrushes, and Jochebed wove them into a tiny boat. She caulked the boat with mud and set it upon the water. It floated. She put in a stone and it still floated, and she knew it was good. She hid the tiny boat in the reeds and went to the cave and suckled her son. Then she took him to the river and waited there, hidden in the reeds, until she saw the princess coming down to bathe.

Jochebed kissed her infant and put him in the ark made of bulrushes. She put the boat upon the water, and shoved it out into the river until the current caught it and began to float it gently downstream.

She took Miriam by the shoulder and whispered, "Be quick and be silent. Creep along the bank and follow the ark until it is taken. Then do as I have told you."

The princess was removing her garments on the riverbank when she saw something floating past. "Go fetch it," she said, and a maiden swam out, caught the bulrush boat, and carried it to shore. The princess looked into it and wept. The baby howled, as if echoing her. She snatched him out of the boat and kissed him. "This is one of the Hebrews' children," she said.

A little girl slipped through the circle of maidens quick as a cat and went to the princess. It was Miriam. She said: "If you are looking for someone to suckle the child, I know a woman of the Hebrews whose son was taken, and she is full of milk."

"Fetch her," said the princess.

Miriam ran back and summoned her mother, who came to the princess. "I have saved this child from death," said the Pharaoh's daughter. "And I shall raise him as my own. Will you suckle him for me?"

"I have just lost my baby," said Jochebed. "Behold, lady, my breasts are big with milk. I will suckle him, and care for him as if he were my own."

And the Pharaoh's daughter was a foster mother to the boy, whom she named Moses, meaning "draw out," for she had drawn him out of the water. She loved him like a son. He lived in her house and was brought up like an Egyptian prince. And he loved his wet nurse, also. As soon as he was old enough to understand, she told him the secret of his birth, and he knew himself to be her son.

He was huge of frame like his ancestor Levi, and very powerful in his body. He learned to be a warrior and handled spear and sword, and was counted one of the royal house. Yet he knew himself to be a Hebrew, and he saw the Hebrews living as slaves under the yoke of the Egyptian, and he was of divided mind. A great confusion fell upon him, muffling his wits and slowing his speech. He envied the Egyptians, and he envied the Hebrews, the slaves — for even in their servitude they knew who they were and were unconfused.

The Pharaoh saw Moses grow up in his daughter's house, and watched him grow to be a giant of a man, skilled in weapons. And the Pharaoh hated him, for Moses was a Hebrew. But the Pharaoh did not wish to separate himself from his daughter and did not declare his hatred. But Moses knew it all the same.

One day he was walking in the field and he saw a taskmaster flogging a slave. The Hebrew fell to the ground. His back was bleeding, and he was moaning and could not arise. The taskmaster raised his whip to flog him as he lay there, but Moses walked to them and grasped the taskmaster's arm. The Egyptian pulled his arm away and struck at Moses, who caught the lash in his hand, pulled the whip away, and reversed it, swinging the stock of the heavy whip like a club. He smashed the taskmaster's skull, and the man fell dead. Moses dug a hole in the sand and hid the body, and went his way.

But he kept thinking of what he had done. Now he walked in the fields among the slaves and watched them at their work. One day he saw two Hebrews smiting each other. They used their shovels as weapons and were trying to kill each other. Moses stepped between them, grasping their shovels. "Why do you smite each other?" he said. "Do you not suffer sufficiently under the blows of the Egyptians?"

One man said: "Who set you to judge over us? Do you mean to kill us as you killed the Egyptian?"

And Moses saw that his deed was known, and he was afraid. When he returned to the palace, he learned that the Pharaoh had said: "My daughter's ward has killed an Egyptian. He is a Hebrew and has killed an Egyptian, and seeks to teach his fellows to rise against their masters. He must die." And Moses fled the palace, and went eastward out of Egypt into the land of the Midianites.

He was a stranger in the land and moved warily, for it seemed a rough, wild place after the tame vistas of Egypt. He came upon a well and rested himself. A flock of sheep went down to the well, driven by seven tall maidens. They were the daughters of the priest of Midian, and they were watering their father's flock. They drew water from the well and filled the troughs, and the animals drank. And Moses watched. The eldest of the girls, the one who led them, was a beauty, free-striding and strong, and her laughter was a shout of delight. He heard the others call her Zipporah. And Moses gazed upon her with pleasure.

Then he heard loud shouting, and a band of shepherds clad in sheepskins, brandishing their staffs, rushed upon the well and drove the maidens' flock from the watering troughs. And the shepherds threatened to harm the girls if they did not take their flock and depart. Moses arose then, and seized the leader's staff and cudgeled him until the fellow dropped senseless. The other shepherds fled. Moses bowed to the maidens but said nothing. He drew bucket after bucket of water and filled the troughs for the sheep, and said nothing. The maidens departed, driving their flock before them.

Their father, Jethro, the priest of Midian, came out to meet them and said: "How is it you came home so early today?"

"A man helped us," said Zipporah. "A stranger. An Egyptian. A mighty man who drew so much water so quickly that we were soon finished. He also drove off the shepherds who attacked us."

"Why did you not invite the stranger home?" said Jethro. "Go call him that he may break bread with us."

So it came to pass that Moses dwelt in the priest's house and told Zipporah his tale. Telling it, he was amazed. He had always been painfully slow of speech, almost tongue-tied. But this girl cast a warmth that unlocked his frozen tongue. He found himself speaking easily to her, discovering new meanings in his own experience.

He told her of the cruel, hawk-faced Egyptians, and how a flower of gentleness and kindness had sprung from that fierce people — the Pharaoh's daughter, who had drawn him from the river and become his foster mother. He told her of Jochebed, his real mother, and of the ruse that had saved his life. He told her of his father, Amram, and his sister, Miriam, and his clever brother, Aaron. He told her of his double life as an Egyptian prince who was known to be Hebrew; he told her how his rage had slowly mounted and boiled over, and how he had killed the taskmaster. And how the Pharaoh had hunted him out of the land. And he told her of the beast gods of Egypt, of cow goddess and cobra goddess and falcon god, and of the great cats carved of stone, crouching in the desert.

Zipporah listened and marveled. She thought his tale most wonderful, and the teller more wonderful still. She questioned him about the Hebrews and their customs.

He told her ancient tales he had heard from his father, Amram, tales of Abraham and Isaac and Jacob. And of Joseph, sold by his brothers into bondage — Joseph, reader of dreams, who ruled Egypt and brought his brothers there from Canaan, those brothers from whose loins had sprung the nation of Hebrews, dwelling now in bondage. He told her how, since the time of Abraham, Hebrews had cut the sign of the covenant into the flesh of their male children, and how his mother, Jochebed, had circumcised him in the cave where she had hidden him, had cut the sign into his flesh with a sharp stone.

Zipporah marveled at it all, and loved the huge, puzzled man who had come to be their guest. And Moses loved her with a great love and took her to wife. She bore a son, whom he named Gershom, meaning "stranger." "For," he said, "I have been a stranger in a strange land."

Moses dwelt in Midian with his wife and son, drove Jethro's flocks, and guarded his watering places. He began to forget Egypt. But as Moses forgot, God remembered. The Hebrews were slaves in Egypt, but they were not docile. Bondage galled their souls even more than their bodies, and they cried out to God. Their cries rose to heaven. God heard them and remembered His covenant. He looked down upon the Hebrews, searching for one to be the instrument of His will. There was no one in Egypt strong enough for the enormous task. His eye fell upon Midian, and He saw Moses.

One day Moses drove his flocks past their usual grazing places, which had been cropped over. He drove his sheep into the wild highlands of the Sinai to a mountain called Horeb. Bushes grew on its slope, and among them a taller bush, really a small tree, the acacia, whose sap is fragrant and whose wood is hard. It was winter and the leaves were brown. As Moses went near, he saw the bushes being pressed to earth by a great wind, but no wind blew. Then he saw that the bushes were bowing low, prostrating themselves before the thornbush, which did not bow. He moved closer, staring at the tall bush. It flowered as he watched, putting out large, red blossoms. The blossoms were fire, and the bush burned. It burned but was not consumed. It stood there, wearing its flame like a giant in a cloak of flame.

A voice spoke out of the bush. "Moses. Moses."

"I am here," said Moses.

The voice said: "Do not step here. Take off your sandals. This is holy ground."

The bush burned and the voice spoke out of the bush: "I am the God of your fathers, the God of Abraham, of Isaac, and of Jacob."

Then Moses knew that God's self burned in the bush. He hid his face; he was afraid to look upon God. The voice said: "I have seen the affliction of my people. I have heard them groan under the lash of the taskmaster and have heard their cries. And I have come down to deliver them out of the hand of the Egyptians; to bring them up out of that land to a good land, to a land flowing with milk and honey. You must go to the Pharaoh and bring out the children of Israel."

Moses said: "Who am I that I should go to the Pharaoh, and that I should bring the children of Israel out of Egypt?"

"You are the one that I have chosen. I will go with you, and this shall be your token. When you bring my people out of Egypt, you shall return to this place and serve me upon this mountain."

"Behold," said Moses. "When I go to the Israelites and say to them, 'The God of your fathers has sent me to you,' and they ask me, 'What is His name?' what shall I answer?"

"I am who I am," said the voice. "You shall say to the children of Israel: 'I AM has sent me to you.' You shall say to them: 'The Lord, the God of your fathers, the God of Abraham, of Isaac, and of Jacob, has sent me to you.' This is my name forever and shall be to all generations. Go! Go down into Egypt and gather up the elders of Israel, and speak my words

149

to them. Say that I will bring them up out of the affliction of Egypt into the land of the Canaanites, a land flowing with milk and honey. They shall listen to your words. Then you shall take them to the king of Egypt, and say to the Pharaoh: 'The Lord God of the Hebrews has summoned us. Now, O Pharaoh, let us go three days' journey into the wilderness that we may sacrifice to the Lord our God.' "

"And if he does not let us go?" said Moses.

"Then I will reach out my hand and smite Egypt with all my wonders. After that he shall let you go."

Moses said: "The elders will not believe me. They will not listen to my voice. They will say the Lord has not appeared to me."

"What is in your hand?" said the voice.

"A rod."

"Cast it on the ground."

Moses threw down his staff. It turned into a serpent. And Moses fled from it.

"Put out your hand and take it by the tail," said the Lord.

Moses put out his hand and caught the serpent; it became a staff again. "Do that and they will believe your words," said the Lord. "If they still do not believe, do this. Put your hand upon your chest."

Moses reached into his garment and put his hand on his chest. When he drew it out it was like a leper's hand, white as snow.

"Put it in again," said the voice.

Moses put his hand on his chest again and took it out; it had turned again to his own flesh. "If they do not believe your words," said the voice, "they will believe the serpent. If they do not believe the serpent, they will believe the leper's hand. And if they believe none of these signs, do this: Take water from the river and pour it on the dry land. It will become blood."

"O Lord," said Moses, "how can I do your bidding? I am not eloquent. I am slow of speech."

The Lord said: "Who made man's mouth? Who makes the dumb or the deaf or the seeing or the blind? You are in my hand, and all your senses. I will teach you what to say."

Moses answered, "There are so many who speak well, O Lord. Why not send one of them?"

And the Lord spoke angrily: "Is not Aaron your brother? Is he not eloquent? You will tell him what to say, and he will speak for you. And keep the staff in your hand, the serpent staff, that you may do signs and wonders and convince the doubtful."

"Shall I go down into Egypt?" said Moses. "There are men there who seek my life."

"They are all dead, these men," said the Lord. "Go down into Egypt and do what I have said."

Moses returned to his home and said to Zipporah: "We must go into Egypt. The Lord has spoken, and I must do His errand." She took the child and provisions for the journey, said farewell to her father and her sisters, and mounted her donkey with the child in her arms. Moses walked before them, and they commenced their journey.

As they rounded a mountain pass, Moses felt a swoon descend upon him, and dimly heard the voice of the Lord but could not comprehend what he heard, and he thought the voice was wrathful. "I have angered my Lord!" he cried. "He spoke to me and I doubted. I hesitated. Now he kills me!" Moses sank to the ground.

Zipporah, seized by terror, remembered the tale he had told, and ripped the garment off her child's body. She took a sharp stone and cut off his foreskin and cast it at Moses' feet, saying, "Surely, you are a bloody husband to me."

The swoon passed, and Moses rose again. He raised his arms to the sky and cried, "Thank you for granting me life! I shall do your bidding without hesitation."

Zipporah said: "I have done according to your ancient rite. I have cut the sign of the covenant into the living flesh of my child and cast his foreskin before the Lord that He might release you from His clutch. Our wedlock is sealed in the blood of our son."

She took the babe in her arms again and mounted the donkey, and they resumed the journey.

The Lord spoke to Aaron, saying, "Go into the wilderness to meet Moses."

Aaron went out of Egypt into the wilderness and met Moses on the way. They met at the mountain called Horeb , and Aaron kissed Moses, and Moses tried to tell him all that God had said out of the burning bush. But he could not find the words. The enormity of it maimed his speech, and he uttered broken syllables. He fixed Aaron with burning eyes and took him by the shoulders and shook him — and stuttered and smote himself on the face to loosen his speech, but could only utter soft howls and grunts.

Aaron struggled against his brother's clutch. But the power of those hands and the fire of those eyes somehow told him that Moses had met God face to face, and that the sight had maimed his speech, and he would never be able to utter what God had told him.

"We shall be as one creature before the Lord," said Aaron. "You are the eyes to see, the ears to hear, and the responding heart; I shall be the tongue."

Moses and Aaron crossed into Egypt. They gathered the elders of Israel, and Aaron spoke all the words that the Lord had spoken to Moses. But the elders doubted. Aaron took the staff and cast it on the ground. It turned into a serpent. The elders fled. Aaron took the serpent by the tail, and it turned into a staff in his hands. He spoke again. "The Lord has seen our affliction. He will deliver us out of the hand of the Egyptian."

But still the elders doubted. Then Moses put his hand upon his chest inside his robe. When he drew it out, it was white as a leper's hand. And the elders were afraid. He put his hand in his tunic again and drew it forth, and it was returned to his own flesh. And still they doubted.

Aaron said: "How many signs, how many wonders?" Moses dipped water from the river and poured it on the ground; it became a pool of blood on the ground. Gulls dived, screaming, to drink the blood. Then Moses passed his hand over it, and it was water again.

"The Lord speaks to you!" cried Aaron. "His words are edicts."

And the elders believed. They bowed their heads and worshipped.

Then Moses and Aaron went to the Pharaoh and said: "The Lord, God of Israel, has spoken. He says, 'Let my people go, that they may hold a feast unto me in the wilderness.' "

"Who is this lord," said the Pharaoh, "that I should obey his voice and let Israel go? I do not know this lord, and I will not let Israel go."

"The God of the Hebrews has met with us," said Aaron. "We beseech you, O Pharaoh, let us go three days' journey into the desert and sacrifice to the Lord our God, or He will fall on us with pestilence and with the sword."

"Your people have labors to perform here in Egypt," said the Pharaoh. "And you, Moses and Aaron, are interfering with their work. Get out of my sight and let your people take up their burdens again."

153

Moses and Aaron departed. The Pharaoh called his taskmasters together and said: "The Hebrews must not rest from their labors. Their burdens shall be increased. Do not give them straw to make their bricks, as you have until now. They shall gather up their own straw for bricks, and still make as many bricks each day as before. For they grow idle. They are putting aside their task and saying, 'Let us go sacrifice to our lord.' They are slaves. Slaves need no god. So lay more work upon them, and do not spare the lash."

The taskmasters went among the slaves and told them they must gather their own straw for bricks and still make as many bricks each day as before. And the people went searching for straw but could not make as many bricks as before. The taskmasters flogged them brutally, and they suffered under the lash. The elders went to the Pharaoh and said, "Why do you treat us so? We are given no straw and are told to make as many bricks as before, which is impossible. We fall under the taskmaster's lash; we are flogged until we die. We pray you, O Pharaoh, be merciful."

"You are idle, you are idle!" cried the Pharaoh. "You say, 'Let us go sacrifice to the lord.' Now return to your tasks. You shall be given no straw, and I want to hear no more complaints, or it shall be worse for you."

When the elders came out of the palace they met Moses and Aaron, who were waiting for them. The elders berated the brothers, saying, "Let the Lord look upon you and judge. You have made us stink in the nostrils of the Pharaoh. You have put a sword in his hand and he slays us."

Moses spoke to the Lord: "I have done what you said and it has made the people suffer. Why did you send me? Since I came to the Pharaoh and spoke in your name, he has done evil to us. And you have not delivered us."

The Lord answered: "Now you shall see what I will do to the Pharaoh. Now you shall see the strength of my hand. Your people shall be delivered from the Pharaoh. For I am the Lord. I appeared to Abraham, to Isaac, and to Jacob, and they knew me by the name of God Almighty. But you shall know me by a new name — Jehovah — which they did not know. Also, I established my covenant with them and gave them the land of Canaan, the land of their pilgrimage, wherein they were strangers. I have heard the groans of the children of Israel, whom the Egyptians keep in bondage, and I have remembered my covenant. Now I say this to you: I am the Lord, and I will bring you out from under the burdens of the Egyptians. I will rid you of your bondage and I will redeem you with a stretched-out arm and with great judgments. I will take you to me for a people and I will be to you a God. And I will bring you to the land that I promised."

Moses and Aaron went again among the Hebrews and spoke the Lord's words. But the people were anguished in their spirit. They were crushed under their cruel burdens, and they did not heed the brothers.

Moses spoke again to the Lord, saying, "They will not heed me."

The Lord said: "Go to the Pharaoh again."

"I did speak to him!" cried Moses. "I spoke to him through Aaron, but he did not heed my words. My people groan under their burdens; they die under the lash."

The Lord spoke: "Go again to the Pharaoh and speak my words again, demanding that he send the people of Israel out of Egypt. If he refuses, he will feel the weight of my displeasure. I will lay my hand on Egypt and summon disaster. I will utter great judgments and bring the children of Israel out of Egypt."

Again Moses and Aaron went to the Pharaoh, and Aaron spoke the Lord's commands. But the Pharaoh did not heed their words. Then Aaron cast down his staff and it became a serpent. The Pharaoh summoned his sorcerers and they cast down their staffs, which became serpents. "Behold!" cried the Pharaoh. "Your magic is ordinary, and not to be feared."

But the serpent that had been Aaron's staff pursued the other serpents and devoured them. "Your serpent does not terrify me," said the Pharaoh. "Get out of my sight! Your burdens shall be increased."

The Lord spoke again to Moses, saying, "The Pharaoh's heart is hardened. He refuses to let the people go. Return to him and show him another sign, which I shall teach you."

Moses and Aaron returned to the Pharaoh. He met them on the palace grounds near the riverbank. Aaron said: "The Lord, God of the Hebrews, has sent us to you. He says, 'Let my people go, that they may serve me in the wilderness.' "

"The very words I heard yesterday," said the Pharaoh. "They have not changed. Nor have I changed."

"Behold," said Aaron. He raised his staff and smote the river. There before the eyes of the Pharaoh and his servants the water turned to blood. Moses and Aaron departed.

In the days that followed the fish of the river died. And the river stank. The Egyptians could not drink its waters. Their wells and fountains gushed blood, and they could not drink. The Pharaoh consulted his oracles and his magicians and his wise men, and did not relent. He ordered new wells dug and sought clean water. But the river ran blood.

The Lord spoke again to Moses. "Return to the Pharaoh. Repeat my words."

Moses and Aaron went to the Pharaoh, and Aaron said: "Our Lord says to you, 'Let my people go, that they may serve me.' "

"I will not," said the Pharaoh.

"Behold," said Aaron. He stretched his rod over the river. Frogs leaped out of the river, a multitude of frogs. They climbed out of the river and swarmed into the palace. Moses and Aaron departed.

In the days that followed, they stretched their staffs over the streams, over rivers and over ponds, and frogs swarmed out of all waters — into houses, into bedchambers, and onto the beds, into ovens and kneading troughs. The land of Egypt was covered with frogs. They were unclean; they were a vermin and a pest.

The Pharaoh called for Moses and Aaron and said: "Ask your lord to take the frogs away, and I will let your people go."

"When?" said Moses.

"Tomorrow."

"By tomorrow the frogs will have departed from your houses, your bedchambers, and your kitchens," said Aaron. "We will entreat our God, who shall call off this pest of frogs."

They left the palace, and Moses spoke to the Lord, saying, "Your will has prevailed. Call off the frogs."

The frogs died in the houses, in the villages, in the fields. The people gathered them into heaps, and the land stank. But when the Pharaoh saw that the frogs were dead, he broke his promise.

The Lord spoke again to Moses and instructed him. And Aaron stretched out his rod and smote the dust of the earth, and the dust turned to lice. And lice crawled upon men and beasts, and all the dust was lice.

"Can you do such enchantments?" cried the Pharaoh to his sorcerers. They took heaps of dust and tried to make lice, but the dust remained dust. Then they spoke spells, trying to kill the lice on man and beast, but they could not. And the lice crawled and were foul.

"We can do nothing, O King!" cried the sorcerers. "We cannot match these enchantments. This is the finger of their god." But the Pharaoh's heart was hardened, and he did not heed his counselors.

Moses and Aaron returned to the Pharaoh and said: "Let our people go."

"No!" cried the Pharaoh.

"Hearken," said Aaron. "If you do not obey the Lord in this, He shall send a plague of flies. Swarms of flies shall descend like a black cloud and shall come into your houses and on the food that you eat, and on your cattle. They shall bite fiercely and crawl with their filthy feet. Observe, O Pharaoh. Flies shall be everywhere but in the land of Goshen, where the Hebrews dwell, so that you may know that God has separated His people from yours, and you will understand His sign."

The Pharaoh did not answer. Aaron raised his rod, and the sky blackened with a swarm of flies. They hung between earth and sky and made a foul dusk. They swarmed upon the Egyptians and into their houses, into barns and sheds. They crawled upon man and beast and bit and moved upon them with filthy feet.

Then the Pharaoh called upon Moses and Aaron and said: "Sacrifice to your god, if you must. But do not go into the desert. Sacrifice here."

"No," said Aaron. "We cannot do that."

"Why not?" cried the Pharaoh.

"We sacrifice calves. We take a calf and cut its throat, and roast its meat, and offer its tender parts upon a stone altar that we raise to the Lord — a calf or cow, as the case may be. But we cannot do that here, O Pharaoh, in your land, where the cow is worshipped as a goddess, as Hathor, your cow goddess. If we sacrifice here, before the Egyptians, they will stone us to death. We must go three days' journey into the wilderness, and sacrifice to the Lord according to our own manner."

"Go into the wilderness," said the Pharaoh. "Sacrifice to your god in your own way. But call off the flies."

"We shall entreat the Lord to do so," said Aaron. "But see to it, O Pharaoh, that you let our people go and do not deal deceitfully with us."

They departed and spoke to the Lord, and the flies disappeared. When the Pharaoh saw that the flies were gone, he broke his promise again. Moses called upon the Lord and was told what to do. Moses spoke to

Aaron, and they went again to the Pharaoh.

Aaron said: "The Lord, God of Israel, sends this message: 'Let my people go, that they may serve me. If you do not let them go; if you harden your heart again, then I will send the cattle pest to attack your herds. Your cattle shall die, and your horses, your donkeys, your camels, your oxen — all shall die of the pest. Your cow goddess shall not save them. And observe, O Pharaoh, that not one head of cattle belonging to the Hebrews shall die. The pest falls tomorrow.' "

Aaron and Moses departed. The next day pestilence began to rage among the royal herds. It spread from herd to herd. The cows' udders dried up and they gave no milk. They parched and died. Also, bulls and calves, all the cattle. The plague spread to horses, to donkeys, to camels, to goats, and fell upon the sheep. They died and lay in heaps in the field. The plague raged through all the herds and flocks of the Egyptians, cutting down the animals like grass. But the herds and flocks belonging to the children of Israel were untouched; not one beast died. The Pharaoh turned away from this dread sight, and he did not let the Hebrews go.

The brothers returned to the Pharaoh. They found him in the place where bread was baked. "Out of my sight!" he cried. "Foul enchanters! Leave my presence before I slay you."

Moses reached into an oven and took a handful of ashes and tossed it into the air. The ashes were taken by the breeze and floated upward, and became a small dust. The dust spread and fell upon the faces of the Egyptians. As the Pharaoh watched, the faces of his wise men and magicians and captains and bakers all broke out in running sores. Boils swelled on their faces, and broke, and became sores that did not heal. The dust spread, and the priests of Egypt were afflicted with boils and sores and could not perform their rites, for now they were unclean.

The Pharaoh was stubborn. He hardened his heart and turned away, and did not obey the word of the Lord.

"What shall I do?" said Moses.

The sky spoke: "Go again to the Pharaoh. Go to the hard-hearted one and have Aaron say what I tell you."

Again Moses and Aaron entered the throne room and stood before the Pharaoh. Aaron said: "These are the words of the Lord, God of the Hebrews: 'I will plague you and I will plague your people, O Pharaoh, so that you may know there is none like me on all the earth. I will stretch out my hand and smite you and your people, and you shall be cut off from the earth. I will show you my power that my name may be declared throughout all the land.' "

The Pharaoh sat on his throne and said nothing. Moses and Aaron raised their hands. Hail began to fall out of the blue sky. Strangely it stormed when the brothers called. The hail was mixed with fire, and the blue sky thundered. Fire ran along the ground, and there was a storm of hail throughout the land of Egypt. Man and woman and beast were killed in the field. And the hail blasted the grass of the field and scorched the crops and broke every tree that stood. But in the land of Goshen where the Hebrews dwelt, no hail fell.

The Pharaoh called for Moses and Aaron and said: "I have sinned again. Your lord is righteous and I am wicked. Now entreat your god to cease his mighty thundering and his fire and hail, and I will let you go."

Aaron said: "As soon as we are gone out of the city the thunder shall cease, and no hail shall fall."

They departed. The thunder stopped, and the lightning, and there was no more hail. But as soon as the storm stopped, the Pharaoh hardened his heart again, and again broke his promise.

Moses and Aaron returned to the Pharaoh. "How long, O King?" cried Aaron. "How long will you refuse to humble yourself before our Lord? How long before you let our people go? If you do not do this, our Lord will send another plague, one more terrible."

The Pharaoh conferred with his wise men, who said: "How long shall this man be a snare to us? Let the Hebrews go, or Egypt will be destroyed."

The Pharaoh said to Moses: "If I let you go, whom will you take with you?"

Aaron said: "We shall go with our young and our old, with our sons and our daughters, and our flocks and our herds. We shall go into the desert and hold a feast unto our Lord."

And the Pharaoh said: "No! I will not let you all depart, only the men. The women and children I will hold hostage so that I know you will return to your tasks."

"What the Lord wants must be given without stint or abridgment," said Aaron. "That is not what the Lord wants or what we require."

The brothers departed. Aaron raised his staff over the land. He smote the air. An east wind sprang up, and blew all that day and all that night.

And in the morning the east wind was freighted with locusts. An enormous swarm of locusts rode in on the east wind and covered the land like a living carpet. They covered Egypt, covered the realms within and the coasts beyond. No man had ever seen such a sight. Locusts covered the earth and the land was dark with them. They ate herb and stalk and every plant the hail had left standing. They ate the fruit off the trees, and ate and ate until no green thing remained.

The Pharaoh called for Moses and Aaron and spoke in haste, crying, "I have sinned against the lord your god and against you. Now, therefore, forgive, I pray! Entreat your god to call away this crawling death."

There before the throne, Moses raised his hand and turned his palm. The wind turned. The east wind backed up and became a mighty west wind that blew away the locusts, blew them into the Red Sea and drowned them all. In an hour all the locusts were swept from the land of Egypt and not one remained. But when the Pharaoh saw that the locusts were gone, he hardened his heart again, and broke his promise.

Moses obeyed the Lord and stretched out his hand toward heaven, and a darkness fell over the land of Egypt. A darkness so thick and heavy it was like a weight upon the head of each man. Never had there been such a thick darkness. And it lay on the land for three days. No flame could live in this choking blackness, flame of candle or flame of torch, and there was no light in the houses. But all the huts of the Hebrews were lighted by torch or candle.

The Pharaoh called Moses and Aaron to him and said: "I have decided to let you go. And you may take your women and your children. All of you may go. Leave only your flocks and your herds."

"It is not to be considered," said Aaron. "Our cattle, also, shall go with us, and there shall not be a hoof left behind. The Lord requires our cattle, also."

"But your flocks and herds are the only ones left alive in Egypt. The others have been stricken by the plague." The Pharaoh could not bear to see his land stripped of cattle, and he cried: "Get out of my sight! Take heed to yourself and never appear before my face again, for the day that I see you, you shall die."

Moses spoke now instead of Aaron. He spoke to the Pharaoh for the first time in his own voice and said: "You have uttered truth for the first time. I shall see your face no more." And they left.

The Lord said to Moses: "I will bring one plague more upon the

Pharaoh. One more time shall my hand lie upon Egypt. Afterward you shall depart. Now speak to your people, Moses. Before you go, let every man take something of value from his Egyptian master, and let every woman take something from her mistress — all manner of treasure, whatever you can carry, jewels of silver and jewels of gold. Spoil the Egyptians."

The Pharaoh sat on his throne and waited. He had hardened his heart against the Hebrews and would not let them go, and had set the taskmasters upon them again. Nevertheless, he knew that another plague would fall upon the land, and he waited.

God spoke to Moses, saying: "This month shall be to you the beginning of months; it shall be the first month of the year to you. Speak now to all the congregations of Israel, saying, 'On the tenth day of this month each man shall take a lamb, a lamb without blemish, a male of the first year. And he shall keep it alive four days, until the fourteenth day of the month. And the whole assembly of the congregation of Israel shall kill the lamb in the evening, and take of its blood and mark the two sideposts and upper doorposts of the houses. They shall roast the flesh in fire and eat of it with unleavened bread and with bitter herbs. Do not eat it raw or sodden with water, but roasted with fire. Eat it all up, and do not let anything remain; anything that remains burn with fire. But eat in haste — with sandals on your feet and staff in your hand. For this night I pass through the land and smite all the firstborn of Egypt, both man and beast. Against all the gods of Egypt, cow god and falcon god and cobra god, I will execute judgment. I am the Lord. And as I pass over Egypt, smiting the firstborn, I shall recognize the blood upon your doorposts and it will be a sign to me that a Hebrew lives therein. When I see the blood, I will pass over you, and will not smite your firstborn, but pass over and smite an Egyptian house.

"It is the Lord's Passover. And this day shall burn in your memory forever. You shall observe it as an ordinance forever. And it shall come to pass when your children shall say to you, 'What do you mean by this service?' you shall say, 'It is the sacrifice of the Lord's Passover, for the Lord passed over the houses of the children of Israel when he smote the Egyptians, and delivered our houses.' "

Moses went among the people and told them all that the Lord had said. They bowed their heads and worshipped.

On the tenth day of the month each man selected a lamb. It was kept four days, then killed. On the fourteenth day, each man dipped his hand in the blood of the lamb and marked the doorposts of his house. Then the lamb was roasted and eaten with unleavened bread and bitter herbs. And the people waited.

And the Pharaoh waited. He sat on his throne and waited. Nine times has that nameless god cursed us, he thought. He has killed our cattle and poisoned our waters and smitten us with vermin and sent strange storms upon us. Yet Egypt, wounded, still lives — and I still rule, and the Hebrews are my slaves. I will not let them go!

Then, as he sat in his throne room that night, a sound came to him. A huge, formless sound like the wind, the wind crying in a human voice. A vast multitude of voices, growing louder and louder, coming nearer and nearer, drowning all other sounds in a giant howling of grief.

A mob of people swept aside the guards and stormed into the palace. They stormed into the throne room and pressed about the throne, weeping. "Speak," said the Pharaoh, and they stammered out their tales. And the Pharaoh knew the nature of the tenth plague. The firstborn child of every family in the land, the eldest son or daughter, all were being stricken in the hours of darkness. One moment, full of life and health; the next instant, without warning, their eyes rolled back, showing only the whites, their bodies went rigid, and they died where they stood.

The Pharaoh rose from his throne, raising his arms to heaven. "No!" he cried. "Fiend god of an accursed race, you shall not rob me of my slaves. Do your utmost — I will not let them go!"

Whereupon, he bade his guards herd the people from his throne room, and summoned his high council. His chief courtiers came to him, led by his son, prince of Egypt, the lean, hawk-faced young man who would succeed him on the throne.

He arose to embrace his handsome son, the only person in the world, man or woman, he had ever loved, and heard himself howling like an animal. The boy's black eyes had gone white, the supple body was stiffening in his arms. The prince tried to speak but could not; the breath rattled in his throat and no words came. And the Pharaoh, the richest, most powerful man in the world, watched his son petrify and die, and could not help him.

The Lord moved among the families of Egypt and death walked with him, scything down young men and women in the flower of their youth. Eldest son and eldest daughter, firstborn of servant and firstborn of priest. Firstborn of captain and firstborn of millhand — all were dying in the plague. It was the night of the Lord's Passover, and He strode across the land, smiting the Egyptians with His sword of vengeance, and passing over the houses whose doorposts were marked with the blood of the lamb.

Howling in his grief, the Pharaoh spoke names. Again and again he called for Moses and Aaron. Servants raced into the night and summoned the brothers. They came, and the Pharaoh cried, "Take your Hebrews and depart! Take your flocks and your herds and begone! Go — and take your curse with you!"

The Egyptians now were mad with haste. They refused the Hebrews nothing that would speed their departure. They gave gold and silver and treasure of every kind. "Begone!" they cried. "Go in haste or we all must die!"

The Hebrews took their dough before it was leavened, and bound their kneading troughs to their shoulders. They coffered up what they had taken from the Egyptians, the gold, the silver, the gems, and the garments; they loaded their donkeys and departed.

Moses went first to the tomb of Joseph. He broke open the sepulchre and took the coffin, thus fulfilling Joseph's dying wish. The coffin rode behind Moses, as he led his people out of Egypt.

Jacob had taken sixty-seven people into Egypt. Now Moses brought out six hundred thousand men and women, and a multitude of children. He led them into the wilderness and headed for the Red Sea. It was the largest migration ever to move over the face of the earth. They swarmed across the plain. They were a nation in size, but not a nation. They were a rabble. They had been slaves. Fear had been flogged into their bodies; shame had eaten into their souls. The men were less than manly. The women, concerned more about their children than about themselves, were stronger. But they, too, were terrified of the Egyptians, terrified of being pursued and slaughtered. They were tattered and filthy.

They followed Moses through a pathless wilderness, a great waste of desert and mountain. The sun of an Egyptian April flayed them by day; the night wind racked them with cold. They realized that they were wandering — that Moses had lost his way. They grew sullen and vicious.

Moses called out to God, "We are lost! Show us the way." He looked

The Red Sea

163

up into the burning blankness of the sky, awaiting an answer. None came.

"What is your will, O Lord? Must we wander in the wilderness until we perish?"

The sun's naked light fell like a hammer on Moses' upturned face. The sky began to spin. He closed his eyes. When he opened them, the sky had darkened, although the sun was still shining. The darkness broke away and became a cloud, a cone-shaped cloud, spinning furiously on its point, funneling down to earth. The mob of Israelites cringed to earth, moaning with fear. The cloud changed shape as it dropped, becoming a great, fleecy ram with upflung head and curling horns, its legs bent as if galloping upon the bright air. The cloud ram floated eastward. Moses followed it, and the people followed him.

All day long they straggled after the cloud — which changed shape as it went, becoming a bear, a whale, a winged ship, a white camel, but in all its shapes sailing east. Then, at the end of day, its fleece took red fire from the sinking sun. And — most strange — after the sun had gone, the cloud kept burning in the darkness and was a pillar of fire. And Moses kept following it, and the people staggered after him.

God had come down into the wilderness. He went before His lost children as a pillar of cloud by day and a pillar of fire by night. He led them to the shore of the Red Sea, and they camped there.

In Egypt the Pharaoh was raging because he had been forced to let them go. "Why have I done this?" he cried. "They are my slaves; they belong to me!" His rage swelled until he could bear it no longer, and he gathered his army. He took six hundred brass-wheeled chariots driven by picked warriors and pursued the Hebrews. He followed them through the wilderness with chariots of brass, and horsemen and footsoldiers. They pressed hard on the trail of the Israelites, and they glittered and jangled like a metal dragon.

Moses waited at the edge of the sea. He waited for the Lord to speak. But waiting was hard. The beach seethed with people. Never was such an encampment seen on earth. The Israelites had no tents. They slept on their wagons, slept on the earth. Moses and Aaron stood on a low hill, overlooking the camp. Aaron said: "Behold our people! Is this a nation chosen by God? It looks like a swarm of maggots when you lift a log."

"Pity them," said Moses. "They hate their past and dread their future."

"It is you they hate," said Aaron, "for leading them out of the safety of

164

bondage. They will turn on you and rend you limb from limb — and me, also."

"For shame!" roared Moses. "You who held the serpent staff and threatened the Pharaoh in the name of the Lord, do you doubt His word? Do you dare to doubt? He who made man out of dust can make a mighty nation out of a swarm of maggots."

Now the Hebrews heard a clanging and saw a far glitter, and they knew the Egyptians were coming. The elders rushed to Moses, crying, "Behold, they come! They will slay us! Were there not graves enough in Egypt, wonderful tall graves, that you took us to die in the wilderness? It would have been better to stay and serve the Egyptians than to come here and die in our own blood, pierced by lance or sword."

"Fear not," said Moses. "Stand still, and await the salvation of the Lord. He who took you out of Egypt will not deliver you again into the hand of the Egyptian. Stand and wait."

He spoke to God, who said: "Do not cry out to me. Speak to Israel. Kindle their spirits with your words, so that they become men instead of slaves. At dawn the chariots will charge. You shall not be frozen with terror; you shall not break and flee. But you shall march toward the Red Sea as if it were dry land. You shall march toward the sea and trust in Him who made the world and placed mountains and seas at His pleasure, whose touch makes mountains tremble and seas divide. Therefore march upon the Red Sea tomorrow, when the chariots charge, and go before your people, holding your staff in your hand. When you come to the sea, raise your staff. And be of good heart, for I march with you."

The Lord stood between the Egyptian army and the Hebrew encampment. He stood there as a pillar of black cloud. The blackness could not be pierced, so the Egyptians could not attack at night and had to wait until the sun rose.

That night Moses and Aaron spoke to the people and prepared them. Then at the first light the children of Israel roused themselves and marched toward the sea. Moses and Aaron walked before.

Behind them they heard the rattle of weapons and the terrible wheels of brass and the battle cries of the Egyptians, which were like hawks screaming. Bewildered, terrified, the ragged horde streamed after Moses and Aaron, who walked steadily toward the edge of the sea. Moses stood on the shore and stretched out his staff. An east wind blew, a wind that sheared like a knife and divided the waters. Before the astounded eyes of the Israelites stretched a road, running along the bottom of the sea, running out of sight toward the far shore.

Moses and Aaron stepped upon the road and the people followed. The waters were a wall on their right hand and on their left. They gazed in wonder at these huge, trembling walls of water that churned with a mighty force within, and wished to tumble back to their place but were restrained by an invisible hand. And they walked along the strip of dry land that divided the waters.

The Pharaoh had reined up his horse in amazement, and all his army halted. His stallion pawed the sand as he watched the children of Israel marching into the sea. He thought they meant to drown themselves, choosing death by water rather than death by sword. He saw the sea divide and the road appear — and the people march along it between towering walls of water.

The Pharaoh raised his sword. The army moved in glittering ranks to the edge of the sea. The king sat his horse and looked out on the divided sea. He could not believe what he saw — the strip of dry land between the towering walls of water, and the horde walking that impossible path, vanishing eastward into a great dazzle of morning light. He grew more wrathful as he watched his slaves vanishing, that enormous force of unpaid labor that had built the treasure cities of Pithom and Rameses, and walls and roads and pyramids. He raised his sword again.

The army surged to the edge of the sea — horsemen and spearmen and brass chariots — and went down into the sea bed. They pressed forward along the dry strip of land between the walls of water. Aha, thought the Pharaoh. The sea that divides for them is divided for me. Where they flee, I pursue. And when I reach them, this sea will run redder still.

The Egyptians pursued the Hebrews along the sea-bed road. But Moses had stopped and stood waiting, as the rest of his people went forward. He stood there, staff in hand, and watched the Egyptians. They were coming fast. They were charging between the walls of water, horses foaming, swords glittering. They were very close now. But he wanted the entire army to come upon the sea bed, and there were still troops on the beach. He waited. The first chariot was almost upon him now. He heard the snorting of the horses and the deadly chuckle of the hub knives that spun on the axles of the chariot wheels. He saw that the beach was empty. "God be with me," he said, and raised his staff.

The east wind fell and the sea returned. In an instant the chariots and the horsemen, the archers and the spearmen, were swallowed up. There was nothing but a third wall of water rearing up before Moses — so close that the end of his staff was wet. But behind him the waters were yet divided and the road remained. He turned and went after his people.

The Israelites walked upon dry land in the midst of the sea between the walls of water, and passed to the other shore. And of all that mighty army not one Egyptian was left alive. They were all drowned when the waters returned. And the people feared the Lord and believed Moses.

Moses and Aaron shouted with joy, and their words became a song:

> I will sing unto the Lord, for He has
>> triumphed gloriously,
> Horse and rider has He thrown into the sea. . . .

Miriam, their sister, took a timbrel in her hand and led the women in a wild dance, singing as she danced. Moses sang, also, and the people sang after them:

> The Lord is my strength and song
> And has become my salvation.
> O Lord, you sent your wind
>> against the Egyptians
>> and the sea covered them.
> They sank like lead in the mighty waters.
> Who is like you, O Lord, among their gods?
> Who is like you for glory and holiness?
> Who is like you for doing wonders?

And as they sang and danced, the shackles of fear melted, those invisible chains that had bound their souls and kept them slaves. In the joy of victory they became men and women, never again to be slaves.

Now, the shortest route from Egypt to Canaan did not lie across the Red Sea at all. The best road ran northward along the Mediterranean coast to the northeast border of Egypt — through the land of the Philistines, who held the seacoast of Canaan. But Moses knew he could not follow this road. It was the great highway for caravans, studded with Egyptian fortresses and custom posts. And even if they could pass through the Egyptian troops, who would be hunting for their runaway slaves, they would have to cross the land of the Philistines, guarded by the walled harbor cities of Gath and Ashkelon and Ashdot, and patrolled by Philistine horsemen.

So the best route was barred to Moses, and he knew that he would have to lead his people through the wilderness where he had once been a fugitive — that vast, barren plain in whose highlands the Midianites dwelt, where his father-in-law, Jethro, still dwelt. Through the land of the Midianites he would have to go, and through the mountain passes of Sinai, past Horeb, where he had first heard the word of God, going eastward through that terrible wilderness, passing to the south of Canaan; then into the Syrian hills, where those who survived the journey could cross the Jordan and go into the promised land.

Now, as they stood on the far shore of the Red Sea, a great wasteland spread before them — desert and mountain, sand and rock, little water, few trees. And the long journey began, a journey that was to last forty years.

They did follow a road, one of the oldest in the world, a road that was a thousand years old when Abraham was born. Less a road than a path, it had been worn into the earth by the feet of slaves, trudging from the Nile to the Sinai mountains, where they had been forced to labor in the mines, digging copper out of the earth, gouging lumps of turquoise and amethyst from the rocks, and dragging the heavy loads on sand sleds to the Nile.

The day's march was the distance between water holes, where they might drink and fill their goatskin bags, and where the cattle could crop the grass that grew only near water. Then Moses led his people eastward into the wilderness. For two days they found no water. By the third day they had drunk the last drop from their goatskin bags. Still they found no water. The desert sun knelt low, scorching them. They burned with thirst.

"O Lord," said Moses, "we die of thirst. Lead us to a river or to a spring."

He walked on. He saw a glimmer in the distance. He did not cry out. For heat waves dance and shimmer in the desert, cruelly deceiving the sight of those who thirst. The people had been fooled before by such mirages, and each time they had viciously abused Moses and Aaron, as though the brothers had flung the mirage in their path to keep them on the move. Moses said nothing, but walked on. Now he could not only see the glimmer of water but smell its coolness, and see the grass growing at its edge. It was no mirage, but a small river.

With a great cry, the people rushed forward in a jostling mob. They knelt upon the bank, thrusting their heads into the water, drinking in great gulps. Moses saw one man stagger away, clutching his belly, retching. Everyone was retching, spewing out the water, screaming. Some tore out handfuls of grass and ate it. Moses scooped up some water and drank. It was bitter; it was foul. It could not be swallowed. He spat it out.

He saw people crouching on the grass in front of him, glaring up at him, like beasts ready to spring. He backed off. He joined Aaron, who had not drunk, and they stepped behind a screen of rocks.

"They will kill us," said Aaron. "They will kill us and drink our blood."

Moses raised his arms to the sky. "How have I sinned, O Lord?" he cried. "You have led us to a river, but its waters are bitter and we can not drink."

The sky spoke: "Cut down a tree."

"No tree grows here," said Moses.

"A tree grows. Cut it down."

There, in the space between the rocks, stood a tree where no tree had been. Moses cut it down.

"Cast it upon the waters," said the Lord.

Moses bore the tree to the river and threw it in. The people watched sullenly. A man shouted, "Now throw yourself in. Drown yourself, old fool, or we shall slay you here on the banks of this bitter river."

Moses reached down and scooped up a handful of water. He tasted it. He cried out with joy and knelt at the riverbank and plunged his head in. The water was sweet and cool. "Drink!" he cried. "The Lord has provided!"

The people rushed to the river and drank and filled their waterskins. The cattle cropped grass. Moses named the river Marah, meaning "bitter."

They struck deeper into the wilderness. They managed to find enough water, but there was little grass. The cattle began to die. The dead animals were butchered, but the meat spoiled in the heat. By the end of a month the herds were gone, the sheep and the goats and the cattle, and there was no meat. They baked unleavened bread, flat sheets of it on the rocks, using no fire; the sun was hot enough to bake it. They ate bread and dried lentils.

Then the grain was gone. There was nothing. They ate goatskin bags.

169

Moses and Aaron feared to move among them now, for the people howled with rage when the brothers passed. "You took us out of Egypt, where we had plenty to eat," cried one of the elders. "We sat by the fleshpots in Egypt; we filled our bellies with meat and bread. Now you have brought us into this wilderness to kill us with hunger."

The brothers walked alone. "Why do they not learn?" said Aaron. "They have seen the Lord deliver them from bondage. They have seen the waters divide before them and fall back upon their enemies. They have seen Him sweeten the bitter waters. Still they do not trust Him. How many wonders must be performed?"

"Four hundred years of slavery have done this to them," said Moses. "To survive, a slave must blind himself. He must deafen himself, cut off his capacity to understand. He must ignore all evidence of how the world is, because his world is unbearable."

"They have been taken out of bondage," said Aaron.

"Now they are like limbs unbound after tight bandaging," said Moses. "The blood rushes in, swelling dry veins, and it is agony. Their freedom is agony still. They have no faith, no endurance. Perhaps this terrible journey is God's way of teaching us to be men."

"Perhaps," said Aaron.

Moses left his brother and went into the desert, for the Lord spoke most clearly to him when he was alone. As he went, he watched a flight of birds across the sky, flying north in a vast migration. The Egyptian soothsayers believed that each flight of birds was a thought crossing the mind of their falcon god, and they studied bird flight to predict events. They also cut open doves to examine their entrails for clues to the future.

"I am no Egyptian," said Moses to the sky. "I cannot read your intention in bird flight or bird gut or the casting of lots. I'm all Hebrew now, and must question you until I am answered. Why do you starve us, God?"

The Lord answered: "Behold, I will rain food from heaven. You shall have flesh to eat in the evening; in the morning, bread."

Moses went back and called the people together. "Tonight you eat," he said.

"What is there to eat?" they shrieked.

"The Lord will provide."

A malicious whisper hissed from elder to elder.

Moses said: "Your murmurings are not against me, but against the

Lord. But He will prove Himself again. He will rain food from heaven."

The crowd was silent. He could feel their need and their anger beating about him like waves. He went to his tent.

That evening the elders came rushing to his tent. "We are lost!" they cried. "The sky is falling!"

Moses went out. Dark things were drifting down. "They are quail coming down to rest," said Moses. "The Lord has sent them. Go take them for your pot."

"Catch quail by hand? They will fly away."

"Behold!" said Moses. He went toward the enormous covey of quail. He walked among them. They sat there, motionless. He reached down and seized two of them and strode back, a quail in each hand.

"Gather the birds," he said. "Take what the Lord has provided."

The quail did not fly away when the people went out to get them. That night they roasted the birds, and ate.

The next morning, after the dew had risen, there on the ground lay small white things, glistening like hoarfrost. It was not hoarfrost. Its fragrance was like newbaked bread, but sweeter. "Manna . . . manna . . ." the people cried. This means "What is it?"

Moses said: "This is the bread the Lord has given you. Gather it up and eat."

When Moses led them from that place they had enough food for many weeks.

They wandered in the wilderness, and the way was long. They had drunk all their water and they found no more. They spoke against Moses, saying, "Give us water that we may drink."

Moses said: "You complain against me, but you anger the Lord." He went out alone and cried, "What shall I do with this people? They are ready to stone me."

The Lord said: "Take them to the mountain called Horeb, to the place where I first appeared to you. I shall be there again. There is a rock there, before the ascent begins. Take your staff and smite the rock."

Moses returned to the encampment and gathered the people. He led them across the wasteland that lies between the Red Sea and the Sinai mountains. It was an enormous plateau they were crossing, a flat place of hot, yellow sand — no waterholes, no grass, no trees. The ground does not rise gradually here. The mountains thrust out of the ground in stark crags. Moses could see them looming in the distance. He led his people toward the mountain. They murmured and grumbled and complained, but he did not let them stop. People were fainting with thirst and falling. Moses harried the others. They lifted the fallen and pressed on.

They came to the mountain. This was Horeb,where Moses had heard God speak out of the burning bush. Now he heard a mighty wailing from the horde that followed him. "We thirst! We thirst!"

Moses stepped forward, shaking his staff at the others to make them stay where they were. No man but Moses could lift this staff. It was an entire young tree, uprooted, and trimmed of its branches. He approached the mountain alone, and the people gaped at him in dull wonder. They hated and feared this huge, bearded wizard, who drove them day and night toward an unknown place. Nevertheless, they followed him, and, complaining bitterly, did what he said. Now, as he stood stretching his arms toward the peak of Horeb, it seemed that he was speaking to the mountain, but they could not hear his words.

"O God," cried Moses, "I have come to your mountain, and the people thirst!"

"Take your staff," said the Lord. "Smite the rock."

Moses saw a big rock standing like a footstool at the base of the mountain. He raised his staff high and struck down. The rock split. A stream of pure water gushed out. And the people drank.

They rested that night in the Horeb valley — but it was no place for strangers to spend the night. The valley belonged to a tribe called Amalek, who pastured their horses on its grassy slopes, and by night rode out to raid caravans. The male children of this tribe rode before they walked, and from their earliest years were trained in the use of sword and spear, noose and dagger. They grew up to be superb horsemen, savage fighters, and a terror to travelers.

They came now at night and camped in a half circle about the people of Israel.

Moses watched as the people slept. He did not know what he feared, but he feared something and could not sleep. Now as he prowled among the tents he heard noises upon the hillside — the creak of harness and the clank of arms. Looking up, he seemed to see movement on the slopes, and, sometimes, the watery gleam of moonlight on metal. For the raiders, feeling contempt for the Israelites, scarcely bothered to conceal their movements. And Moses knew that these horsemen of the night would wait through the hours of darkness and attack at the first light.

"O God," he whispered, "these are the Amalekites. They are savage and disciplined. They will fall upon us like wolves upon a flock of sheep and eat us alive. What can we do?"

God answered in a whisper, but the whisper filled the valley with a great rustling sound like the wind. "You must stand and fight."

"Will you help us?"

"When you begin to help yourselves."

Moses chose a young man named Joshua to be his captain. Joshua was a stalwart man, brave and stubborn. Out of all that vast throng, he was the only man who bore suffering without complaint, and spoke out against those who reproached Moses and sighed for Egypt.

Moses said to him: "We are about to be attacked. You are my captain. Choose your men."

"There is not much choice," said Joshua. "None of them has ever fought before."

"There is always choice," said Moses. "Pick the youngest and strongest."

Joshua said: "This is a rabble, choose as I may. The Amalekites are trained warriors, without mercy, without fear."

"And without God," said Moses. "Do you think that He who made man from a handful of dust cannot make our young men into warriors?"

"All I know of God is what you tell me."

"Then I tell you this: Pick the youngest and strongest of our men. Lead them out at dawn to fight the Amalekites. I will stand on top of the hill and implore God for victory."

Joshua led the men out before dawn, and Moses climbed to the top of the hill. Aaron went with him, also Hur, who was the husband of Miriam. Now red fire touched the sky, and the Israelites saw their enemy for the first time.

The Amalekites, wise in warfare, knew that the sight of one's blood gives courage to the enemy — so they wore red robes in battle, and red headcloths so that their blood would not show. Now, riding out of the dawn with the red sky at their back, they seemed cloaked in fire. Joshua had exhorted his men, trying to instill them with courage, and they stood awaiting the charge, making a hedge of spears. But they saw red demons riding out of a bloody sky. They heard the merciless drumming of hoofbeats growing louder and louder; they heard the Amalekite war cry, which was the screaming of eagles multiplied. They saw red light smoking on horses' manes, red light dripping off curved swords.

And the Israelites had been slaves for four hundred years. For sixteen

173

generations they had been trained to submit; fear had been drilled into their marrow. They fled. And the horsemen were among them. Curved swords rose and fell. Men fell in their blood. And those who were left kept fleeing, and the horsemen pursued, cutting them down as they ran.

But there was one who did not flee. Joshua raged about the field, and his great sword was a circle of fire about his head. He ducked under the horses' bellies, slashed upward at their riders, and where he passed, he left empty saddles and dead bodies. At first, the Amalekites had tried to take him alive, for he was a big, powerful young man, one who would fetch a high price in the slave market at Damascus. But they saw they could not let him live; he was too dangerous. Three picked horsemen began to hunt him across the field, trying to hem him in and butcher him where he stood. But he was racing away across the plain now, on a course that would intercept the nearest group of his fleeing men. He cut across their path and tried to rally them. He shouted at them, implored them, beat at them with the flat of his sword, but they feared the enemy more. They flowed around Joshua as a river parts upon a rock, and kept running.

Then Joshua, heart bursting with grief and rage, turned to face the horsemen — ready to be killed rather than to survive this shame, but wanting to drag some Amalekites into death as he fell.

Moses stood on the hilltop and watched what was happening on the field below. Aaron and Hur were with him, watching in horror. Their faces were wet with tears. Moses' face was like one of the rocks. He stood huge and motionless; only his white beard moved in the wind. He could not understand what he was feeling. He had trusted God, and ordered his men into battle, and now saw the battle becoming a massacre. But Moses felt only love for the God who had broken His promise — puzzled love and utter faith. He looked up at the sky and raised his staff in a kind of final salute to Him who wielded such wonder and terror.

A hook of blue fire seared the pink sky. It touched the tip of his staff. And Moses felt an awful, scorching power pass through his arm and his rigid body. He saw the fire striking down toward Joshua's sword.

The Amalekites had surrounded Joshua, hacking down at him with their curved swords. He was wounded in many places. One sword cut had laid his jaw open, and he was choking on his own blood. He felt his life draining away, and knew that he was about to fall. He cast one last look at Moses on the hilltop, murmuring, "Forgive me, Master. I have done poorly today." He saw blue fire hook out of the sky, saw the flame pass through Moses and stab down, down, flowing past the horsemen and touching his own sword, which turned radiantly blue.

Suddenly, the blood in his mouth tasted like wine. And the air was scorched and strangely sweet; he drew it deep into his lungs, and felt a gigantic strength flushing through his body. He no longer felt the blades slashing down at him. He reached for a horse, seized it by mane and girth band, and, as the Amalekites gaped in wonder, swung it off its feet, the startled rider still clinging to his saddle. Joshua held horse and rider over his head, then hurled them at the knot of horsemen. Man and animal fell under the hurtling weight, horses kicking and screaming, men tangled in the harness, unable to rise.

Joshua gave them no time to recover. He leaped into the tangle. His great sword rose and fell, scattering diamond-blue splinters of strange light over the plain, summoning the Israelites like signal fires, drawing them back onto the field, toward the miracle of Joshua restored and the Amalekites fallen, drawing them out of panic, back to manhood. With a savage, joyous shout, they raised their weapons and charged the Amalekites, who had recovered from Joshua's assault and were surging forward again. The Israelites raced across the field to meet the galloping horsemen. The dismounted men met the cavalry head-on. They flung themselves under the flying hoofs, grasped the riders' legs and pulled them out of their saddles, then met them sword to sword.

Only a few moments had passed since the holy fire had touched Joshua, but what had been a shameful stampede was again a battle. And the Israelites were holding their own. The fire from heaven touched each man, lending him power he had never known. They dragged the Amalekites from their saddles and attacked them furiously with their swords. Those who had dropped their weapons in flight fought like animals, flinging themselves at the red-robed ones, wrestling them down, strangling them with their bare hands.

Moses' arm grew weary. The staff dipped. Then the Israelites lost their special strength, which was the power of God in them, passing through Moses' staff. And the Amalekites rallied. They regrouped their horsemen and charged again. The Israelites broke.

Moses tried to lift his staff again, but his arms were without strength. He called upon Aaron and Hur, and sat upon a stone. Aaron stood on one side, Hur upon the other, and they propped up his arms. His hands were heavy upon the staff and he held it high. Again the men of Israel felt themselves fill with a marvelous, hot, fighting energy. Yelling to his men, Joshua ran toward the line of horsemen. His men followed, running swiftly. And the Amalekites, seeing them come, seeing the wild light on their faces, turned and galloped away. But the men of Israel outran the horses. They cornered the Amalekites in a rocky pass and killed them all.

Moses built an altar there. He called it Adonai-nissi, or "the Lord is my banner."

A voice spoke out of the mountain: "Moses! Come near."

Moses climbed toward the voice. He had been there before, but not so high. He found himself inside a wild battlement of rocks, mighty towers of stone carved by some vanished water. Black lava, green copper, red, brown, a deeper red, and whites strangely mixed with lilac and black. All in flame tones. The sun, like a golden whip, flogged the very color of blood out of the hills. And the voice of the Lord was the wind among the rocks.

"I will come to you in three days," said the voice. "I will show myself to the people. Go to them; let them make themselves clean. I shall appear on the mountain. But set bounds around its base; if they come too near they will die."

Moses went back to the tents of Israel and consulted with Aaron. Aaron was fearful, but Moses ignored his fear. Stammering with great intensity he told his brother exactly what to do. And Aaron was incapable of saying no to this huge old man with his blazing eyes and beard like spun sea foam.

Moses then called the elders together, and Aaron addressed them, speaking for Moses: "We have seen what the Lord did to the Egyptians, how He smote them with storm and pestilence, how He bore us out of bondage on eagle wings. Now He has brought us to this place to hear His commandments. If we obey His law and keep His covenant, then He will treasure us above all people. We shall be a kingdom of priests and a holy nation. O elders of Israel, are you ready to do His will?"

"We are ready," answered the elders.

"Bathe yourselves in clear water," said Moses. "Wash your clothes. Prepare for the coming of the Lord."

The people bathed themselves and washed their clothes and waited. Two days they waited.

On the morning of the third day they saw a thick, black cloud descend on the mountain. Great hooks of lightning scorched the air; there was enormous thunder, and the terrible blasting voice of a trumpet. Moses led them toward the mountain. They cried out in terror as they saw flame burst from its crest. They fell back then, and Moses did not stop them, for the heat was becoming unbearable. The mountain was a furnace gushing fire and smoke. The crash of falling rock mixed with the thunder and the voice of the great trumpet, and the people were terrified.

The elders said to Moses: "You speak with Him. If He speaks to us, we shall die. If we go closer we shall die."

Moses called out to the Lord, "They are afraid. Will you speak with me?"

The voice spoke in thunder: "Come to me on the mountain, and receive my commandments."

Moses said to the elders: "Wait here."

He went up into the mountain, and a cloud covered him. Moses vanished into the cloud. And the glory of the Lord dwelt on that mountain. The sight of that glory was like fire to the children of Israel. The mountaintop burned. Moses was in that smoke and flame. And there he stayed for forty nights, and the Lord spoke to him as He had never spoken to anyone before. And Moses listened as no man had ever listened before. Every word that the Lord uttered, Moses carved on a tablet of stone. For forty days and forty nights he did not eat or drink or sleep, but nourished himself on God's words. They were like meat and drink to him; they filled him with joyous strength. The days and weeks passed like a flash, for Moses did not wish that voice to stop; he did not wish to leave that presence.

Now, the first law that God gave to Moses was this: "I am the Lord thy God, and thou shalt have no other gods before me." And even as God was uttering His first law on the mountain, the people below were preparing to break it.

For forty days and forty nights the people of Israel waited at the foot of the mountain. And Moses did not come down.

Now they were afraid with a different fear, and their fear made them forget their vows. Now, without Moses, who was like a father to them, they crouched like children in the dark.

They remembered the many gods of Egypt — the falcon god, the cow goddess, the cobra god. They remembered the cat gods, whose statues crouched in the desert, guarding the tombs of kings and promising death to any invader. They remembered these undemanding beast gods — to whom many an Israelite had secretly prayed — and they yearned for something to worship that would not utter itself in plague and volcano, strict edicts, and long ordeals. They went to Aaron and said: "Where is Moses?"

"On the mountain," said Aaron.

"He is dead. He has been burned in the fire. He will not return. God has departed and Moses is no more. What shall we do?"

"Wait for him," said Aaron.

"No!" they cried. "We must have gods. The wilderness is huge and we do not know our way. And our enemies wait. We must have gods!"

"There is only one God," said Aaron. "He speaks to Moses. And Moses will descend and return to us."

"No! Do not deceive us. Moses is dead and God has departed. You must make us gods, gods that will go before us and lead us out of this wilderness."

They pressed upon Aaron, gabbling and screaming and waving their fists. Aaron was afraid. He said to them: "Bring me gold, the gold in your coffers and more. Break off the golden earrings that your wives wear, and your daughters. Break all their earrings and bring the gold to me."

When the women heard that the gold was to go for a beautiful new god that they could hear and touch and that would not trouble them with ordinances; when they heard that such an easy god would be theirs again, they tore the earrings from their ears and gave them to their husbands — not only their earrings, but brooches, armlets, anklets, necklaces, and rings. All that was gold they gave, and rejoiced.

Aaron took the gold and cast it into a huge pot, which stood on a fire. The gold melted, and he made a golden calf, and cried, "This is your god, O Israel!"

The people recognized it. They remembered the cow goddess of Egypt, which their masters had worshipped when they were slaves. Aaron made an altar for the calf, and said: "Tonight we feast the golden one. Tonight we worship."

They killed goats and roasted them, and placed them upon the altar as burnt offerings. They feasted and drank, and began to dance. Miriam played the timbrel, and danced, and led the women in dance. And they all sang. The dance grew wilder and wilder — until the sound of it rose to the mountaintop.

The Lord said to Moses: "Go! Go down! Your people are corrupt. They have made a golden calf and are worshipping it, crying, 'This is your god, O Israel.' I have seen them, and behold, they are a stiff-necked people. Therefore go, and leave me alone, for my wrath grows hot against them. I will consume them. You alone shall be left, Moses, and of you I will make a nation."

Moses pleaded with the Lord: "Why does your wrath grow hot against your people, whom you brought out of the land of Egypt with a mighty hand? If you slay them, the Egyptians will say: 'It was for mischief He brought them out, to slay them in the wilderness and consume them from the face of the earth.' Oh, my Lord, turn away from your fierce anger and repent of this evil against your people. O God whom I love, remember Abraham, Isaac, and Israel. You swore to them that you would multiply their seed as the stars of heaven and give them Canaan as an inheritance. I beg you, O Lord, do not destroy Israel."

And the Lord changed his intention. He heeded the words of Moses, and withheld His wrath.

Then Moses went down the mountain. He carried two gigantic tablets of stone. Written on that stone was all that the Lord had told him during those forty days and forty nights. At the foot of the mountain he found his young captain, Joshua, who had been waiting for him all this time, and had been absent from the assembly.

"Hearken, Master," said Joshua. "There is a noise of war in the camp."

"No, not a noise of war," said Moses. "Not the voice of those who shout for mastery, nor the voice of those who plead for mercy. It is the voice of those who sing and rejoice and make strange revel."

He strode away, holding the two enormous tablets of stone, and Joshua followed. When they reached the camp, it was full night. Fires burned; huge shadows danced. Among the shadows danced the people. They danced before a stone altar. On the altar stood a great golden calf, the calf of Hathor, the cow goddess, mother of the beast gods of Egypt. The sound of Moses' voice, bellowing with rage, froze the dance.

The dancers turned and saw Moses. He looked gigantic, standing there in the firelight, multiplied by shadows. He looked like a piece of the mountain descended, a giant carved of stone, holding two huge stone tablets. "Foulness!" he cried. "Abomination!"

179

He raised the tablets of the law. He raised high the enormous slabs of stone and smote the altar, smashing it. He used the table of the law like a great mallet. He smashed the golden calf, then stamped on the pieces, grinding them to powder. He mixed the golden powder with water, and dragged the elders to the trough and made them drink of this foul brew, for his wrath was consuming him. He seized Aaron and cried, "What have you done?"

"The people were set on mischief," said Aaron. "They said to me: 'Make us gods that shall go before us, for Moses is dead.' And I took their gold ornaments and melted them and made this calf. I was afraid they would kill me."

Moses mounted the broken altar and cried, "Who stands with the Lord? Who belongs to the Almighty God, maker of heaven and earth, the living God, whose image cannot be cast in gold?"

The sons of Levi gathered about him. Also, Joshua and Joshua's first officer, Caleb, and their young fighting men, who were drawn from all the tribes. Moses said: "Let every man gird on his sword and go from gate to gate and from tent to tent. Let every man slay his brother, his companion, and his neighbor. Let every man be slain who does not stand here with us and declare for God."

And those who stood with Moses fell upon the others with sword and spear. That night three thousand men fell. To those who were left, Moses said: "You have sinned a great sin. Now I must go to the Lord and try to atone for what you have done."

He went up the mountain and spoke to the Lord. "Oh, these people have sinned a great sin. They have made gods of gold. I pray you, forgive their sin. If not, then blot my name, also, out of the book that you have written."

The Lord said: "Go down. Lead the people to the place I have promised you. I will send an angel before you, but I will not go myself, for they have offended me."

"Will you not visit us?" cried Moses.

"I will visit you. And on that day I will visit your sin upon you."

"So be it," said Moses.

"Depart," said the Lord. "Lead the people. Lead them to Canaan, to a land flowing with milk and honey. But I will not go in your midst, for you are a stiff-necked people, and I will not go now, lest my wrath consume you on the way."

Moses said: "I thank you, Lord. If I have found grace in your sight, show me the way that I may know you. I beseech you, show me your glory. I want to see you."

The Lord said: "You cannot see my face. No man can see it and live. Stand here on this rock, and I will let my glory pass before you. I will cover you with my hand as I pass, and you shall not see my face but you shall see me as I depart. And you shall be the only man who has seen me."

There was a great flashing of golden light. It was like sunlight but it was like sound, also, and the sound was song. And its voice was more boundless than the sea's voice when it calls to the sailor. The voice stretched to the horizon and was one song, and the song was light.

Moses saw a great slab as of sapphire; the golden light sank into it and turned blue. The voice murmured, and it was a song of night and wind and sea and stars. And Moses swooned with the glory of it. When he awoke the light was ordinary, but he was filled with strength and happiness, and felt young again, and a giant in strength.

He heard the Lord's voice: "Hew two tablets of stone like the first tablets that you broke. And you shall write again upon stone the words that I utter. And when you go down from the mountain, you shall coffer up these tablets in a great chest made of acacia wood inlaid with gold, which shall come to be known as the ark of the covenant. This ark must go with the people of Israel wherever they go in their long wanderings, and become the most holy furniture of whatever temple they erect to me. Thus they shall be an eternal nation, surviving slavery, massacre, and exile, finding a home always in my law."

For many days and nights the Lord spoke again to Moses. The words that he spoke were laws and were carved on the stone. He finished and departed.

Moses took up the tablets of stone and descended. The people assembled in a mighty multitude, and he read them the words that were written on the stone, crying, "These are the statutes and ordinances spoken by the Lord, to be your law unto the last generation."

The people stared at him in wonder. His face was streaming light. It had been kindled by the radiance he had seen upon the mountain, and it burned like a star. It was too bright to look upon; they hid their eyes. And Moses veiled his face and read the words that God had uttered on the mountain:

" 'I am the Lord your God, who brought you out of the land of Egypt, out of the house of bondage.

" 'You shall have no other gods before me.

182

" 'You shall not make for yourself a graven image; you shall not bow down to it or serve it, for I, the Lord your God, am a jealous God.

" 'You shall not take the name of the Lord your God in vain.

" 'Observe the sabbath day, to keep it holy. Six days you shall labor, and do all your work, but the seventh day is a sabbath day to the Lord your God.

" 'Honor your father and your mother.

" 'You shall not kill.

" 'Neither shall you commit adultery.

" 'Neither shall you steal.

" 'Neither shall you bear false witness against your neighbor.

" 'Neither shall you covet your neighbor's wife; and you shall not desire your neighbor's house, his field, or his manservant, or his maid-servant, or his ox, or his ass, or anything that is your neighbor's.' "

It was thus that Moses gave the law, beginning with those we call the Ten Commandments, which the people of Israel were the first to receive and not the last to forget.

This was thirty-five hundred years ago. There was no law then, as we know it. The strong decreed, the weak obeyed. A king could order a subject beheaded, impaled, enslaved, or thrown into a dungeon to rot — and there was no appeal. There was no check at all upon the power of a slave owner. He could flog his slave to death, or work him to death if that seemed profitable, or use the body of man, woman, and child for his pleasure. A favorite way to correct a lazy slave was to grill him in an iron cage over a charcoal fire.

Into this world Moses strode, bearing his stone tablets. Inscribed on those tablets were laws decreed not by king, priest, or slave master, but by the supreme judge, who punished disobedience with disaster. These statutes for the first time in the history of mankind embodied the idea of justice; they restrained the strong and protected the weak. On the tablets were rules for honest and humane behavior that attached the power of divinity to the most generous impulses of the human heart, and gave them the force of law.

At first, Mosaic law was practiced only by the Hebrews — not always, never perfectly — but sufficiently to kindle a concept of righteousness, whose light has never quite gone out, even in the darkest days. Fifteen hundred years were to pass between the establishment of the law and the destruction of the Second Temple. During that time other peoples learned that the Hebrews, instructed by their God to treat one another decently, derived an inner strength that translated itself into military victory — and, when victory was denied, retained the ability to rebuild their nation after defeat and exile.

The Mosaic law was enormous in scope, detailed, absolutely specific. Besides endless rules for ritual, it ranged from an elementary code of sanitation to statutes protecting widows, orphans, paupers, and slaves.

Besides the Ten Commandments, some of the other laws inscribed on the stone tablets were:

You shall not steal, or deal falsely, or lie to one another.

You shall not bribe or coerce a judge.

When sitting as a judge, you shall not take a gift, for a gift blinds the eyes of the wise, and perverts the words of the righteous.

You shall not curse the deaf, or put a stumbling block before the blind.

If an escaped servant comes to you, you shall not deliver him to his master. He shall dwell with you in the place he shall choose.

If a stranger sojourns with you in your land, you shall not vex him. The stranger that dwells with you shall be as one born among you. You shall love him as yourself, for you were strangers in the land of Egypt.

But the great law bore heavily upon the people. Their souls flinched under the stern purity of these statutes. They stumbled into disobedience, fell into sin. In God's judgment they were not ready to enter their inheritance, and He kept them wandering in the wilderness.

Moses cried out to Him, "How long, O Lord, how long?"

The Lord answered, "Your people have sinned against me. They have broken my law and ignored my word; they have grieved and offended me. But I have chosen them and will abide by my choice. Nevertheless, they must be punished. And this is the punishment: They shall wander in the wilderness for forty years. All those who came out of Egypt shall perish in the wilderness. Of this weak and wicked generation only two men, Joshua and Caleb, shall go into the promised land."

"And I, shall I not go into the promised land?"

"You shall go to its borders but not cross into it."

"Why not, O Lord, why not?"

"You have intervened for this people. You have stood between them and my vengeance. For love of you I spared them. I must consider that they *are* you or my wrath will consume them. Yet you, too, shall perish in the wilderness. Of the generation that I delivered out of Egypt only

Joshua, your captain, and the valiant Caleb shall enter the land that I promised — these two and all the children born in the wilderness, your children and your children's children; they shall enter their inheritance. They shall be my nation."

"Then I shall have done my work," said Moses. "The task that you have given me I shall have fulfilled. I thank you, God, for the fulfillment."

So God kept the people of Israel wandering in the wilderness for forty years. By this time Moses was a hundred and twenty years old. He knew that his time on earth was ending. "I pray you," he said to the Lord, "allow me one glimpse of the promised land, although I may not enter it."

The Lord said: "Among the mountains called Pisgah the highest peak is Nebo. Climb to the top of Nebo, and I will show you the land that I have promised."

Moses felt the years fall away. Strength returned. He climbed to the top of the mountain. His eyes were no longer dim. He looked upon the land that was to be Israel's. He saw all of Canaan, from the mountains of Lebanon to the southern desert, from the mountains of Syria to the sea. Lying before him was a scimitar-shaped land of astounding variety, mirroring the richness of the world. Northward stood the mountains of Lebanon, where cedars grew. Eastward were the mountains of Syria, sloping down to the Jordan valley, where a river ran, the Jordan river, widening into a great lake at the base of the mountain where he stood. To the south, past the sullen glare of the Dead Sea, was the desert he knew so well; beyond that, Egypt. To the west, the sea. And that sea, now under a westering sun, was a pool of blue fire.

Moses stood upon Nebo, and God showed him the length and breadth of the land — its hills and streams, the wide, green fields of standing wheat, the harbors and cities, the fig trees, palm trees, and the orchards heavy with fruit, its flocks and herds and grazing places. And it was not only landscape he looked upon, but the terrain of legend. Swimming past him as he stood upon Nebo were the story fragments that had fed the hunger of his people in exile and slavery — Abraham heaping stones onto an altar as a child watched; Isaac digging his well; Jacob grappling a huge fire-robed angel; a lad in a coat of many colors riding a donkey toward his tall, bearded brothers. He heard sounds, also. The wind that grieved among the crags was Esau bewailing his legacy; the sound of the river was Sarah's laughter.

Moses stood alone upon his peak under a darkening sky. For the last time he looked down upon the land he could not enter, looked upon it all from the edge of the wilderness to the utmost sea.

"Thank you, Lord," he said. "This rich glimpse will nourish my soul through eternity."

He went down from the mountain and passed the leadership of all the tribes of Israel to Joshua. Then he died.

And of all the patriarchs and prophets and holy men of Israel, there was none like Moses, for he alone spoke with God face to face.

IN THE PROMISED LAND

F inally, after wandering in the wilderness for forty years, the Israelites crossed over into the land that God had promised. Moses was dead, and all who had left Egypt had perished on the journey, except Joshua and Caleb. So that it was a horde of young men and women, all born in the wilderness, who followed Joshua into Canaan.

Now, those who went into Canaan were very different from those who had left Egypt. Born into a nomadic life, polished by ordeal, trained in the Mosaic law by those who had heard Moses utter it, they were tough, fervent, literate. Branded upon their soul was a hatred of slavery and a contempt for idolatry. Bred into their very marrow was the conviction that they had been brought by God to Canaan to take it away from those who lived there.

In His instructions to Moses, God had assigned a portion of the land to each of the tribes descended from the sons of Jacob, very strictly defining their borders — the largest portion to the largest tribe, Ephraim; the smallest to the smallest tribe, Benjamin. Now Joshua took a census of the tribes, according to God's instructions, and set bounds to the territory each was to possess once it had been taken.

But this division of Canaan was done without the permission of the Canaanites and of the other people who dwelt there — the Philistines, the Moabites, the Ammonites, the Edomites, the Jebusites, the giant Anakim. Hundreds of years had passed since Jacob and his sons had departed from Canaan and gone down into Egypt. And the departure of the Israelites had been far more welcome than their return.

All the people who dwelt in Canaan — except the Philistines — were descended from the Hamitic tribes. Canaan was the son of Ham; Ham was the son whom Noah had cursed. But the most powerful of these peoples, the Philistines, were descended from Cretan sea raiders who had taken the west coast of Canaan and held it against all enemies. The Philistines were a clever, warlike people. They were seafarers, fishermen, pirates. They built the great harbor cities of Gath and Ashkelon. They worshipped the fish god, Dagon, and Astarte, the moon goddess, great whore mother of the groves.

The Moabites and Ammonites dwelt in the hills ridging the Dead Sea valley. They were fierce mountaineers, goatherds, robbers. They worshipped a fire god, Molech, an idol made of brass, hollowed like an oven. On feast days the hollow was filled with charcoal, and the charcoal set on fire. The idol grew red hot; into its brass hands live babies were put to roast.

The other Canaanite tribes worshipped the stone idol, Baal, and the moon goddess, Ashteroth, another name for Astarte. They, too, practiced temple prostitution, child sacrifice, ritual orgy, and ritual murder.

These rites were a foulness to the Israelites. The Hebrews were so fired with the idea of a single, all-powerful, law-giving God that they went into battle with a matchless zest. They felt that they were not only reclaiming their land but cleansing it of abomination.

Rumors of the Israelites had traveled before them — terrible rumors of a people who despised all customs and all gods except their own. And this God was invisible and almighty; He devoured all other gods, and awarded miraculous victories to His chosen ones. This God wielded calamity as a warrior used his spear — hurling tempest upon the enemies of Israel, assailing them with volcano, tidal wave, earthquake, and shooting fever-tipped arrows of pestilence into their camp. Now these Hebrews were coming out of the wilderness into Canaan, claiming that their dreadful God had promised it all to them, from the Nile to the Euphrates.

A mighty host gathered against the children of Israel. Joshua had to fight for every foot of land. And God gave him victory. Nevertheless, there were defeats, as well.

DEBORAH

At this time there was no king in Israel. For the first three hundred years after they reached the promised land, each tribe was governed by a council of elders. However, from time to time, when menaced by an enemy, or seeking to cast off the yoke of an oppressor, a single chieftain would emerge from one of the tribes, and, by virtue of his strength and his wisdom, would be accepted as leader by all the tribes. These leaders were called judges. There were thirteen judges, twelve men and one woman. The woman's name was Deborah, and she was perhaps the most remarkable of all the judges.

She dwelt in a village on the slope of Mount Ephraim. She was a wife and a mother. She was also a woman whose nights were full of dreams and whose days were full of deeds. For often the Lord appeared to her at night and told her what to do, and she would arise to do it. Her fame as a prophetess spread, and the children of Israel went to her for judgment. She sat under a palm tree and heard disputes, summoned witnesses, and gave judgment. And the palm tree she sat under was looked upon as a sign of God's favor toward her, because palm trees did not grow in that mountain region; hers was the only one.

Now, at this time, the children of Israel had swerved from the Lord's narrow path, and had begun to worship the gods of the Canaanites — the blood-hungry stone god, Baal, and Ashteroth of the groves. God was angered. In His anger dwelt spearmen and chariots. His anger was defeat and death and slavery. He gave Israel into the hands of Jabin, king of the Canaanites, whose captain was Sisera, a mighty warrior. Sisera attacked with nine hundred iron chariots and scattered the men of Israel. He delivered the land to his king, who oppressed the Israelites most cruelly for twenty years.

One night, Deborah spoke to God: "What of your covenant, O Lord? Did you save us from the Pharaoh only to give us into the hand of Jabin?"

God answered: "Jabin shall be given into the power of a woman." He said no more, but sent Deborah a dream of battle.

The next morning, she summoned a man named Barak, a man of valor, who would not bow to the Canaanite and who was a fugitive in the hills. "God has spoken to me in the night. He named you, Barak. Go, muster ten thousand men of the tribe of Naphtali and of the tribe of Zebulun, and array them for battle upon the heights of Mount Tabor."

"Ten thousand men," said Barak. "Sisera will bring a hundred thousand against us. And he has iron chariots, and we have none."

"The Lord will walk with you," said Deborah. "In His presence, numbers cease to count. He multiplies the few and reduces multitudes. Besides, chariots cannot charge uphill."

"I go up the mountain with my men; then what?"

"Then, the Lord promises, Sisera will lead his army through the valley along the bank of the river Kishon. You shall attack downhill and drive the Canaanite into the river."

"When I hear your words, it all becomes possible," said Barak. "But I know that when I leave you this battle order will seem again like the death trap it is."

"Then I will go with you," said Deborah, "and keep you believing in the impossible. It is right that I should go, for the Lord said He would give Sisera into the hands of a woman. Up! Let us go! The Lord goes before us!"

Barak gathered ten thousand men of Naphtali and Zebulun, and led them to the top of Mount Tabor. Then Deborah, standing on a peak of the mountain with Barak, felt herself sinking into a dream. For she saw exactly what she had seen in her night vision: Canaanite spearmen marching through the valley between the hills; the iron chariots along the river bank — and Sisera on a huge, black horse, the sun glinting off his brass armor.

"It is well," she said to Barak. "These are the men, these the chariots, this the array the Lord showed me in my dream. Blessed be the name of the Lord! He stands with us today. Salute Him with your sword, brave Barak, and take what the Lord has given you."

Barak raised his sword high and shouted a shout so loud and joyful that the hills rang with it, and the sound of it fired his men's hearts with courage. The Israelites surged downhill and struck the ranks of Canaan like a mailed fist. The Canaanites broke. They were driven into the river and drowned in their armor. Some made a stand, and Barak and his men cut them down like men scything down wheat.

Sisera's horse was killed beneath him. But he leaped off and hacked his way through his attackers, and plunged into a copse of trees. He ran with long strides, and drew away from his pursuers. He went swiftly through the copse and out the other side. The sounds of battle grew dim. He walked over a darkening plain. He was exhausted, battered, faint with hunger, but he did not lie down to rest because he saw the glow of a fire far off. He forced himself to walk, and finally came to a tent, which he recognized as a Kenite dwelling. The Kenites had wandered in the desert with the children of Israel and gone into Canaan with them, but they did not war against the Canaanites.

He saw a tall woman come out of the tent. "Who are you?" she said.

"I am Sisera, captain of hosts, under Jabin, the king. I am wounded and weary, and men hunt my life."

"I am Jael," said the woman. "Come into my tent and do not be afraid."

He went into the tent. She led him to a pile of rugs, and he lay down. She covered his feet with a mantle.

"I pray you, give me a little water to drink, for I am thirsty."

She took him cool milk in a cup. He drank it, and she covered him again. He said: "I must sleep now. Please stand in the doorway. If anyone comes, asking for me, say there is no man in your tent."

Jael means "mountain goat." She had been given this name because, as a girl, she had roamed the hills wild and free. She could run uphill as swiftly as a goat, and jump nimbly from rock to rock. Her husband was a smith, and she helped him in his work. She stood at the anvil and smote the red-hot iron with a hammer. She was a tall, lithe, powerful woman. Although she was a Kenite and the wife of a Kenite, her heart inclined toward Israel. For she had heard the old tales and knew that the Kenites were descended from Jethro, the father-in-law of Moses.

She stood in the door of the tent, looking at the huge stars studding the sky, and thought, He is Sisera, captain of hosts, a mighty man. But now he flees through the night like a runaway slave, like a whipped boy. Surely, his army has been defeated by the Israelites. And if so few can scatter the iron chariots of Canaan, then their God must have marched with them, trampling the iron chariots, crushing them like grasshoppers under His foot. Truly, He is mightier than stone Baal or Ashteroth of the groves.

She saw a star fall, trailing light, and thought, Does He crack the stars like walnuts? How big are His hands? She shuddered, half with dread, half with delight. Has He brought this captain to my tent? Has He brought him to me for punishment?

She went back into the tent, stepping softly. Sisera slept. She went out again and pulled a tent peg from the ground. It was a long, heavy

196

wooden stake, sharpened at the end. She took the sledge hammer off the anvil, and went back into the tent. She stood over Sisera. He moaned and stirred in his sleep, but did not wake. She put the point of the stake to his temple, raised her hammer, and struck down. The peg split his head and drove deep into the earth. He died without waking.

She heard a noise of horses. She went out of the tent. A troop of horsemen reined up. Their leader spoke to her. "I am Barak. I seek a Canaanite named Sisera — a large man in brass armor, wounded perhaps. Have you seen anyone?"

"Descend, my lord," said Jael. "Come into my tent."

"I cannot," said Barak. "I seek Sisera."

"You have found him. Come inside."

Barak followed her into the tent and saw Sisera lying in his blood. His head was nailed to the ground by a wooden peg. Barak cut off that head and took it to Deborah. She was old. But she seized a timbrel and danced as joyously as a young girl. She led the people in dance and song. She sang:

> The kings came and fought.
> Then fought the kings of Canaan
> >   in Taanach
> >   by the waters of Meggido.
> They fought from heaven; the stars
> >   in their courses fought against Sisera.
> The river of Kishon swept them away,
> >   that ancient river,
> The river Kishon.
> Blessed above women shall Jael
> >   the wife of Heber
> >   the Kenite be; blessed shall she be
> >   above women in the tent.

The Canaanite king was utterly defeated. He did not dare attack the children of Israel again. And his sons inherited his fear, and kept the peace. There was peace for forty years.

SAMSON

There was a man named Manoah, whose wife was barren. She prayed to the Lord, saying, "Please open my womb."

Manoah spoke to the Lord, also: "O God, do not let her wither in her prime. Let her bear."

An angel appeared to the woman and said: "The Lord hears you. You shall bear a son. Now you must beware: Do not drink wine or strong drink; eat nothing unclean. The son you bear shall be consecrated to God, and shall deliver Israel from the hand of the Philistine. As a sign of this mission he must keep his hair uncut and braid it into seven locks. He shall be given giant strength; its virtue shall reside in his hair."

The woman ran joyfully to her husband. "We are to conceive! I am to bear a son! An angel told me."

"How do you know it was an angel?"

"He was terrible and bright. I hid my eyes. He was beautiful and said strange things. That I must not drink wine or eat anything unclean. And that the boy's hair must never be cut. What does that mean?"

Manoah was a learned man. He said: "The law given to Moses lays down rules for those selected by God for some special purpose. These men do not drink wine or eat anything unclean. Nor are they permitted to cut their hair."

"I don't know what it all means," cried the woman. "But I know that I am to bear, and I know that he will be special. And I thank God for him."

She conceived, and drank no wine or ate anything unclean. She bore a son. Her happiness bathed him in a golden light when she first saw him, and she named him Samson, meaning "like the sun."

At the age of eight Samson was working in the fields with his father, and doing the work of a grown man. He was almost as tall as his father; it was plain to see that he would be of gigantic stature. His wits were keen, also, and he asked questions all day long.

"How is it, Father, that we dwell in the land that God promised us, but that the Philistines dwell here, also, and hold the strong places, and are better fighters? What good is such a promise?"

Manoah said: "The Lord brought us here, but He made it clear that the promise was ours to keep, also. For when Moses gave us the law we vowed to keep it. And we have continually broken it. We forget our own customs and adopt the ways of the Philistines and Canaanites and yearn after their easy gods. We kiss our hand to the moon, and worship the moon queen in the groves and high places. Even that stone demon, Baal, who eats babies, even him we run after, forgetting our own God, maker of heaven and earth. And every time we of Israel offend the Lord in this way He punishes us. He deprives us of our strength and courage. And when the enemy comes against us, we submit. We have seen the Amorites and the Moabites and the Hivites; now we are oppressed by the Philistines."

The boy had been listening intently all this while. "When I grow up," he said, "I will smite the Philistines."

He grew to be a young man, and he was as big as two men. He had the strength of a wild bull, and men feared him. But he was merry-hearted and playful, and he hungered for adventure. Alone and unarmed he went to the Philistine city of Timnah, an unheard of thing for an Israelite to do; it was certain death. The Philistines gazed in wonder at this huge young Hebrew with his unsheared pelt of hair. They thought him more a bear than a man, and were careful not to offend him.

A young woman, fresh as flowers, looked at him from the window of her house, and he saw her. She smiled at him, and he blazed up like stubble. He raced home to his parents.

"I have been to Timnah! I saw there a daughter of the Philistines, and I must have her. Get her for me as wife."

His mother cried, "Are there no women among the daughters of your people?"

His father said, "Can you not choose a wife among your own kind? Must you go courting among the daughters of the uncircumcised?"

"Get her for me, Father. She pleases me well."

His parents saw that he was moved beyond himself. And since there was always a margin of him that was unknowable to them, they did not stand against him in this, and gave him their blessing.

He went down again to Timnah, and was passing through a vineyard, when a lion attacked him. He heard the terrible roar that is meant to freeze the spirit of the prey, making flight impossible. But his blood danced as though he had heard a trumpet. He whirled about and caught the lion in midleap. He held it aloft, and with one quick movement shifted his grip to its back legs, and dashed out its brains against a rock.

He went into Timnah and saw the maiden at the window. She smiled at him. He said: "I want you. Will you have me?"

"I never thought to marry a Hebrew," she said. "But they are all afraid of you, the young men. Yes, I will. Send your father to see my father."

Samson returned to the lion. He wished to give her its skin to make into a cape. A swarm of bees had lighted in the lion's body and had made honey there. Samson took the combs of honey and ate some, and took the rest to his mother and father. They ate the honey and it was good. He did not tell them from where he had taken it. And his father went to see the girl's father, and the marriage was arranged.

Samson gave a nuptial feast for the young men of Timnah, according to custom. There were thirty young Philistines, hot-blooded and arrogant — and not well pleased to see this girl, who was the beauty of Timnah, marry an Israelite. But they dared not move against Samson.

He was joyous, and said to them: "I will give you a riddle to solve, with a wager attached. If you can guess the answer in seven days, I will give you each a fine new set of garments. If you do not guess it, then you shall give me thirty sets of garments."

"Speak your riddle," they cried.

He said: "Out of the eater came meat, out of the strong, sweetness."

For three days the young men tried to guess, but no one could begin to think of an answer. They went, all thirty of them, to Samson's bride, whom he had left in her father's house, for she was loathe to go among strangers. The leader of the young men said to her: "Coax the answer to the riddle out of your husband so that we may win our wager."

"I want him to win!" she cried.

"Oh, no. If you don't do as we say, we will burn your house down, and you in it. For you enticed us to a feast that we might be robbed by your Hebrew, and there is death in our hearts."

These were the most savage young fighting men of Timnah, eager for the kill. And she was afraid. When Samson came to her, she wept and said: "You don't love me. You must hate me."

"What do you mean?"

"This riddle. Why don't you tell me the answer? If you loved me, you would tell me."

"I want to keep it secret till I win the wager."

She wept and wept, and said: "No, you don't love me. You won't tell me what I want to know."

He told her. And on the seventh day the young Philistines went to him and said: "We have guessed the answer. Honey and lion, lion and honey!

Ho, ho, ho!" They jeered him. And he knew that they had gotten the answer from his bride and did not know what more she might have given them. But he held back his rage and departed.

Now he knew the time had come for him to smite the Philistines. He went down to the great harbor city of Ashkelon, killed thirty men, stripped the corpses of their garments, and took them back to Timnah to the young men who had won the bet. Then he sought his wife. But his father-in-law stopped him and said: "What do you want?"

"My wife," said Samson.

Her father said: "After the affair of the riddle I thought you hated her. So I gave her to another young man as wife. She has a younger sister, though, very beautiful. Take her, instead."

Samson said: "No matter what I do to the Philistines now, I shall be more blameless than they."

He went into the woods and caught three hundred foxes and tied their tails together, two by two. Between the tails he tied torches, and set the torches on fire. The foxes ran toward the river to put the fires out, but the fields and orchards of the Philistines lay between them and the river. As the foxes passed through, they set the crops on fire. The shocks burned, and the standing wheat, and fig trees and olive trees.

When it was reported that Samson had done this, the young Philistines went to Timnah and set fire to the house belonging to his father-in-law. The house burned and all in it, his wife and her father. Samson hunted down the young Philistines who had killed his wife and slew them all. They fought against him with sword and spear, but did not draw a drop of his blood. He cut them down like grass, and they died where they stood.

Now the Philistines hunted Samson like a wild beast. He went up into the hills and dwelt on the top of the rock called Etam. This rock towered above villages belonging to the tribe of Judah. The Philistines marched against Judah and encamped near the villages. They sent heralds, saying, "We want the man, Samson, who has fled to your rock. Deliver him into our hand, or we shall take your villages and slaughter you all, men, women, and children."

A band of Judeans climbed the rock and found Samson. They said: "Do you not know that the Philistines are our rulers? What have you done to them?"

"I have done to them what they have done to me and mine," said

Samson. "I avenged the blood of my wife."

The leader of the Judeans said: "We have come to deliver you into the hands of the Philistines."

"Do you intend to kill me yourselves?" said Samson. "Must I fight my brothers?"

"We shall not kill you," said the Judean. "But we must bind you fast and give you to them. Else they will attack our villages and kill us all, men, women, and children, as they have vowed."

"Bind me," said Samson. "Deliver me. They may not thank you for your gift."

They bound him with rope and took him down the rock, and handed him over to the Philistines. A picked guard of Philistines, big, burly men in helmets and breastplates, raised their spears against him. He lay trussed on the ground and they pressed about him, raising their spears high. He did not wait for death. He felt no fear. He fixed his eyes on the sky and waited calmly for the word of the Lord.

The Lord did not speak, but He sent a spark of His spirit to earth, and it lodged in Samson's breast. He felt a great, warm glow swelling within him. He took a huge breath and stretched his arms. The ropes that bound him burst like threads. He leaped up, leaped away from the half circle of Philistines. He had no weapon, but saw the skeleton of an animal lying on the ground. He snatched up a big bone; it was a jawbone — the jawbone of an ass. Swinging it like a club, he charged the astounded Philistines. The bone cudgel was a white blur in his hands. Bone crashed against metal, and the metal split. Bone of ass crashed against bone of man, and the bones of the men were shattered. He moved among them steadily like a reaper advancing on a stand of corn. With his bone sickle he winnowed their ranks, killing a thousand of them. The rest fled. He threw away the jawbone and danced for joy. And he named the place Ramath-lehi, meaning "jawbone hill."

His labors had brought a great thirst upon him, and there was nothing to drink. Dead bodies lay in the stream and the water was unclean. He burned with thirst. He said to the Lord: "You have delivered me from my enemies. Must I now die of thirst?"

The jawbone split; he heard it crack. He picked it up and looked at it in wonder, for he had beaten in the helmets of the enemy with it and it had not chipped. Now it was split. He lay it on the ground again, and water spouted from the bone. It was clean, cold water, pure as a spring. He

202

drank of it, and revived, and said: "Thank you, Lord, for wonders large and small."

After this great deed, the Philistines feared Samson and retreated to the cities of the coast. And the people honored Samson. The tribe of Dan and neighboring tribes chose him judge, and he judged them for twenty years. His judgments were wise, but he never put on the gravity of a judge. He kept a certain playfulness of spirit and a joyous heart before the Lord. And the Lord was pleased and stoked up the fires in Samson.

He was a huge man and his passions were a furnace. And the Philistine women beckoned to him. One day he went into Gaza, a city of the enemy, went there carelessly, as was his wont, defying attack. He went to the house of a certain harlot. He was seen, and the word flashed among the Philistines: "Samson is here." They set an ambush. Armed men lay in wait for him. They hid in the shadow of the city's gate. They were sure that they would kill him this time. The walls were too high to climb, and manned by sentries. The gate was the only way to come in and go out.

The captain of the guard said: "He will not leave her till morning. We shall wait all night. He will come out in the morning and meet his death."

But Samson arose at midnight and left the harlot's house. There was no moon; it was very dark. Silently as a deer he raced to the city gates. Before the sleepy men knew what was happening, he had burst through them, knocking them out of his way as if they were children. He came to the gate. It was locked. He seized the iron bars, and with an enormous tug tore the gates out of the stone walls, and bore the entire huge grating aloft. He held the gate between him and his attackers, and their weapons clanked vainly against the massive bars. He laughed a great, joyous laugh and strode off with the gates on his shoulders. He carried them to the top of the hill that overlooks Hebron.

The Philistines held a war council in Gaza. All the chieftains went, and the captains. "Behold," said the high chief. "Behold the broken gates of this city. Who would believe that one man could tear them out of their stone sockets and bear them on his shoulders to the hill above Hebron? But a man did so. His name is Samson. He is the Israelite who has plagued us for many years, and driven us from our inland holdings. We must rid ourselves of this man once and for all."

The warriors brandished their swords, crying, "Kill! Kill! Kill!"

"Yes, of course," said the chief. "Killing is what is needed. But with this man it is easier to say than do. He is enormous. His strength is beyond imagination. When you behold him, you feel not like a man but like a grasshopper. Let us not underestimate him. He wrings the necks of lions as if they were sparrows. With the jawbone of an ass he slaughtered a thousand of us and routed our army. And you have seen the shattered walls of this city, where once the tall gates stood. By force alone we cannot overcome him. We must use guile. But he is not easy to trick, either. We need a plan."

A crafty man arose and said: "Even the strongest person has his weakness. We must seek out this weakness, and through that one crack in his armor deliver the death blow. Now, this man was visiting a harlot in Gaza when you sought to entrap him. And we know how he rioted among the women of Timnah. And there have been other tales. Undoubtedly, his weakness is women. He lusts for women and will dare anything when his desire is upon him. What we must do now is find a woman of great beauty. And this woman will be in our pay and will be a snare to him."

He was interrupted by a great clamor. "Yes! Yes! A woman. Yes! Yes!" And there were other shouts: "Delilah! Delilah! Delilah!"

"Who is this Delilah?" he said.

"A little whore from the valley of Sorek," said the chief. "But very expensive. And worth it."

"So be it," said the crafty one. "Let us employ this worthy Delilah."

The lords of the Philistines came to Delilah's house in the valley of Sorek and told her what they wanted. The crafty one said: "This man Samson is a giant, true. But his strength is beyond that of a hundred giants. It must have some magic source. And every magic can be nullified if you know its secret. What you must do, Delilah, is entice him and see wherein his great strength lies, and by what means we may prevail against him. If you find out what we need to know, we will each give you nine hundred pieces of silver."

"Fifteen hundred," said Delilah.

"Do you dare to bargain with us?" said the chief.

"You have set me a very large task," said Delilah. "My price is fifteen thousand pieces of silver, or fifteen hundred from each of you."

"You seem to think you have an alternative," said the chief. "Allow me to remind you that we here are the lords of the land. You are in our hand. All we have to do is close it, and you are crushed."

She smiled at him. "I know I'm crushable," she purred. "But what good would I be to you dead? Say fourteen thousand?"

The crafty one said: "You will have profit from him, also. He is a lavish spender."

"Oh, well," she said. "Out of esteem for you, great lords, I shall lower my price. Say eleven hundred pieces of silver from each of you."

"Agreed. Do not fail us."

She stretched and smiled. Her eyes were half closed. "Oh, no," she murmured. "I'm looking forward to this."

They departed. She wrote a letter and sent it to Samson by a servant. It read:

> Greetings, mighty one.
> I dwell in the valley of Sorek.
> I saw you striding up the hill
> > bearing a gate on your shoulders.
> My heart shivered with the anguish of love,
> > and I wept that you were a stranger.
> Let us not be strangers.
> Come to me and I will welcome you.
> Come at night.
> I am Delilah.

Her house was a bower of flowers. It was dusky, lit only by three tall candles set in silver sticks. Samson saw a young woman whose face was narrow with yellow eyes. She walked to him, and her body was lithe and indolent and full of sleepy fire, like an Egyptian temple cat whom it is forbidden to thwart, and who feeds leisurely upon doves. She greeted him. Her voice was hoarse and full of sleep. She led him to a couch, and they conversed. His desire was upon him. He took her in his arms, but she slid away.

"No," she said.

"You sent for me," he said. "Was it to mock me?"

"No one would dare to mock you," she murmured. "But I have changed my mind."

"Change it again. I am rich."

She said: "Men buy me — those who can afford it, who are not many. But I will never sell myself to you. I love you. And where love is, there can be no buying and selling."

"There can be giving and taking," he said. "If you love me, then we love

205

each other and it is all simple. Come here."

"You must prove your love. For my passion is great, and if you deceive me I must die."

"I am ready to prove my love."

"That is not what I mean. Bulls show such readiness for any heifer. I know all about men as animals. From you I wish different knowledge. I want to know you through and through. I want to read your soul."

"It resides in my body."

"Tell me a secret."

"What secret?"

"A fatal one. The secret of your strength."

He was drunk with desire. But the warrior was not quite asleep in him, and he smelled danger. "My strength is known. There is no secret."

"You are a giant in stature, but your might exceeds any giant of fable. It must have a magic source." She stroked his shoulders. "Your strength is you. I love your strength. If you love me you must let me share its mystery."

"Very well. If I am bound with green vines, then I shall lose my power and be like other men."

She drifted into his embrace. She was pliant in his arms, serpentine and inventive. Her body was a garden of spices. He took her; he glutted his desire. And it was her art to rekindle desire in the most sated lover. But now she let him sleep. She bound him with seven green vines. She set a candle in the window. A band of Philistines who had been lying in wait outside saw the signal and roused themselves. They entered the house. Samson slept.

"Awake!" she cried. "The Philistines are upon you!"

The men rushed upon the sleeping giant, but he awoke and burst his bonds like thread. He seized a sword, wrenched it from the man's hand, and butchered the Philistines before he was fully awake.

His hands dripped blood. His hair had come loose from its seven plaits and hung free. He seized Delilah. "You betrayed me," he muttered.

"And you lied to me! You lied about the secret of your strength."

"And saved my life. You bound me with vines and called the Philistines. If I had told you the truth, I would be lying there in many pieces."

"I prefer you in one piece," she murmured, and kissed his bloody hand. She slid out of his grip, into his embrace.

Her lips were bloody, but she smiled. He felt his bones melting. "I knew you were in no danger," she said. "I bound you with vines and called the men to prove your lie."

"They came when I slept. They could have killed me."

"I awoke you from sleep. Remember? I knew you could not be killed. There were only twelve of them. How could they possibly kill my beautiful ogre, who has slain a thousand in one afternoon?"

He lifted her and carried her toward the bed. "No!" she said.

"No?"

"You must go. I know that you do not love me now, and I can't bear it. Depart in peace. But depart. I shall always love you, but you must never come here again."

He departed, telling himself it was better so. But in the evening he returned. She knew that he would come back and had informed the Philistines. Fifty of them now lay in ambush in the orchard beyond her house.

He entered. She retreated. "Please go," she said. "The sight of you breaks my heart. I love you but you use me only to sate your lust. You mock me and tell me lies."

He lifted her off the floor and dandled her like a child, laughing.

"You can force me," she said. "I am powerless against you. But I cannot be enjoyed in that way."

"I shall not force you," he said. "I love you, also, foolish child."

"Then tell me the secret of your strength."

"My hair."

"Your hair?"

He was about to tell her the secret, but a last prudence gripped his tongue. "It is plaited in seven locks, as you see. If these locks are woven in a web, then my power departs."

She turned in his hands and kissed his mouth. He took her to bed, and then slept. She did not sleep. She left him and took up a spindle and returned to the bed. She unplaited his seven locks and spun them into a web. Still he slept. She set a candle in the window.

Fifty armed men entered the house and rushed upon him. "Wake up!" she cried.

Samson arose from the bed. His hair was a web about his head. He seized the captain, and lifted him in his hands, and flung him against the advancing men. They turned and fled. He caught one in each hand and smashed their heads together, cracking their skulls. He seized a third who screamed in terror. "Take them and bury them," he said. "And thank your stone god that you do not lie with them." The man dragged his dead companions out. Samson felt his web of hair and turned to Delilah, who was sobbing.

"More treachery?"

"More lies!" she cried. "Go now. Do not come again."

He departed, telling himself she was a treacherous slut and that he would not return. But when the sun fell, his desire rose like sap. He fought with himself, but it was hopeless. He could not stay away. He returned to the house in the valley.

He walked about the orchards and the garden to see if anyone was lying in wait. But Delilah had sent a message to the Philistines: "Come tonight. But do not wait in the orchard. Wait in the woods beyond, for he is suspicious. But tonight I will learn his secret. Bring money."

The Philistines waited in the wood beyond, and Samson did not see them. He entered the house. It was dark. "Delilah," he called. There was no answer. But he smelled her spice-box fragrance and knew she was there. He heard a sound. It came from the bed. He went to the bed. She lay huddled like a child, sobbing. He took her in his arms. She slid away and seized a knife from under her pillow. She raised it above her breast. "Farewell, Samson. You do not love me, and I must die."

He seized her wrist, twisting the knife away. He tried to comfort her. But she would not look upon him, or speak to him, and she wept.

"When you go," she said, "I will kill myself. You mock me and lie to me and I cannot live."

The night passed so and he could not go to her. And her weeping and reproaches vexed him beyond his endurance. Finally he said: "I will tell you now what I have never told anyone else."

"Tell."

"Will you betray me again?"

"Betray you?" she cried. "Never! Don't you see my life is bound up with yours, and that I would kill myself for your favor. Tell me. Tell me."

"My strength does reside in my hair, as I told you before. It has never been cut. For I am a Nazarite, dedicated to the service of God from birth. I may not drink wine or eat anything unclean. And my hair may not be cut. If it is cut, my power will go from me, and I shall be as weak as any other man."

She caressed him then, and made love to him. And when he slept she caressed him until he awoke and rekindled his desire. For she wished to weary him, so that he would sleep a deep sleep and not be easily awakened. Again and again that night she used all her art to rekindle his desire. Finally, at dawn, she let him sleep. He slept upon her knees. She took a knife and cut off the seven long, plaited locks of his hair that had never been cut and were the sign of his separation from other men and his service to God. She cut them short, then laid his head gently upon the pillow, slipped away, and put a candle in the window.

The Philistines rushed into the house. "Awake!" she cried. He awoke and sprang from the bed. He felt the coolness of air upon his shorn head, and a weakness in his arms and legs that he had never felt before. And he knew that the spirit had departed from him, taking his strength. The enemy was upon him. He tried to fight but could not resist them. They bound him. With the same knife that Delilah had used on his hair, they stabbed out his eyes.

But blind and shaven and strengthless as he was, they still feared him. They loaded him with fetters of brass and took him down to Gaza, the city whose gates he had carried away in the days of his strength. There they put him with the other slaves, turning a mill wheel and grinding corn.

But they could not forget their hatred of him. They were not content to have him toil at the mill wheel. From time to time, they took him out and stood in a circle about him, pricking him with the points of their swords. He would try to seize one tormentor, who would dodge away, and another would go and prick him. And he would whirl and try to catch that one. And the young men would stab at him and dodge and laugh. They called it the blind man's game, and they had much sport.

When he was taken back to grind, he said to himself: I can manage my own death. Why do I allow myself to live in this misery? Then he thought: I must live for vengeance. I will not allow them to torment me into suicide. I will wait until my hair grows again, and I will pray to God for my strength to be restored. Then we will see what I can do without eyes.

But his strength did not return, although his hair had grown somewhat. And he despaired. In the next month the Philistines gathered to offer a sacrifice to Dagon, their sea god, and to hold a great feast. "For our god has delivered our enemy into our hands," they said. "The destroyer of our troops, the slayer of thousands, is now our slave."

All the lords of the Philistines gathered in Gaza, and their captains,

and their best warriors. And their women, too. There was a great crowd of them, about three thousand, the cream of the Philistine nobility. They feasted in an enormous hall, the temple of Dagon. They sacrificed to Dagon a bull, a ram, a stallion — and an unborn child, also, for it was gilled like a fish and was pleasing to the sea god. They cut it out of its mother's belly and laid it on the altar with the bodies of the beasts.

Then they feasted. They caroused. They glutted themselves on meat and drank much wine. Then the prince of Gaza called, "Bring us Samson! We will have sport!"

Samson was taken from the mill. A small boy led him by the hand, and the blind giant ambled after him. The young men formed a circle about him in the courtyard of the temple. Everyone streamed out to watch. People climbed to the roof and watched from there. The players of the game stabbed him lightly with their swords, and he chased them. They dodged away, and whirled about, and stabbed him again. He heard enormous laughter and knew that he was in a mob of people, entertaining them all with his helpless fury. And he knew a great anguish. The shame of it stabbed to the very depth of his soul.

"Lord," he cried, "remember me, I pray you. Strengthen me again only this one time, O God, that I may be avenged. Lord, Lord, give me vengeance for my two eyes."

There was a great clamor about him and he did not hear God's voice. But he seemed to feel strength flowing back into him. A current of energy was running into his arms and legs; he felt the great muscles of his back begin to harden. "Is it so?" he said to himself. "Or does my wish make it seem so?"

They had finished their game now, but they wished him to remain on view to the multitude. They set him between the pillars of the temple. And he said to the little lad: "Lead me to the pillars, for I am weary and would lean on them." And the little boy led the blind giant by the hand to the pillars of the temple.

Samson stood between the two great middle columns that supported the roof of the temple. He placed his right hand on one and his left hand on the other. "Dear God," he said, "forgive me my transgression. And allow me enough of the strength you have taken to do this one last thing."

He bowed his head and spread his legs and pressed outward upon the pillars of the temple. And in a great, swelling, bitter joy he knew that God had answered him, for the harder he pressed the stronger he grew.

"Thank you, God," he said. "Now let me die with the Philistines."

Those in the courtyard gazed in wonder as they saw the marble columns begin to sway. The roof sagged.

The people on the roof shrieked in terror. Great chunks of marble fell. Still the blind giant, planted upon the portico with bowed head and spread legs, pressed upon the pillars, pressed outward, outward. The pillars were like bows now; they crumbled. The walls fell. Men and women ran screaming to the doors and to the windows. But they could not escape. The walls caved in on them. The roof fell, and crushed all those who were in the temple. And the stone idol that was Dagon was crushed, also. Three thousand died in the temple — the lords and the captains of the Philistines and their best fighting men. And Samson.

Now the enemy was sorely weakened, and the Israelites swept them from the field, and took back their strong places, and were triumphant. They went to Gaza and took the broken body of Samson and buried him beside his father, Manoah.

THE COMING OF KINGS

There was a truce upon the land, and the Israelites began to pick up the ways of their neighbors. They were seduced by the Canaanite gods and worshipped them in the groves and high places. They sacrificed to Ashteroth, moon goddess, barley mother, mistress of revels; they rutted in plowed fields and honored her with orgies. They turned to Baal, also, whose stone image smiled upon ritual prostitution and whose seasonal wrath was appeased by the blood of babies. How much easier to please were these Canaanite gods than the stern Father in heaven who demanded your whole soul, who wrenched you into righteousness, thwarting every impulse toward robbery, rape, and murder.

So the children of Israel wandered from the way and broke the holy commandments and whored after strange gods. The Lord turned His face away, and they were sapped of strength and courage. The truce ended; the enemy attacked. The Hebrews called upon their new gods, Ashteroth and Baal, but they were useless in battle, and the enemy prevailed. Every tribe was threatened with defeat and enslavement.

The captains of the tribes clamored for a leader. Not many separate leaders but one supreme war chief for all the tribes. And since each of their enemies had a king who led them into battle, the Israelites — who had never had a king — began to want one.

Now, there was a man named Samuel whom everyone respected. He was a strange figure. He had been a judge. He had driven from office certain corrupt priests, whose interest was not to serve God but to enrich themselves. But he did not like to govern; he wanted to make his people wise enough to govern themselves. It was known that he conversed with God. He went up and down the land preaching against idolatry — warning that the children of Israel must return to God's law or be punished by defeat in battle.

It was to this man that the captains came, and the elders of the tribes, clamoring for a king.

Samuel answered them, "You want a king to reign over you. Do you know what a king will do? He will take a tenth of your harvest, and one beast in ten of your flocks and herds. He will take your sons to be his charioteers and his horsemen, and some will run before his chariot. Your sons will labor for him; he will set them to sow his ground and reap his harvest and labor at the anvil, forging armor for him and tall gates for his palace. He will take the best of your fields and your orchards and your vineyards and give them to those who flatter him. He will take your daughters to be concubines, cooks, and house maids. And in time to come you will cry out because of the king you wanted, but the Lord will not hear you on that day."

So Samuel warned, but the captains refused to hear his words. "Nay," they cried, "we wish to be like other nations. We want a king to judge us, and go before us, and fight our battles."

Samuel consulted the Lord, who said: "Do as they say. Find them a king."

"Where shall I find him, O Lord?"

"I will show you the way. Go to the least of the tribes, the tribe of Benjamin, and seek out the poorest man of that tribe. His name is Kish and he has sons. You want his youngest son."

Samuel did as the Lord had commanded. He went to the domain of the Benjamites, and sought the youngest son of Kish. When the young man was brought before him, Samuel saw the tallest man he had ever seen, towering head and shoulders above his tall brothers, and powerfully muscled. His name was Saul.

Samuel presented Saul to the captains, and anointed him king, the first king of Israel. And Saul was humble in his greatness. He thanked God for His favor, and implored God for strength and wisdom. And God answered, promising victory.

The troops gathered. They came from every tribe to serve under their king. Saul was a wild bull in battle and a fearless leader. He led the armies of Israel to victory on every field. The foe was beaten back. And Israel rejoiced in its king.

Saul reigned for many years. He held court. He took wives and concubines and they bore him sons and daughters. His heart grew fat with pride, and he put on pomp. And all that Samuel had spoken came true. Saul taxed the people and stuffed his treasury. He kept a multitude of servants and lackeys and courtiers, and flew into a murderous rage when anyone opposed him in anything. No one dared stand against him except Samuel, who feared only God and always spoke his mind.

Then Saul began to whore after other gods. He assembled his court in the groves and high places and performed the abominable rituals of Baal. He honored Ashteroth with orgies.

The Lord was displeased and raised an enemy against him. The Philistines marched against the Israelites and smote them. Saul's army was driven from the field. He retreated and regrouped. But the spirit of God had departed from him. Nothing was the same.

DAVID

Saul was king in Israel. He had been mighty in war, but was now losing battle after battle. He did not know why — and resisted knowing. Again and again he had been warned by the prophet Samuel: "God is the source of power," said Samuel. "When you walked in His way, He lent strength to your arm and brought you victory. Now that you have grown disobedient, He withdraws His favor. Repent, O King! Keep His statutes, or lose your power."

But Saul did not heed the old prophet. He pursued a mean-hearted, brutal course. He was suspicious of all men, and feared by all men when he fell into one of his wild fits of wrath. In one savage tantrum he had tried to thrust his spear through his own son, Jonathan, whose beauty and valor had endeared him to everyone except Saul.

The Philistines were pressing hard. The king led out his armies, but the flame of command that had burned in him when he was God's own young captain was damped now by sloth and arrogance. The inspired power of leadership had gone from him, and the Philistines were everywhere triumphant.

Samuel spoke to God: "Must the Philistines prevail, O Lord? You raised a king to drive the heathen out of our holy land, and the king was Saul. Now you withdraw your favor and his heart faints. Must your people be vanquished again? Shall the stone images be raised where your altar now stands?"

God said: "How long will you mourn over Saul, seeing that I have rejected him? Fill your horn with oil. Find another to be king and anoint that one."

"Where shall I find him, O Lord?"

"Behold, the sheep are lost, the wolves prowl. Seek a shepherd."

"Where?"

"Go to Bethlehem."

Samuel begged the Lord for more exact directions, but the Lord was silent. And Samuel knew that God wanted him who had found Saul to find his successor and would give no further clue. Samuel begged no more. He was old and very wise, and he knew that the Lord liked to test His prophets, also. Without saying a word to Saul, he left the palace and hastened toward Bethlehem.

Now, there was a man named Jesse who dwelt in Bethlehem, and he was of the tribe of Judah. He had eight sons. Seven were grown men; the youngest was a boy named David. And David was a shepherd lad and kept his father's flocks.

He was small and slight, of auburn hair and fair skin, but made ruddy by sun and wind. He was light-footed as a wild roebuck and very swift in all his movements. But what marked him most was his joyous heart. He lived outdoors. He saw the sun rise out of the eastern mountains and climb to the top of the sky and dive into the western sea. He watched the huge darkness gather, saw the moon swim out of the sea and touch the great chandelier of stars with its silver fire. Then, under the enormous jewelry of that sky, he made a last round of his flock and lay down to sleep.

David was a poet — with a poet's generous greed. He claimed each of the stars as his own, and the sun and the moon. And returned them as song.

He touched his harp and sang. His voice was beautiful. It was said of him that the staid old rams rose on their hind legs and skipped like lambs when his song was merry, and that his night song would make the marauding wolf lie down and sleep. These are the words he sang:

> O Lord, when I consider your heavens,
>> the work of your fingers,
>> the moon and the stars that you have ordained,
> I ask what is man that you are mindful of him,
>> and the son of man that you visit him.
> For you have made him a little lower than the angels
>> and have crowned him with glory and honor.

He welcomed all weather. He loved even storm. He watched the sky blacken and the first low thunder growl. He sang:

> The voice of the Lord is upon the waters;
> The glory of God thunders; the Lord is upon many waters.
> The voice of the Lord breaks the cedars;
>> yea, the Lord breaks the cedars of Lebanon.
> He makes them also skip like a calf,
> Lebanon and Sirion like a young unicorn.
> The voice of the Lord divides the flames of fire.
> The voice of the Lord shakes the wilderness.
> He shakes the wilderness of Kadesh.

217

His father wondered at him. His brothers mocked his ways and thought him half a lunatic. But he answered them gently and held his peace. He knew that he was not like the others. He knew that the starry joy that flooded his soul and compelled him to song was a good thing and had nothing of evil in it. So he held his peace and walked in his own way.

As the grazing grew more sparse around Bethlehem, he sought farther slopes, other valleys, places where the grass was lush and no flocks went. But here, also, prowled beasts of prey; it was the lair of the wolf, haunt of lion and bear. He had two dogs that were fierce and true. Otherwise, he was armed only with his shepherd's staff and a sling.

He had made his sling out of calfskin. He had cured the skin himself, working it till it was very supple. He had made its pouch of a size to fit the exact size of the stone whose weight and shape he found best for slinging. And he made a dance of the slinging, humming a song and spinning on the balls of his feet, whirling the sling about his head with all the speed of his spinning behind it. As he whirled, he fixed his whole mind upon the mark, felt his whole soul launch itself upon the chase, and released one end of the leather thong just as his soul clutched the souls of his prey. He rarely missed.

A chill wind blew that night, and David built a fire and slept. He was awakened by barking, bleating, snarling, and awoke to find a bear at bay being attacked by his dogs. He saw the bear's paw catch a leaping dog and smite it to earth, but the other dog kept circling. Now David was whirling his sling. The stone flew and hit the bear under the eye. The beast howled in agony and fled. David ran to the fallen dog. The animal lifted its head and whimpered, licked David's hand, and died. The other dog was barking far off, chasing the wounded bear. David wept.

He was snatched from grief by the crying of a lamb, and he saw that a lion had crept out of the shadows and was bearing the lamb off alive. He did not use his sling for fear of hitting the lamb, but flashed after the lion. He seized it by its beard and pulled the lamb from its mouth. The lamb tottered away. The lion roared. The lamb froze in its tracks. The lion swung its great head back and forth between David and the lamb, trying to decide where to pounce. But now David was whirling his sling. Spinning on the balls of his feet, he sang: "Break its teeth in its mouth, O Lord. Break its great teeth." And he let the stone fly just as the lion pounced. The stone caught the beast in midleap, its force doubled by the force of the lion's leap. David heard the lion's teeth breaking. It sank to earth, bleeding from the mouth. David stood off, watching. He put another stone in his sling and whirled it again. The stone hit the lion's head, smashing it.

"Thank you, Lord," said David, "who has given me dominion over the great beasts, and strengthened my arm to guard my flocks." He heard a slight sound, saw eyes glowing. His hand went again to his bag of stones.

"Hold your hand," said a voice. "I come in peace."

An old man stood in the firelight. He was tall and very thin, with a tangled white beard and white hair that blew in the wind. His eyes smoldered in their sockets.

"Who are you?" said David.

"I am Samuel. And you are David, son of Jesse, who dwells in Bethlehem."

"Venerable sir," said David, "welcome to my fireside. Repose yourself, I pray. And partake of my fare — bread and cheese, olives, figs. Will you share my meal?"

"I thank you," said the old man. "But I come upon urgent business and must not tarry. I have been to your father's house in Bethlehem and seen your brothers. Now I seek you."

"Did my father send you?"

"The Lord sent me here, unless I mistake His purpose. David, son of Jesse, remove your garments and wash them in the stream. Bathe yourself; purify yourself. Then return."

The night was cold, but David did not think of refusing. For Samuel's words came with easy power, with the authority of natural things, river flow and wind and rock fall. A great force seemed to flow through him, having its source elsewhere. David stared at him, at the emaciated body, the hair and beard, the burning eyes.

"Samuel?" he whispered. "Are you he, even that one, that Samuel, prophet to the king?"

"I am the Lord's prophet," said the old man. "I serve the king only when he serves the King of kings. But of kingdoms and such we will speak another time. Go now. Purify yourself and return."

David went to the river. He stripped himself and washed his clothes and laid them on a rock. He leaped into the icy water. But the blood heat of the beast hunt was still upon him, and he was strangely stirred by the old man. His blood ran hot and he did not feel the cold. When he came

219

out of the stream, he found that his clothes were miraculously dry, and fragrant of wild grass. And his joy grew. But he was a little frightened, also. The man stood tall in the firelight. He held a horn in his hand. "Kneel," he said.

David knelt. The man poured a little oil from the horn. It fell on David's head and ran down his face. It was oil but not sticky. It smelled of sandalwood and cinnamon; it felt like balm.

Samuel spoke as he poured: "O Lord, you sent me into this wilderness without a guide and instructed only by hints. But I have found a young shepherd who guards his flocks well. I offer him to you, and anoint him with holy oil. If I have read your intention, accept him, I pray. If I have erred, forgive me, and instruct me afresh."

"Why do you anoint me with holy oil?" said David. "What have you done to me? What does it mean?"

"If I have done right, the meaning will come clear," said Samuel. "At this time I can tell you no more. Besides, my lad, things take on the meaning you give them. You must gather your flocks now and drive them all night to reach Bethlehem by dawn, and put them in your brother's care. Then you must leave your father's house and go to the king."

"To Saul?"

"He is your king."

"O venerable sir, what shall I do at court among the mighty? I am a poor shepherd."

"That is a form of words. Modesty becomes the young, but this hour demands truth. Do you really deem yourself poor?"

David looked into the sunken fire of the old man's eyes. The flame licked at his own marrow, burning away trivia and inconsequence. Only truth could be spoken.

"I don't know what I am," he said. "The oil you have poured upon me this night has entered my blood, and I am changed, changed. It is pain and it is joy. What have you done to me?"

"Go to the king," said Samuel. "Go to the palace of King Saul. He will welcome you, for he esteems the music of the harp and sweet song. Play to him. Sing to him. Look into the heart of that bitter, stormy man and seek to learn his strength and his weakness. Watch his ways with captain and charioteer and man-at-arms. Observe the court and the ways of the court. Study kingship, its perils and possibilities."

"To what end?" whispered David.

Samuel looked at him sternly. "David, son of Jesse," he said, "you have been chosen, and, being chosen, must justify the choice. You are unripe yet for your destiny. Go to the court and do as I have said."

David knelt and kissed the old man's hand. He looked up at him and saw that his beard was a thicket of silver fire in the starlight.

"Samuel ... teacher ... anointer with strange oils, I will do your bidding in all things."

"Go, then, and begin."

"Shall we meet again?"

"Doubtless. Farewell."

The old man embraced David and kissed him. Then he stepped into the shadows and was gone. And David, standing alone in the profound darkness, in the great hush, under the immense sky, thought it was all a dream. But his garments were newly washed and the fragrant oil was in his hair. He whistled to his dog, rounded up his sheep, and headed for Bethlehem.

Pain sat upon Saul's brow. His crown was a hoop of fire. He swept it off his head, but the circlet of fire burned into the king's skull, scorching his wits, filling him with a murderous unfocused rage. Light stabbed his eyes. He ordered the windows veiled. The great throne room filled with dusk.

A voice came out of the shadows beyond his throne. It was the voice of the new harp boy sent by Samuel. Fresh as a running stream this voice, and words seemed minted for the first time in its melody. No fatness of self-admiration in its tones; it was easy and cool as birdsong.

> The king shall joy in your strength, O Lord,
> In your salvation how greatly shall he rejoice;
> You have set a crown of pure gold on his head,
> His glory is great in your salvation.
> Honor and majesty have you laid upon him. . . .

The melody curled about the king and he sank into its coolness. The words *gold* and *crown* made him wince, but then he seemed to hear other words singing behind those and they were: "Your pain is your crown, but your crown is of kingship. In splendor is responsibility."

He turned to see the new harp boy, but the shadows were too thick. He saw only a slender arm, a blur of face, and the gleam of the harp. A tension went out of Saul's huge body. The melody quenched the fire in his head; his pain eased. He turned again and closed his eyes, and sank into a healing sleep.

Now each afternoon after the war council, he dismissed his captains

and sent away the magnificent prince, his son Jonathan, and sat alone in the shadowed throne room and listened to the harp boy sing. The young voice seemed to burst with joy, and the songs were of praise and wonder.

> *The lines have fallen to you in pleasant places, O King;*
> *Yea, you have a goodly heritage;*
> *Therefore shall your heart be glad and your glory rejoice.*

The king had always been told of God in the most dire terms and was tormented by the fear of divine wrath. Now in these songs a new vision of the Creator was being painted.

> *Sing unto the Lord: His anger endures for but a moment.*
> *Weeping may endure for a night, but joy comes in the morning.*

And Saul, cooled by strange song, eased by shadows, did not summon the lad to him or look upon his face. He wanted to keep that voice steeped in mystery. He wanted it separate from everyday knowledge; he did not want it attached to a name or face. For this voice out of the shadows was the only ease to his torment. He was like one who listens in a dream and does not wish to awaken.

Swathed in shadow, David touched the strings of his harp and studied the king. He saw that Saul, who listened half absently in council to reports of Philistine victories, was more bedeviled by private woes than public peril. But what was troubling him so, this man of power and wealth and fame, who had bedded beautiful women and begotten strong and beautiful sons? Why did he sit there brooding, when he should have been out in the field leading his armies, inspiriting his men as he alone could do? What fanged shapes of guilt and remorse were feeding upon those royal guts?

David began to feel a puzzled tenderness for the big, agonized man whose grief he could not fathom. He plucked his strings and sang his verse and felt the music of praise surging through him, stiffening his fingers into rods of power. And when the power was upon him in full flood in the shadowed afternoon, he tried to believe that the sound he made was passing through the king, cleansing him of those foul private devils.

He sang new songs:

> *O King, you who love songs and admire prophesy,*
> *Know that I, David, shall incline my ear to a parable*
> *And open my dark saying upon a harp.*

223

The king sat erect on the throne, staring out in front of him. The tension did not leave his body; the song did not reach him. David pondered. What sin had Saul committed that God should punish him with such unhappiness? Or, perhaps, was his unhappiness itself the sin? Was unhappiness ingratitude? Was it the worst sin, the father of sins? The thought began to sing itself:

> Praise the Lord!
> In His presence is the fullness of joy;
> At His right hand there are pleasures forevermore.

Tidings from the battlefields grew worse and worse. Bloody, dusty messengers arrived daily at the palace and told the war council their tales of terror and loss. Finally, the captains' alarms pierced the torpor of the king. Saul sent heralds to every corner of Israel, calling upon each tribe to send forth every man who could bear a weapon. And David knew that his brothers must obey this summons and leave his father's flocks untended. He knew that the time had come for him to leave the king and return to his sheep.

He bade the king farewell. The man looked at the boy with stony eyes. David knelt and seized the great, knotty hand and kissed it. Then he arose swiftly and left the palace. He mounted his donkey and hastened toward Bethlehem.

David and Goliath

The Philistines came in a mighty host and encamped on the slope of a mountain. Saul mustered his forces on another mountain; the valley of Elah lay between.

There was a great clanging of metal against metal. The astounded Israelites saw a gigantic figure striding out of the Philistine camp. It was a man, but almost the size of two men. Nine feet high he was, and as broad as a span of oxen. His spear's shaft was the trunk of a tree, its point like an ordinary man's sword. His shield was of brass and as big as a chariot wheel. He beat spear against shield, making an awful din. He called out and his voice was a thunderous bellow.

"I am Goliath, Goliath of Gath, and I challenge you all! Saul, do you hear me? You, King Saul, who slew your thousands, I challenge you to single combat. Why let your men be slaughtered? You and I will fight. If you win, we Philistines shall bow the knee to you and serve you. If I win, then you and your Israelites shall serve us. Or, if you are afraid to fight, then choose another champion. Send out your best man against me, or two or three, and the battle will be settled between us. Ho there, Saul! My challenge awaits an answer."

Saul stayed in his tent. He was a brave man, but the sight of this giant froze his marrow. He knew that Goliath would squash him like a beetle. Goliath stood on the mountain, bellowing and jeering. There was no answer.

The giant laughed and shouted, "No answer, Saul? I give you seven days to consider my challenge. If no one comes forth to meet me in that time, then I will fall on you, followed by the host of Philistines, and not one of you shall be spared, not your women or your children. All of you shall be put to the sword. We will scour this land of Canaan once and for all of the Israelite pest."

He strode off. Saul remained in his tent and did not go out. The troops were bewildered, fearful. Men began to drift away. And all knew that if the Philistines attacked, there would be a dreadful rout and a massacre.

Now it was that the brothers of David, answering Saul's desperate call for men, came to join the army. They were strong, brave young men, but they were amazed at what they found. The proud troops of Saul had become a sullen, terrified, half-mutinous mob. The brothers of David saw Goliath flaunting himself upon the mountain and heard his terrible bellowing. And they, too, were afraid.

Upon this day, David was summoned by his father. "I wish you to go on an errand," said Jesse. "You must go to the valley of Elah. You will find your brothers there, among the tents of Saul. Take them this food — this parched grain, these ten loaves. And take these ten cheeses as a gift to their captain, so that he may treat them well. Hurry now. Do not fall a-dreaming and tarry on the way."

David departed. He mounted his donkey and rode swiftly to Saul's encampment. There was a circle of wagons around the tents. The men stood in ranks with their weapons, for Saul expected an attack. David left the loaves and the cheeses and the bag of grain with the wagoner, and ran to find his brothers.

"David!" cried his eldest brother, Eliab. "Why are you here?"

"Father sent me. I've brought you food — a sack of wheat to make bread, and ten newly baked loaves, and cheeses for your captain. Do you fight today? Will there be a battle?"

225

His heart danced as he looked about the ranks of men with sword and spear. He could hardly contain his excitement. But he saw his brothers looking at him grimly, and said nothing. Then he heard a great clanging and a voice that bellowed terribly over the valley. He saw a gigantic warrior stride out of the Philistine lines and post himself on the slope opposite, and call, "Do you still skulk among your tents, O men of Israel? I defy your armies, O Israel. Why don't you find a man who will fight me?"

David couldn't wait to see who would answer the challenge. He looked for Saul, but the king was in his tent. And no man stepped forward. David felt himself choke with shame. He said: "Who is this uncircumcised monster, that he should defy the armies of the living God? Why does no one go forth to meet him? Are you all afraid?"

Eliab grasped his shoulder and shook him. "Why did you come here?" he cried. "Why did you leave your sheep? I know your pride and the wickedness of your heart. You didn't come to bring us food, you came to watch the battle. Do you think it's a boy's game, this warfare? Men's bodies are broken; they die screaming. Now leave this place and go back to your sheep, or you shall feel the weight of my fist."

David did not answer. He turned away from his brother and moved off, and listened to Goliath roaring. He looked about again to see if there would be anyone coming out to fight. But there was no one. The shame swelled in his chest until he could hardly breathe. He cried out, "Men of Israel, fear not this giant who serves a god of stone! Remember Samson, who slew a thousand of these same Philistines with the jawbone of an ass! He was alone and weaponless, but God armed him and gave him strength. Have you forgotten the power of God?"

Saul, coming out to his troops, heard these words. "Come here!" he roared.

David approached and knelt before him. "O great King," he said, "you whom the Lord anointed and whose mighty deeds have fired the spirit of all Israel, I pray you, let me go out and fight the Philistine. The blight of fear has fallen upon your troops. Their hearts fail. I swear by the living God that I do not fear this giant and will fight him."

"How can you go against this Philistine?" said Saul. "You are but a youth. He is a mighty man of war. Behold him; he is a giant. You are small even for your age."

"I was tending my father's sheep in the wilderness," said David, "and a bear came. And a lion. I drove off the bear. And the lion snatched a lamb from the flock. I did not wish to cast a stone, lest it hit the lamb. And I grasped the lion by the beard and took the lamb from its jaws. Then I slew the lion. Yes, King, I swear to you that I slew both lion and bear. And this uncircumcised Philistine shall die in the same manner, for he has defied the army of the living God."

"You are raving, my lad," said Saul. "It cannot be. Look you, I have sought a man among my troops. I have tall men here, strong men, skilled at arms. I have offered great riches to the man who kills Goliath, and promised that he should marry my daughter and be like a son to me. But no one dares to meet the giant. They are afraid. And they have reason to fear."

David said: "The Lord has delivered me out of the paw of the bear and the maw of the lion, and He will deliver me out of the hand of the Philistine."

Saul looked into the lad's eyes. Arrows of light seemed to come from those eyes. They pierced Saul's heart, and he heard himself saying, "Go, then, and the Lord go with you."

The king called for weapons and clad David in armor, put a helmet of brass on his head and a coat of mail. He gave David his own sword, saying, "This has tasted the blood of many Philistines. May it serve you well."

David walked a few steps. He swung the sword. He could hardly move for the weight of the metal. He said to Saul: "I thank you, O King. But I cannot wear this armor or wield this sword. My fighting is a kind of dance. I do not know how to tell it. But I must go light-footed and with my own weapons, this staff and this sling."

He cast off the armor and took his staff and sling, and knelt at the brook and chose five smooth stones, and put them in the pouch that hung at his belt. He said to Saul: "When you see me again I will be bearing Goliath's head — or you shall not see me again. Farewell, O King."

He departed. He went down the hill into the valley and climbed the hill where Goliath stood. Goliath saw the lad coming, this small, slender boy, clad in sheepskin, bearing a staff. He thought it was some mockery of him by the Israelites. He roared, "Am I a dog that you come against me with a stick?"

"I am a shepherd," cried David. "I esteem dogs. You are no dog, but a beast more foul."

227

"Come here, little one," shouted Goliath. "Vulture and rat shall pick your bones."

David said: "You come to me with a sword and a shield, but I come to you in the name of the Lord of hosts. Today the Lord delivers you into my hands. I will smite you and take your head from you and give your great carcass to the hungry vermin of earth and the birds of air, that all men may know there is a God in Israel."

Goliath did not advance. He wanted the advantage of the high ground, and waited for David to come to him. Then David vanished. Goliath lost sight of him among the rocks, and thought the boy had fled. David kept himself hidden and climbed the hill out of Goliath's sight. He was circling away, trying to get to higher ground and attack the giant from above.

Goliath laughed. He roared with glee. "So you have scuttled away, little rat. All you Hebrews are cowards, from the youngest to the oldest." He pranced and clanged spear against shield. And he called across the valley, "There is not a man among you Hebrews, so you sent a boy. Now the boy has fled, also. I challenge you no more, for you are cowards. Today we attack! I will smite you and you shall flee before us. We will pursue you even unto your thresholds and destroy you all, men, women, and children, until there is no Hebrew left anywhere on earth."

He heard a shout: "Goliath! Goliath! Turn, Philistine, and meet your death!"

He whirled to see David moving above him, coming toward him. He snarled deep in his throat, raised his shield, drew his sword, and walked slowly uphill in a fighting crouch. Even crouching he was enormous, and fearful to look upon.

David whispered, "Deliver me, O God, out of the hand of the wicked, out of the hand of the unrighteous and cruel man. A giant is arrayed against me. But your favor will magnify me, O Lord, and make me mightier than the giant."

And it seemed to him that God answered only one word. It was like an eagle screaming, and the word was *yes*. He fitted a stone into his sling and began to whirl it above his head. The giant was trudging up the hill toward him. The sun glinted off his huge brass helmet. Goliath's spear was the trunk of a tree, its point as long as a sword. David whirled his sling. He felt his whole soul launching itself out of his body and flying down the slope toward Goliath. Past shield and breastplate it darted

228

and grappled in stinking darkness with the brutal, lardy soul of the giant. At that instant David cast his stone. It sped downhill and struck Goliath in the middle of the forehead, hit so hard that it sank into the bone of his head and stood out like a third stony eye. The giant swayed like an axed tree and fell face downward with a great crash.

David ran down the slope, skipping like a goat, caroling with joy. He stood above the fallen giant and took Goliath's sword from his hand. He had to use both hands to lift it. He raised the huge blade and slashed down and smote off the giant's head. He lifted the head toward the sky like an offering and cried, "Beloved God, you are my rock. You are my shield, my honor, my high tower, my refuge, my savior! Your word is my strength, your favor my victory!"

David ran down the hill and across the valley and up the other slope toward his own lines, swinging the head by its hair and shouting with joy. When the men saw him coming, when they saw the starry light streaming from his face, and realized that the head he bore was as big as a bull's head and that his victory was a miracle — then they felt the spirit of God entering them and felt their own hearts grow hot with it. They raised a mighty shout and charged down the hill. They charged the Philistine lines. And the sun flashing off their swords was no brighter than David's face as he watched.

"Rebuke the company of spearmen, O Lord!" he cried. "Scatter the people who delight in war."

And the music of David's praise pleased God more than the words of anyone since Moses. His favor shone upon the Israelites that day. They scattered the Philistines and pursued them. And slew them by the thousands and by the tens of thousands.

King Saul stood on the hilltop and watched his men penning the Philistines in the valley below. But he could not rejoice in the victory. Echoing in his ear was that first amazed triumphant yell of his men when they saw David coming with the head of Goliath. At that moment, at the very instant of triumph and joy, Saul's heart was bitten by envy, and the envy festered into hatred.

David went toward him. He knelt before Saul and laid the enormous, bloody head of Goliath at the king's feet.

Saul said: "Whose son are you?"

"I am the son of Jesse the Bethlehemite," said David.

"'You have done well, young man."

"Done well?" cried Jonathan. "He is blessed of God and performer of wonders. His victory is a miracle." The tall young prince swept David into his arms and kissed him, and those about the king raised their voices in a shout of approval.

"Father!" cried Jonathan. "You vowed that he who slew Goliath would marry your daughter and be as a son to you. Will you keep your oath?"

"Truly a day of wonders," growled Saul. "I seem to hear a son instructing his father."

"Pardon, O King," said Jonathan. "But I want this lad to be my brother and share princely honors with me. For his deed this day has swept the enemy from our gates and preserved our land from the heathen hordes."

"Thank you, Prince," said David. "But all victories belong to the king. We are his subjects, and our hearts and arms belong to him."

"Gently said," said Saul. "Perhaps you can teach courtesy to princes, as you teach courage to kings. Do not return to your father, David. Stay here with me. I shall keep my promise and reward you as you deserve."

The king turned abruptly and departed. "Come with me, brother," said Jonathan. He was very tall and broad-shouldered, and his legs were columns of muscle. He was the best young warrior in all Israel.

David looked up at him and smiled. "I am yours to command, brother, elder brother. Will you teach me to use sword and spear, to ride the chariot and guide its swift horses?"

"If you teach me shepherd things," said Jonathan. "To cast deadly stones with that little sling and to pluck sweetly upon the harp."

"You recognize in me the harp boy who sang for your father?" said David.

"Come," said Jonathan, "let me tell you what I know about you. And you shall tell me all that I do not know."

The two youths loved each other like brothers and more than brothers. Each delighted in the other's feats of strength and daring, and there was no envy in either of them. The soul of David knitted with the soul of Jonathan; they were seldom apart.

One of the king's counselors, a man named Doeg, knew that Saul secretly hated David, and saw a chance to curry favor. "Truly that little shepherd is puffed up with pride," he whispered in the king's ear. "He struts like a prince in the robes that Jonathan has given him, and tries to make people forget his origins."

"He has made me forget," said Saul. "Perhaps you had better forget them, too."

But Doeg was a subtle man and easily read the king's heart. He knew that Saul was pretending to defend David so that Doeg would continue to vilify him. "I am a blunt and honest man, O King," he cried. "And my one wish is to serve you. Though you slay me for it, I must speak the truth as I see it."

"Speak," growled Saul.

"Yesterday you passed among the populace at the head of your troops, with David at your side. You were undoubtedly occupied by weighty matters of state and did not notice what happened."

"Crowds cheered as I passed," said Saul. "And women came singing and dancing to meet me. Aye, the fairest of them, they came to greet their king with taborets and with joy and with instruments of music."

"Your generous nature did not allow you to hear what they were whispering."

"Whispering? What did they whisper?"

" 'Saul has slain his thousands,' they said to one another, 'but David has slain his ten thousands.' "

That night, after Saul and his favorites had dined, David tuned his harp to play to the king. Saul sat watching him. He saw the lad's flushed face musing over the harp strings. The blood pounded in his ears and became a voice: "Saul has slain his thousands, but David has slain his ten thousands." The fury swelled in Saul's head until he felt his eyeballs bursting. He seized his javelin and hurled it at David. Just then a harp string broke. The boy bent suddenly to it, and the javelin sheared the air where his head had been an instant before. As in battle, David's reflexes were quicker than thought. He slid out of the room like a shadow. And Saul sat on his high seat and no one approached.

The king never offered explanations for anything he did, and no one dared question him. Nevertheless, as a leader of men he was attuned to the feeling of those he led, and when his spasm of fury had passed he knew that he had made a mistake. David had become a magical hero to the army, and the men were seething with resentment. David had vanished; Jonathan was nowhere to be seen. And Saul knew that if the youths quit the court, a faction would form itself about them, and resentment would ripen into rebellion.

Swallowing his wrath, Saul pretended to bend to the popular mood. He sent for David again, and set him high among his captains, giving him a thousand men to lead.

Doeg went to him and said: "Is this prudent, O King, to give David a thousand men? He will win their hearts with his sly, ingratiating ways and forge a weapon to strike at the throne itself."

"For a son to attack his father is sacrilege," said Saul. "He may be ambitious, the little jumped-up shepherd, but I do not think he is prepared to break a holy statute. I shall bind him to me in fealty by making him my son-in-law. I shall give him my daughter in marriage. My youngest girl, Michal, seems to have developed a sudden interest in harp music. Little fool's mad for him. Well, he can have her."

"Excellent," murmured Doeg. "Generous . . . politic . . . profound and subtle. May I suggest a refinement?"

"You may."

"You have dowered him royally by making him a captain and giving him a thousand men to lead. Now you must ask a groom gift, as is the custom."

"Gift? From him? What can he give me? His shepherd's crook? One of his father's stinking sheep?"

"That is the point, O King. In tactful recognition of his humble means, you will ask him to supply out of his courage what his purse cannot."

"A deed of valor . . . " muttered the king.

"Of exceeding valor. He prefers to fight against odds, apparently. Set a task to challenge the mettle of him who slew Goliath."

"Dead enemies!" roared Saul. "What gift more fitting to a warrior-king from a hero son-in-law? The heads of two hundred Philistines slain in battle — that is the gift I shall ask. To slay two hundred of them, he will have to engage a force ten times as great."

"And," said Doeg, smiling, "the fortunes of war are uncertain, especially when you are outnumbered. It may be that a tragic circumstance will befall the young miracle worker."

"Nevertheless, we are moving ahead of events," said Saul. "I have not yet offered him my daughter, so I can ask no groom gift. I appoint you my emissary in this matter. Go to David, wise Doeg, and offer him the princess Michal as his bride."

Doeg went to David and said: "O giant killer, I know that your modesty is as great as your valor, and that you may not have allowed yourself to recognize what is so plain to everyone else, that the king loves you dearly. He loves you like his own son."

Very much like his own son, thought David. He's tried to kill Jonathan many times.

But David had learned enough about the ways of the court to mask his thoughts, and said: "Your words please me, Doeg. Indeed I owe the king my love and fealty and obedience."

"Nay, I speak not like a smooth-tongued courtier!" cried Doeg. "I come to you with no ceremonial rhetoric, but with the simple truth. I tell you that the king delights in you. He wishes to make you his son, in fact. He offers you his daughter Michal as your bride."

"He has empowered you to tell me this?"

"He has."

"What can I answer?" said David. "Do you think it is a light thing to be the king's son-in-law?"

"Not a light thing at all," said Doeg, "but a supreme honor."

"Do I merit this supreme honor? Who am I that I should be son-in-law to the king?"

"You are he who slew Goliath, he who preserved Israel. You are no shepherd now, but a captain and high among Saul's captains. And he wishes you to marry his daughter."

"I cannot even afford a groom gift," said David. "I have no princely fortune to draw upon. I am a poor man."

"The king who thinks of everything has thought of this, too. He asks only a token gift — the heads of two hundred Philistines slain in battle."

"Convey my profound gratitude to the king," said David. "When next I appear before his august presence, it shall be with the heads of two hundred Philistines slain in battle."

David led his men toward Ashkelon, where a mighty host of Philistines were encamped. Gorgeous among the tents was the pavilion of Ashkelon's king, for the Philistines had three kings, each holding a section of the coast. Their harbor cities were Gath and Ashkelon and Ashdot.

The king of Ashkelon had ten thousand men; David about eight hundred. David spoke to his men: "Do not let us consider our numbers. For the Lord multiplies us. Did He not guide my small stone and make it prevail against the gigantic spear and sword of Goliath? He is the Lord of

233

hosts, wielder of man's destiny, bestower of victory. He will magnify you against the Philistines until you are like a plowman stepping upon an anthill."

His men shouted until the thunder of their voices filled the plain, and followed him in a headlong charge against the Philistines. This was the first time that David had led his own troops, and they followed him as lost men follow a ray of light in the darkness. They cut through the brass ranks of the Philistines, divided them, and wheeled and sliced a bloody path through them again, cutting the enemy into smaller and smaller pockets. The spirit of God rode upon their banners and they were irresistible. The enemy fought bravely, but suffered huge losses and had to flee the field. David beheaded two hundred of the corpses, and presented the helmeted heads to Saul.

"He is more a hero than ever," said Saul to Doeg. "Is this the fruit of your wise counsel?"

Now, it is a courtier's task to accept blame for the king's bad ideas, and to give the king credit for all ideas that work. And Doeg said: "David is your captain, O King. His victories are your victories. Give him Michal as bride. Celebrate the marriage with royal splendor. You will be the master of revels, the great benefactor; his glory will be absorbed into your own. And consider this: Michal is your daughter. It may be that in days to come she will prove a snare unto David's feet."

"She's in love with him. She will not betray him."

"Not yet. She is not yet his wife. Give her time. But it may be wise to let passion wear itself out on the nuptial bed."

Saul kept his promise. He gave his daughter Michal as bride to David. The marriage was celebrated with a round of magnificent feasts. But it was not Saul's way to be crafty and diplomatic. His nature craved direct, brutal action. And his hatred of David robbed his days of purpose and his nights of sleep. He burned with rancor, and he knew that nothing would quench his torment but the sight of David dead. Nor did he seek to hide his feelings — even from Jonathan, who loved David.

The prince spoke to David: "My father means to kill you, and soon. Do not sleep at home. Hide yourself, and stay hidden."

"Why? Why?" cried David. "I have offered him only loyalty and obedience."

"Hide yourself in the field beyond the palace gates," said Jonathan. "I shall walk in that field tomorrow and speak with him. I shall speak of you.

234

You will hear him, and judge."

David did not return home that night but slept in the field. In the morning Saul and Jonathan walked in the field. David heard Jonathan's voice: "O King, my father, let me speak to you of David. Do not sin against him. He is your servant; he is innocent of any wrong. Consider his deeds. They are good, very good."

David heard Saul's voice answering, "You speak the truth, my son, and I shall hearken to your voice. As the Lord lives, David shall not be slain."

Jonathan could not read his father's mind. Had the venomous hatred passed like a fever? Or was the king dissembling, trying to disarm suspicion? But David wished to believe the king and went into his presence. He played the harp for Saul and sang to him, and Saul was pleasant to him.

Reports came that the Philistines were gathering in strength again. David went against them at Gath. He led his men in another brilliant, headlong charge and won another great victory. The people rejoiced and lined the roads where he marched, and split their throats cheering. And Saul's rancor flared anew.

He called certain men to him and instructed them. They ringed David's house. Michal saw them through a window; she knew who they were. She said to David: "My father has sent his assassins. Leave this house, beloved. Leave tonight, or you will be slain tomorrow."

She let a rope out the window. David slid down and disappeared. She stuffed David's robes with straw and placed them on her bed under a sheet, and set a pillow of goat's hair as his head. She drew the blinds, so that the room was full of shadow.

The assassins waited outside the house all that night and the next day, but David did not appear. Their leader went to Saul and said: "He must suspect something, O King. He stays in the house and does not come out."

Saul sent a message to David's house, bidding him report to the palace. Michal met the messenger at the door and said: "My husband cannot leave the house. He is sick."

"I must see him. I bring a message from the king."

"You may see him," said Michal. "But he is too ill to speak."

She took the messenger to her bedroom. The man saw a shape in the bed and spoke the king's message — but received no answer. "Go," said Michal. "When he has recovered a little, he will go to the palace."

The messenger returned to Saul and told him that David was too sick to leave his bed.

"Sick!" roared Saul. "I'll make sure it's fatal! I shall go there and drag him from his bed and slay him."

He stormed to David's house at the head of the Royal Guard. They burst into the bedroom and tore the sheet from the bed, and saw the robes stuffed with straw and the goat-hair pillow. Saul took Michal by the throat and said: "Why have you deceived me? Why have you helped my enemy escape?"

She put his hand aside and said: "You gave him to be my husband before God's altar. In that holy place we vowed to be of one flesh. How can I help you slay him?"

Saul departed, but sent his men to pursue David, bidding them not to return until they had slain him.

David fled the city. He hid himself by day and traveled only by night. He made his way to Ramah, where the prophet Samuel dwelt. The fame of Samuel's wisdom had spread, and a company of young men had come to dwell near him and learn from him. For it was believed that Samuel spoke directly to God.

Each day at noon, the old man would stand in an empty place before a stone altar, stand with his head bared to the full blaze of the sun, stretching his arms to the sky. No one spoke; there was absolute silence, a silence so profound you could hear the light vibrating. Upon certain days Samuel just stood there staring at the sky, staring and waiting — until his beard and hair and white garments were drenched, and his arms fell of their own weight. Then he would bow his head and walk away, for God had not shown Himself.

On other days his face would light up with joy and he would speak in a voice so deep it was like the mountain speaking. Some words were Samuel's own, questioning and imploring; other words were God's words, uttering themselves through Samuel. The young men wept for joy. Certain of them remembered the words that had been spoken, and, when they returned to the shade of their tents, wrote them down on tablets of clay.

Here it was that David came, fleeing Saul's assassins. He sat among the company of young men the first day. It was a day when God did not speak. But when Samuel had dropped his arms, David leaped up and cried to the sky, "Deliver me from my enemies, O my God; defend me from those who rise up against me. Deliver me from the workers of iniquity; save me from bloody men. Lo, they lie in wait. They make a noise like a dog and go about the city. Scatter them with your wrath and bring them down, O Lord. Consume them with your wrath and let them know that God rules. And I will sing of your power. Yea, I will sing aloud of your mercy in the morning."

They marveled to hear. David's voice was not like thunder in the hills, but like a song. Like water dappling in the sunlight and birdcall — sometimes like a trumpet. The young men marveled, and Samuel was pleased.

Saul's men went to Ramah seeking David. They went with swords to the altar. They saw a white-bearded old man talking to the sky. He turned on them and thundered, "O you who come with swords to this place, know this: The wicked are estranged from the womb; they go astray as soon as they are born. O God, let them melt away. He who bends his bow, let him be cut to pieces. As a snail melts under salt, let every one of them melt away. Let them pass away like the untimely birth of a woman. Let them not see the sun again!"

Saul's men were terrified. The swords dropped from their hands. They fell to their knees, gibbering with terror. Samuel turned and walked away as they knelt on the ground. And Saul's men stayed among the company of young men. They did not raise their hands against David, nor did they return to Saul.

When they did not return, Saul sent other men to pursue David. And they did not return. He sent others under strict instructions to go to Ramah and kill David. Saul waited. No man of this troop returned. Then Saul himself led a company of picked warriors to Ramah. He went to a well. His men drank and watered their horses. He inquired of the people where Samuel and David were, and was told, "They are in Naioth in Ramah."

Saul led his warriors to Naioth. He saw a congregation of white-robed men standing still as trees; among them he saw his own men who had not returned. They were crowding about an altar. Before the altar stood Samuel and David, their faces transfigured with joy. Saul's sword was in his hand, the great blade that had scythed down so many enemies, and the grip of his hand was mighty upon it. He shouted to his men, but the tongue froze in his mouth and no words came. The sword was twitched from his hand. A terrible, nameless pain gripped his bowels. He staggered forward, lurching like a blind man. His robes burned like nettles. He tore his clothes off and knelt before the altar, sobbing like a child: "I seek you, O God; my soul thirsts for you, my flesh yearns for you in a dry and thirsty land where no water is. Return to me, and my soul shall be satisfied as with marrow and fatness; my lips shall praise you. I will remember you upon my bed and meditate on you in the night watches. Return, return, forgive and return!"

"Glory be to God!" cried David. "The king repents!"

"Do not delude yourself," said Samuel. "He repents as easily as he sins, and will sin again."

But the sight of King Saul groveling naked in the dust moved David past prudence. He wanted to forget all the evil Saul had done. He wanted to believe in the king again. Samuel led him some paces away and said: "Leave this place. Leave now. The king's mood will change, and the thought of how he has abased himself before you will make him hate you more than ever."

David heeded the words of Samuel and left that place. He sought out Jonathan and said: "Your father hunts me from place to place. Truly as the Lord lives, there is but a step between me and death."

"How can I help you, my brother?"

David fell silent. He studied Jonathan's face. "We are more than brother, and we love each other," he said. "Nevertheless, you cannot risk your father's displeasure. I ask this: Do not let your father kill me. Slay me yourself, so that my last sight on earth will be the face that I have loved."

"I would rather lift my hand against myself," said Jonathan. "Let me try my father one more time. I will go to him and speak for you."

"Go," said David. "You will find me in the wheatfield where I hid before."

Jonathan went to Saul and pleaded for David's life. Saul's face writhed with fury. Foam flecked his lips. "Perverse rebellious fool!" he cried. "You are so enamored of that sly little demon that you conspire against your father and forfeit your own legacy. When I die, he will brush you aside like a gnat and exterminate your children and seize the throne for himself. I may as well kill you now and save him the trouble."

He snatched up his javelin and hurled it at his son. Jonathan moved away just in time. He did not flee. He looked silently at his father, then walked away. He went to David in the wheatfield.

"You must flee," he said. "I will come to you as soon as I can."

"Do not come to me," said David. "Your father has lost his touch in warfare. You must act like his eldest son and lead the army. You will have work enough. The Philistine grows stronger each day."

"We are bound in brotherhood forever," said Jonathan. "I know you love me and will be kind to me while I live. But swear this to me, that when the Lord has swept the enemies of David off the earth and brought you to the triumph He has designed for you, then, if I be dead, extend your kindness to my children and do not cut them off."

"I swear it," said David. "Let this be a covenant forever between the house of David and the house of Jonathan."

David went first to the valley of Elah and took the sword of Goliath from the place he had hidden it. Two years had passed since his battle with the giant, and David had grown from a youth into a young man. He was not a large man, and the sword was huge. But he felt a fire from heaven coursing through his arms and shoulders, filling him with weird strength. He lifted the sword and swung it easily, and knew that God was with him in his troubles. He swung the gigantic blade and sang to himself, and was not afraid. He went into the hills ringing the Dead Sea a few miles east of Bethlehem, and hid in a great cave called Adullam.

Word went out that David was at Adullam. Magic dwelt in his name, though he was a fugitive and hunted by the king, and men went to join him. Men who were in debt and could not pay; men who had lost their farms or their flocks; and those who were discontented with the king's rule went to the cave at Adullam and made David their captain. Now he commanded four hundred men, hardened, fearless men who trusted him utterly and would follow him wherever he led.

Saul sent troops of his best warriors against David. They hunted him through the length and breadth of the land, in desert, forest, and mountain. But David had trained his men to run like deer, to climb like wild goats, to swim rivers, and to move silently and hide themselves like creatures of the wild. Saul's troops wearied themselves in pursuit but could never come to grips with David's men. The king offered a bounty for every man of David's killed or captured, and a huge reward to the one who would kill David. Still the little band eluded the king's army.

Many times David's men could have turned light-footedly upon their pursuers in mountain passes or marshy places, and hunted down their hunters and slain them. But David did not allow this. They grumbled,

239

saying, "Must we always fly, never fight?"

David addressed them, saying, "You shall not attack Saul's men except to protect your lives. They, also, are children of Israel. They are our brothers; I will not have brother fighting brother. I will lead you into battle, I promise. But it will be the Philistines we fight."

And the Philistines, sensing Saul's weakness, were pressing hard again. The three kings led great armies out of their coast cities against the strongholds of Israel. And Saul called back the troops he had sent to pursue David, for they were needed against the Philistines.

Now it was that David forged his band into a deadly weapon. They roamed far behind the Philistine lines, ambushing small detachments and slaughtering them, stealing mules, stampeding horses, looting food wagons. And God marched with David. His spirit rode David's banners, and the tiny band did more damage than all Saul's army.

Saul was not grateful. He felt himself strangling with envy and hatred, and called certain men to him. "There is a truce now with the Philistines," he said. "And I can strike against the foe who devours us from within like a worm in the fruit. I send you as spies throughout the land. Search out David's haunts, and find those who have seen him there. Bring them to me that torture may be applied and the last drop of information wrung out of them. Those who come to me with sure news shall receive vineyards and fat flocks and much treasure. Go now, friends. Hunt the fox. Run him down and get rich."

Spies fanned out through the land and looked everywhere and questioned everyone, and went back to Saul, reporting that David had led his men into the wilderness of Engedi.

Word came now of Samuel's death, and David wept for the old man who had anointed him and counseled him so wisely. But he did not dare to go to Samuel's funeral, for he knew that Saul would be there.

"Forgive me, teacher, old friend," he said. "Forgive me for not attending your final rites. But know this: In my own way I shall erect a memorial to you that your name may live in man's mind forever."

Saul led three thousand men into Engedi. It was steep, hilly country, very difficult for troop movement. But Saul drove his men up and down the hills in search of David. High upon the mountain where wild goats play, David had found a large cave and encamped there with his men, and Saul marched his troops uphill in swift pursuit. But when he reached the sheepcotes on top, he saw no sign of anyone. He let his men rest then, but was too impatient to rest himself and scouted ahead. He climbed farther and came to the mouth of a cave. He went into the cave. It was very dark after the bright sunlight. He saw nothing, and lay down to sleep.

David's sentry came across the sleeper, and, to his amazement, recognized the king. He ran to David and said: "Behold the day that the Lord promised you, saying, 'I will deliver your enemy into your hand.' He has kept His promise, my captain, for your enemy, Saul, lies at the mouth of the cave fast asleep."

David went to the mouth of the cave, sword in hand. He looked down upon the sleeper. The exhausted king was fathoms deep. He did not twitch or mumble. David studied the face he knew so well. It seemed to have aged greatly. He was looking at the face of an old man. He raised his sword, but could not strike. He knew that he was laying up much trouble for himself, but he could not kill the sleeping man. With his sharp sword he cut off the edge of Saul's robe, and went back into the depths of the cave.

His men crowded about him, crying, "Did you kill him? Is he dead?"

"God forbid that I should do this thing," said David. "He is the one that the Lord has anointed, and I cannot raise my hand against him. For God has made him king, and in His own good time, if He repents of His choice, will pluck the king He made from his throne. Go now, quickly! Go down into the valley, for the king's men are up here. Hasten! Go! I shall come to you in the valley."

The men left. They went through a narrow, rocky tunnel, and out a hole in the side of the mountain, which was a secret way. David waited until he saw Saul arise and leave the cave. Then he followed, and cried out after him: "My lord, my King!"

Saul whirled and looked behind him. He saw David stooping with his face to the earth, bowing to him.

"Why do you believe that I seek to harm you?" said David. "Behold, this day God delivered you into my hand in the cave. My men bade me kill you. But I spared you."

Saul stared at him silently.

"See this in my hand," said David. "This is the skirt of your robe. I cut it off with my sword as you lay asleep. Yes, I used my sword against you as you lay helpless before me. But it was not to kill you, only to cut your robe in proof that I mean no evil toward you. Yet, my father, though I do not sin against you, you hunt me like a wild beast. May God judge between you and me, and if you have done evil, I will leave vengeance to Him. But I will not raise my hand against you. Wickedness proceeds from the wicked. My hand will not be upon you."

Still Saul stood motionless, silent. He was like a rock upon the mountain, and David continued to speak to him.

"Why does the king of Israel march forth with his thousands of troops? Whom does he pursue? A dead dog, a flea, and no more. If you will not hear my words, then let God plead my cause and deliver me out of your hand."

Finally Saul spoke. His voice was so low that David could hardly hear him. "Is this your voice, my son David?" The king wept. David saw tears running down that iron face. "You are more righteous than I," said Saul. "You have done good for the evil that I have done you. The Lord delivered me into your hand and you did not kill me. What other man, finding his enemy thus, would let him go his way? Now, may God reward you for what you have done this day. And know this, too: You shall surely be king after me. The kingdom of Israel shall be established in you."

Again David bowed to the ground.

"Come home now," said Saul. "Bring your men into my army, and be my chief captain."

"I shall find my men and follow after," said David. He bowed to the king, turned, and went his way. When he reached the valley, he mustered his men and hurried them away from the mountain as fast as he could. He had welcomed Saul's words, but he also remembered what Samuel had said: "Do not delude yourself. He repents as easily as he sins, and will sin again." And David knew that Saul would change again, and again seek to kill him. So he kept his men together, and roamed the hills and wild places, and did not return.

After Samuel died, Saul, in a fit of piety, had obeyed an edict of Samuel's and exiled all witches and wizards and those who trafficked with ghosts and demons, and had forbidden them to return on pain of death. But now the king was troubled. Word had come to him that the Philistines were gathering in a mighty host. He called off the pursuit of David and returned to Gibeah, where he dwelt. He mustered his entire army and marched eastward. The three kings of the Philistines came with a huge, well-trained army and encamped at Shunem. Saul pitched his tents at Gilboa.

But when Saul saw the host of the Philistines, he was afraid. He prayed to God, but received no answer. God did not speak to Saul or send him dreams or visions or the word of a prophet.

"I am lost," said Saul. "I am in a fog of fear and doubt. I must have help that is beyond human help. Prophets fail me, so I must find a witch." And he said to his servants: "Find me a witch."

A servant said: "There is a woman who lives at Endor and speaks with spirits."

Saul took off his armor and dressed himself in ordinary clothing. He took two men and they went to Endor. There was no moon; it was black night. The three men entered the old woman's house. Saul regarded the woman, who looked like a bundle of rags with a wig on top. He said: "I pray you, call up your familiar spirit and bid him usher from the Land of the Dead him whose name I shall say to you."

"You ask me to practice witchcraft," said the old woman.

"Are you not a witch?" said Saul.

"No more," said the woman. "For the king has forbidden it. He has forbidden wizardry and witchcraft on the pain of death. Why do you lay a snare for my life?"

"I stand close to the king," said Saul. "Pardon resides in my office. Do as I say, and you shall earn no punishment but a fat purse."

"Whom shall I call up from the Land of the Dead?" said the woman.

"Bring me Samuel."

She lit a fire in her hearth and dropped a powder upon it, muttering. Fragrant smoke arose. The smoke thickened and was a tall spout of smoke, and that became the vague, steamy figure of Samuel.

"You who ignored my counsel while I was yet alive," said the voice of Samuel, "you, Saul, why do you summon me from my final place? Have I not earned repose?"

"You have deceived me!" cried the witch. "You are Saul himself. You are the king and will slay me."

"Be quiet," said the king. "No one shall harm you." Then Saul bowed before Samuel.

"Why have you disturbed me?" said Samuel. "Why have you brought me here?"

243

"I am sore distressed," said Saul. "The Philistines come against me in a mighty host. And God has departed from me and does not answer me, not by word or vision or dream. And there is no other prophet to speak His word. Therefore do I call unto you, Samuel."

"I cannot help you now," said Samuel. "The Lord has departed from you. He has done only what I told you He would do. He has rent the kingdom out of your hand and shall give it to David. You did not obey the word of the Lord; therefore He does this thing to you. Tomorrow He delivers Israel into the hand of the Philistine. And by tomorrow night you shall be with me, and your sons shall be with me."

Saul's heart was split by terror. He crashed to the floor. He was also enfeebled by hunger; he had eaten nothing for a day and a night. Samuel had vanished. The old woman bent to Saul and said: "Behold, your servant has obeyed your voice. I put my life in your hand, and did what you said. Now, I pray, do what I say. Eat a morsel of bread. Restore your strength so that you may leave."

"No," groaned Saul. "I will not eat."

But the old woman spoke to the men and told them that the king would not have strength to walk if he did not eat, and they persuaded Saul. He arose from the floor and sat on the bed. The woman roasted a fat calf and baked a new loaf of bread. She had no yeast and the bread was unleavened. She served the meal to Saul and his men. They ate, and left the house. That was Saul's last meal.

Saul's Death

The next day the Philistines attacked. Wave after wave of armored men and brass chariots hurled themselves against Saul's lines. The men of Israel broke and fled before the Philistines. The enemy followed them, and there was bloody work. The children of Israel were slaughtered by the thousands, and the Philistines were triumphant.

Saul fought bravely. His men formed a hedge of spears around him, and he fought on after the battle was lost. He saw Jonathan fall, and his other two sons. And an archer of the Philistines drew his bow against Saul and sent an arrow through his breastplate, wounding him sorely.

Saul spoke to his armor bearer: "Draw your sword and thrust me through. Or these uncircumcised dogs will come and worry my body." But his armor bearer did not dare to kill the king. Saul placed the hilt of his own sword carefully on the ground and fell upon it. It pierced him through.

It was total defeat. Throughout Israel the people forsook their cities and fled into the wilderness. The Philistines went and dwelt in the abandoned cities. Saul's body and the corpses of his sons were taken to Bethshan. The bodies were stripped of their armor and impaled, naked, on the city walls. But first the Philistines struck off Saul's head. They took his armor and hung it as a trophy in the temple of their mother goddess, Astarte. The king's head was laid upon the altar of the sea god, Dagon, who was half fish.

David was in the wilderness when news came to him of the Philistine victory, and of how Saul and Jonathan had died. When David heard this, he saw Jonathan again in all his beauty, and he felt his heart breaking with the loss of his friend. In his love and grief he forgot any resentment toward Saul, and remembered only the great, robed figure in the shadowed throne room listening to a boy play a harp. He remembered the proud king in his armor leading his warriors. He remembered the naked man groveling in the dust before Samuel. He remembered the sleeper in the cave. And David cried:

> The beauty of Israel is slain upon its high places;
> How the mighty are fallen!
> Tell it not in Gath, publish it not
>   in the streets of Ashkelon,
> Lest the daughters of the Philistines rejoice,
> Lest the daughters of the uncircumcised
>   triumph.
> Ye mountains of Gilboa, let there be no dew,
> Neither let there be rain upon you, nor fields of
>   offering.
> For there the shield of the mighty
> Is vilely cast away.
> Saul and Jonathan were lovely and pleasant
>   in their lives.
> And in their death they are not divided.
> They were swifter than eagles;
> They were stronger than lions.
> Ye daughters of Israel, weep over Saul
>   who clothed you in scarlet.

245

O Jonathan, you were slain in your high place.
I am distressed for you, my brother Jonathan.
Very pleasant have you been to me.
Your love to me was wonderful,
Passing the love of women.

Now all the men about David within the sound of his voice were sobbing. David dashed the tears from his eyes, leaped upon a rock, and cried: "Now must I go and gather up the scattered remnants of Israel, and knit them to a whole again. Our king has been taken from us, and our beautiful prince, and now it falls upon us to refire the hearts of our people and drive the heathen from our holy places."

It happened so. The scattered soldiers of Saul's army made their way to where David was and arrayed themselves under his banner. The elders of Judah came and anointed him king. He sent messages to all parts of Israel where the people had fled the conqueror, calling every man who could bear arms to him. They came. He trained them in his own way, and spoke to them daily, reviving the word of God in their parched and fearful hearts. And out of the broken pieces of a defeated nation he forged a mighty army. They marched against the enemy. The spirit of God walked with David into battle and he prevailed. The Philistines were driven out of Israel, back to their coastal cities.

Israel was whole again and David was king. But he never forgot Jonathan, and he never forgot Saul.

David and Bathsheba

Saul was dead and David was king. The spirit of God, which had departed from Saul and bereft him of victories, returned now tenfold to David, and his armies swept the foe from the field. David was a war chief such as had never been seen before. Young, joyous, with a smile always for his men, and a personal word, he saved his wrath for the enemy, and in his own troops punished only cowardice. It was said that his men would march after him off the edge of a cliff.

Now, Saul's defeats had left Israel weak; its enemies occupied most of the strong places. And David had to drive them out of the land. But he never fought until God gave him the word, and when he went into battle God went before him. A cloud or eagle by day, a torch by night, God went before him with a sound like the wind in the mulberry trees. And David was everywhere victorious.

"May I get you a city, Lord?" he asked. "A high and beautiful city in which to build your house?"

"Get me a city," said the Lord.

David led his men into the hills of Judea toward the City of the Hill, the beautiful walled city of Jerusalem. This city stood so high, its walls were so thick and its Jebusite defenders so fierce, that it had never been taken. Egyptians had marched against it, Hittites, Hivites, and Assyrians, but its walls had never been breached.

David stormed the heights of Zion and took Jerusalem from the Jebusites. There he made his home and planned a house for God. Now, the ark of the covenant, that holy of holies, had been built in the wilderness according to the instructions given Moses on the mountain. It was made of acacia wood inlaid with gold. In it reposed the tables of the law, a pot that had held manna, and Aaron's rod. It was set with brass rings; through them staves were placed so that the ark could be carried by two strong priests. It had been kept by the children of Israel as they wandered in the desert, and had been taken from place to place, according to the fortunes of battle. It was the holy of holies, the most sacred object that had ever been — not because of the richness of its wood or metals or the skill of its design, but because this ark and its furred tent held God's words to Moses and the rod of power he had given to Aaron. The ark rested now in a small village in Judah, attended by its priests. David ordered it brought to Jerusalem.

With thirty thousand men, the cream of his army, he went to escort the ark on its journey. They set the ark on a new cart. Musicians walked before it, playing joyful music. They played the harp, the psaltery, timbrel, cornet, and cymbals. The sun was bright and the people rejoiced.

With shouting and the sound of the trumpet, David carried the ark into Jerusalem. "Make a joyful music unto God, all ye righteous!" David cried. And the players played and the people shouted.

David snatched a psaltery from a player, and played as he danced, and sang:

> I will also praise you with the psaltery,
> I will sing your truth, O my God.
> Unto you I will sing with the harp
> O ye haven of Israel.

He was flooded with gladness before the ark in the city that he had taken, and danced with all his might. In front of all the people, the king

247

cast off his garments and danced before the ark. Clad only in a linen shirt, he leaped with joy before the tabernacle, leaped high over all the people, the sun flashing on his legs and on his bronzed wet shoulders.

Michal, his wife, Saul's daughter, looked out the window of the king's house and saw David leaping and dancing before the ark. And she despised him in her heart.

When David returned, glowing with pleasure, to bless his household, Michal came out to meet him and said: "How glorious the king who uncovers himself before the multitude, before his servants and his handmaidens like a drunken lout."

"I danced before the Lord," said David. "Before Him who chose me out of all the people and anointed me king over Israel. You may chide me all you wish, but I will play before the Lord."

"Vile," she said. "Shameless."

"If I am vile in your eyes," said David, "then I shall act out my baseness among those handmaidens you speak of — who are beautiful and who honor me."

From that time on David never went to Michal's bed, and she was childless.

As David led his armies from victory to victory, he trained his men in the art of war, and chose the best warriors as his captains. The greatest of these captains, a man named Joab, went to him and said: "Forgive me, O King, for presuming to advise you."

"Speak," said David.

"I have conferred with your other captains, and they are with me in this. We do not wish you to lead your troops into battle. You place yourself always in the hottest part of the fighting. And you are the first to scale the walls of a beleaguered city."

"I am king," said David. "My privilege resides in my duty. I must be first in battle."

"Not so," said Joab. "You have led us in battle where no other could. You have inspired our hearts with courage. You have trained us in the art of war. You, O King, are our heart and our mind. Without you we are simply men, some good, some bad. And since we are fewer than the enemy, we must be vanquished without the special virtue that you inspire. You are worth ten thousand troops to us. If you are killed, as you must be one day with your headlong rush into the thick of battle, then

Israel dies with you. For the host will fall on us and will prevail."

"I thank you," said David, "and shall weigh your words carefully. I shall pray to God for guidance."

David asked God what to do. The Lord answered: "I wish you to live and reign. Guide your captains from Jerusalem."

When Joab returned the next day, David embraced him and said: "Thank you for your wisdom. We shall plan the campaigns together, brave Joab. You will lead the armies and I shall send you messages."

Shortly afterward Joab marched against the Ammonites and laid siege to Rabbah, their city. David tarried in Jerusalem. He was very restless away from his army. After one sleepless night, he sought the shade on his terrace during the heat of the day. The terrace of his palace was high over the roof tops and he could see into nearby courtyards. He saw a woman bathing. She raised a silver ewer over her head and let the water fall upon her, and stood there naked, being sponged by a handmaiden. She was tall and very beautiful. He did not know whether she was wife, widow, or virgin, and he did not care. He sent for her and she came to the palace.

She was taken to him on the same terrace from which he had seen her bathing. It was night, but the heat had lingered and there were no stars. She knelt to him and said: "You have sent for me, O King, and I am here."

"What is your name?"

"Bathsheba, daughter of Eliam, wife to Uriah."

"Is your husband at home?"

"My husband is with your army, my lord, on the field before Rabbah."

"Do you know why I sent for you?"

"No, my lord."

"I saw you bathing today. You are very beautiful."

"You are kind to your servant."

"Servant? You are my mistress. Your beauty reigns over my heart. Will you lie with me?"

"What of my husband?"

"Do you love him?"

"He is my husband. He stood with me before God's altar, and we exchanged vows."

"Do you love him?"

"Ah, my lord, I am dazzled by you. How could it not be? I am a simple

249

woman; you are a glorious king. Your name is golden to us, your fame like music in the air. When I behold you now, it is like looking at the sun with unshaded eyes; you are clothed in fire. And when I think that you, who can have any woman in the world, have chosen me, then I am suffocated with pride and joy. Is this love?"

"It can become love."

"What of my husband?"

"He shall be honored in other ways."

They burned for each other in the darkness of the terrace. He could feel her heat from where he stood. He felt his bones fusing as she came to meet him, and he entered her embrace.

He kept her with him for two days and nights, and kept himself private, and allowed no one to come to him. He had their meals brought into his chamber. They were together all the time and glutted themselves upon each other, and delighted in each other. And his lust grew with fulfillment.

The campaign against the Ammonites dragged on, and Uriah was in the field with the troops. Bathsheba came to the palace every night but went home before dawn, because David wished to keep the affair secret. He did not want it said that he had stolen the wife of one of his officers while the man was away, fighting.

Then Bathsheba informed him that she was pregnant. David sent a message to Joab, asking that Uriah be sent home on leave, the pretext being that David wanted a firsthand report of battle conditions. Uriah reported to David, who questioned him at length about the progress of the siege, the spirit of the men, and the fighting quality of the Ammonites. Uriah answered with intelligence and precision; David saw that he was a very good officer. He thanked him and said: "You have been in the field for months, and deserve a few days' rest. Go home and embrace your wife, and refresh yourself."

But Uriah did not go home that night. He slept in the courtyard of the palace. David sent for him, and said: "You have a beautiful, loving wife at home, and you sleep on cold stones. Are you mad?"

Uriah replied, "I am grateful for your concern, O King, but it is impossible for me to enjoy the comforts of home, knowing that my comrades are in the field, hourly risking their lives against the fierce Ammonites. I pray you, let me depart from Jerusalem, and return to the siege."

When David heard this, he was sickened with shame. He had always led his men against the enemy, sharing every hardship, thrusting himself into the most dangerous places. Now every word of this brave man, whose wife he had stolen, pierced him like a poisoned arrow. And David, unaccustomed to shame, began to hate this man.

"Very well," he said. "Return to Rabbah. Go now."

Thereupon he wrote a letter and sealed it with the royal seal. He sent for a messenger and said: "Take this to Joab."

The letter read: "Uriah has impressed me. He is a man of valor. Put him where he may prove his worth."

In three days the messenger returned. He bore a letter from Joab that said: "We have had a battle. The enemy made a sortie from the city, surrounded our forward troops, and killed five men before they were beaten off. Among those who fell was Uriah — who fought very bravely. Do not think me rash for pressing so close to the walls. We have cut off their food and water. The city must fall within three days. And we will cast down their stone idols and raise an altar to the living God. I know that you itch for action, O King, but you reside in the hearts of your men, and inspire us to victory."

David went to Bathsheba and said: "You are a widow. Your husband has fallen in battle."

She did not want David to see her face. She bowed her head and thought: Thank God he died in ignorance of my guilt.

She was shaken by a gust of bitter grief, which became more bitter still as she realized that she was mourning not the loss of her husband but the loss of her honor; that, in fact, she had killed Uriah in her heart before the swords of the Ammonites had touched him.

She raised her head and said: "I cannot weep."

"You must leave me now," said David, "and mourn for a time. You shall not be a widow long. I will find you a husband."

"Another husband?" she said.

"Myself," he said. "You will be my wife and my queen."

Joab took the city and the troops returned. There was a victory celebration, and another feast for David's marriage to Bathsheba. And when the feasting was done, when the music had stilled and the guests had departed, there came a man whose name was Nathan.

He was a wise man, a prophet of the Lord, and David had consulted him about the building of God's house. He reminded David of Samuel who had visited him in the wilderness. He was also pared down to the shape of the bone, and his eyes burned in their sockets, and his voice held the authority of natural things. He said to David: "I come for justice, O King."

"Speak," said David.

"I will tell you a tale," said Nathan. "There were two men, one rich, the other poor. The rich man owned great flocks and herds. The poor man had nothing except one little ewe lamb that he raised himself. He fed her by hand and made her a pet, and she played with his children. She ate out of his dish and drank out of his cup and slept at the foot of his bed. She was like a daughter to him. And it happened that the rich man passed the house of the poor man and saw the lamb playing in the garden. And, since he was entertaining a guest that night, he thought he would take this lamb instead of one from his own flock. He led the lamb away and killed it, and dressed and roasted it, and served it to his guest."

David's wrath was kindled by this tale. His anger choked him; he could hardly speak. Finally he said to Nathan: "As the Lord lives, the man who has done this thing shall die. He shall restore the value of the lamb many fold, and then he shall die because he has done this thing and has no pity. Who is this man?"

"Thou art the man," said Nathan. "The Lord God of Israel has spoken to me, and He is greatly displeased with you. He anointed you king. He took you out of the hand of Saul. He gave you Saul's house and Saul's daughter to be your wife, and your choice of other wives. He gave you the throne of Israel and of Judah. And if you had thought all this too little, He would have given you other things. But you have despised His commandment and done evil in His sight. You have killed Uriah as surely as though you had cut him down with your own sword, and you have taken his wife to be your wife. Now, therefore, says the Lord, the sword shall never depart from your house, because you have despised His statutes and killed a man and stolen his wife. The Lord says that He will raise up evil against you out of your own house. And He will take your wives and give them to your neighbors, who will lie with them before your eyes."

David answered Nathan, saying, "I have sinned against the Lord."

"You have sinned indeed," said Nathan. "But the Lord still loves you. You must pay for this sin, but you shall not die. But because you have done this thing, the child that is born to Bathsheba shall surely die."

Nathan's words filled David with terror. And when the child was born, it was very sickly. David pleaded to God for the child's life. He fasted and went out of the castle into the courtyard and lay all night upon the earth. The elders of his house went to him to raise him up from the earth. He would not rise. Nor would he eat. He ate nothing and drank no water. They were afraid their king would die.

He continued to fast and sleep on the ground. On the seventh day the child died. David's servants feared to tell him that the child was dead, thinking that since he had punished himself so sorely during the child's illness, he would surely kill himself at the news of its death.

They went to him, and he said: "Is my child dead?"

They said: "He is dead."

David arose from the earth and washed and anointed himself and changed his garments. He went into the house of the Lord and worshipped. Then he went to his own house and asked for food. He ate meat and drank wine.

An elder asked him, "How is it, O King, that you fasted for the child while he was alive, and now that he is dead you have regained your appetite?"

David said: "While the child was yet alive I fasted and wept. This was my way of asking God to spare the child. But why should I fast now that he is dead? Can I bring him back again? I shall go to him one day, but he can never return to me."

And David comforted Bathsheba and made love to her. She conceived again and bore a son. They named this son Solomon.

But Nathan's terrible words burned in David's mind, and he kept brooding about how the prophecy would fulfill itself — how evil might come to him out of his own family. He considered many possibilities but never suspected that the evil would be done by his favorite son.

David had many wives and they bore him many children. The child he loved best was his third son, Absalom, who was a young man by the time the last son, Solomon, was born. Throughout Israel this young prince, Absalom, was praised for his beauty. He was tall, much taller than his father; his eyes were gray, like David's, and he had a mane of red-gold hair, which hung down below his waist. Once a year he cut it. The shorn locks, it is said, weighed more than ten pounds. Girls and women fought like wildcats for one shining curl. He was as brave as he was handsome, skilled with spear and bow. David set him high among the captains, and his troops loved him.

That the king favored Absalom was known to all; he was accepted as the heir to the throne. But he was impatient. He wanted to be king and he could not wait for his father to die. He set out to wean the people from their loyalty to David. He began to live with great ceremony, spending more money than the rest of his brothers combined. He kept chariots and horses and fifty men to run before him. And people began to accept that he was unlike anyone else.

Once a month people went to Jerusalem to be judged. The king sat upon his throne and heard all those who had quarrels or complaints and judged among them. From all over Israel they came thronging to Jerusalem, many more than David could hear. Those who could not be heard were told to go home and return the next month. Absalom saw a chance here. He would arise early on the morning of judgment day and stand at the city gates, greeting each man who came, asking his name and his dwelling place and the nature of his complaint. Then Absalom would pretend to look around, and call out, "Ho there! Is there a man of the king here? Is there a man to handle this business and take these good folk to the palace?" Then Absalom would turn back to the visitor and say, "You have come here on weighty business, but there is no one sent by the king to hear you. Oh, that I were judge in this land. Any man who had any suit or cause of complaint could come to me and I would do him justice. And swift justice. For justice delayed is no justice at all."

When the petitioner thanked him, Absalom would say, "It is for us, the king's sons, to thank you for your patience in this matter." He would embrace the man. And the man embraced by this glorious prince would feel himself princely, and would return to his village praising Absalom, saying that he should be king. Thus did Absalom steal the hearts of the men of Israel.

David was told how his son paraded himself before the people. Hushai, an old friend of David's and his chief advisor, cautioned him. But David brushed off the warning, saying, "Absalom, my son, is princely and beautiful. People love him wherever he goes. Shall I blame him for this? It is rather a cause for rejoicing."

"He is more than princely," said Hushai. "He means to be kingly. And he will not wait to inherit. Unless you wake up and bestir yourself, O

King, he will snatch the crown off your head."

But another of David's counselors, a man named Ahithophel, a subtle and deceitful man who had secretly cast his lot with Absalom, said: "No one is wiser than my brother Hushai. But in this matter, O King, his love for you, I fear, colors his judgment. Absalom is generous, impulsive, warm-hearted. But he worships you next to God and would never lift a hand against you."

David believed what he wished to believe. He welcomed the words of Ahithophel and coldly dismissed Hushai.

For three years Absalom wove his web of conspiracy. In the fourth year he judged that events had ripened. He went to David and said: "God has been good to me, O my father, and I wish to thank Him. I wish to go into Hebron, and sacrifice at the tomb of Abraham and Sarah."

David was pleased at Absalom's piety. "Go in peace, my son," he said.

That night Absalom called together two hundred of his most faithful followers in Jerusalem. They all left their houses and went out of the city. Absalom chose eleven of these men, and sent one to each of the tribes of Israel. "Await my summons," he told them. "When you hear a man coming on a horse, blowing a trumpet, then proclaim to the tribe you dwell among that Absalom reigns in Hebron. Then gather men of valor from each tribe and come to me here, and we shall march on Jerusalem."

Absalom dwelt in Hebron. Men flocked to his standard. Among them went Ahithophel, David's counselor. But there were those loyal to David in Hebron. They hastened to Jerusalem and told David. "Rise, O King, for the hearts of the men of Israel are with Absalom."

Then David knew that Hushai had spoken the truth and that Absalom had been conspiring against him all this time. He was sickened by the thought of his beloved son doing this, and he could not rise to the peril with his old fighting spirit. He could not bear the thought of fighting his son. He called his counselors together and said: "We must flee. We must leave Jerusalem, for Absalom is coming. He comes with an army and will take the city and put us all to the sword."

That night David departed with all his court. He left his city of Jerusalem, which he had taken from the Jebusites, the city that he had so joyfully entered, bearing the ark of the covenant, dancing before it and singing his glad song. As he rode through the gates out of the city, he felt all his triumphs turning to ashes. All his memories were repealed, and his pride withered.

Six hundred men went out of Jerusalem with him, and his wives and his children. Of those who dwelt in the palace he left only ten concubines. He rode northward into the wilderness of Judah, into those hills where he once had hidden while Saul pursued him. The cold, piney wind off those mountains reminded him of the days of his youth, when he himself had been a rebel against the king, hunted by Saul's entire army. He sat up in the saddle and drew a deep breath. He felt his heart reviving. He said: "The Lord gives, and the Lord takes away. Blessed be the name of the Lord forever."

He led his men out of Judah, across the river Jordan into the land of Gilead. This was a place of hills, also, a stark country. But there was a valley there, where a kind of pine tree grew; and the sap of this tree, when boiled in a certain way, made the most soothing balm for wounds and bruises. David thought of this and said to himself: "Perchance for me, also, in these hard straits there is a hidden sweetness." His spirit flamed up in him again, and he became the war leader who had smitten the Philistine and the Moabite and the Ammonite and all the enemies of Israel, and made his name great among nations.

Entering Gilead, he kindled the hearts of the men there, and they arose and followed him. They were tall, strong hillmen, good with the spear, deadly with the bow. They came to swell his ranks. Now David led an army, and the army had to eat. The matter became known. The women of Gilead came. They brought bread in earthen vessels. They brought wheat and barley, parched corn, beans, and lentils — also, honey, butter, sheep, and cheese. There was enough food for the army. The men rested themselves and were refreshed and ready for battle.

David went into a walled city in Gilead, and made that his stronghold. "But we do not shelter here," he said to Joab. "We attack. We will divide our men into three parts, a larger force and two smaller ones. You shall command the larger force, and we will appoint two subcaptains for the other two. We will draw Absalom into the valley, and then attack from the hills. I will go out with you myself and ride with you into battle, as in days gone by."

But the people heard this and sent a spokesman to David, who pleaded with him: "Do not go forth, O King. You are our father, our shepherd. If you are killed, we shall be like lost sheep, and be slaughtered like sheep. Stay here. You are worth ten thousand men. Do not risk your life."

257

"I will do what seems best to you," said David. Then he said to Joab: "I wait here, for the people wish it. And I trust you utterly, my brave one. I know we shall prevail. God sent me a dream last night, and I saw the enemy fleeing before you. But I pray you, Joab, deal gently with my son. Scatter his forces, destroy his army, but do not slay Absalom."

Joab drew his sword and saluted the king. Thousands of swords flashed in the air. Thousands of voices merged into one voice and rolled across the hills like thunder: "David! David! David, our king!"

Absalom led his troops across the river into Gilead, and they were a mighty horde. He rode a tall white horse and wore a breastplate of brass. He carried his helmet on his pommel and his red-gold mane streamed out behind him. That shining head was like a banner, and men followed it heedlessly, certain of triumph. So sure of victory were they behind their radiant young prince that the captains sent out no scouts, no outriders.

But David's work was not yet done, nor did the Lord intend that Absalom should be king. The prince led his men into a valley. A rain of arrows fell upon them. Huge boulders fell upon them, crushing man and horse. They heard a keening like eagles — David's war cry that was a cry in the throats of all his captains. One troop charged downhill at them on the right flank; another troop charged down the left-hand hill. Joab led his troops straight up the valley toward them. They were hemmed in, trapped. They were slaughtered like sheep in a pen.

Absalom's tall, white horse was swift as a stag. He spurred it through a break in the ranks, angling across a slope and beyond the battling men. He rode behind a screen of rocks, and out the other side of the valley, into a copse of trees. He heard pursuers behind him and spurred the horse on, throwing off his breastplate to make himself lighter. He threw away his sword and his shield. He wore no helmet and his hair streamed out behind him. A great oak stood in his path; its branches grew low. He ducked down to the neck of his horse to pass under the branches. But the wind took his hair; it caught upon the branch and tangled there. His beautiful long hair, strong as a rope, swung him from the saddle, and he hung there. A spearman ran past the tree, looked up and saw Absalom, but did not stop. The spearman ran through the woods until he came to Joab.

"Captain!" he said. "I saw Absalom in the wood, hanging by his hair from a tree."

"Did you kill him?" said Joab.

"No!" cried the spearman.

"You saw him hanging there and did not spear him where he hung? I would have paid you ten shekels of silver."

The man said: "Not for a thousand shekels would I raise my spear against the king's son. I stood there in the ranks this morning as the king charged you, saying, 'Deal gently with my son Absalom. Do not slay him.' Can I disobey the great king? It would be my own death."

Joab did not answer but pushed past him and strode off through the woods. He came to the oak, and saw Absalom hanging by his hair. "Prince Absalom," he said, "are you still alive?"

"Thank God I still live, brave Joab."

"It is well," said Joab. "You die with the Lord's name on your lips."

He took three darts from a quiver and thrust them through Absalom's heart. The young man died, still hanging by his golden hair.

Joab blew a great blast from his trumpet. His warriors came running. He gave orders. They cut Absalom down and cast him into a great pit, and covered him with a heap of stones.

David waited at the city gates for news of the battle. A sentry stood watch on the wall. He cried: "A man comes running, O King!"

David climbed to the wall and watched the man come. "I know him," said David. "He comes with good tidings."

The runner came near. "All is well!" he called. He ran to David and fell to the earth upon his face, crying, "Blessed be the Lord God! He has delivered up the men who have rebelled against you."

"Is Absalom safe?" said the king.

"There was a tumult and a confusion," said the man. "I do not know. I did not see Absalom."

Then a second runner came. He, too, called joyously to David, "Great tidings, my king! The Lord has avenged you this day upon all those who rose up against you."

"Is Absalom safe?" said David.

"May all your enemies suffer his fate," said the second runner.

"Is he dead?"

"He is dead, my lord."

The king did not rejoice in the victory. He walked away and avoided everyone. He wept. Great wrenching sobs were torn out of him. "Oh, my son Absalom," he cried. "My son, my son Absalom, would to God I had died for thee."

David kept to his chamber and would not go out. No one saw him.

Joab came back from the battlefield and searched for the king. He was told: "The king weeps and mourns for Absalom." The word was passed among the troops, and the day of victory was turned to a day of mourning. People slunk out of the city as if they were ashamed. They looked like defeated men, instead of warriors who had vanquished a foe many times their own number.

And Joab, warrior and captain, could not bear this. He ran up the stairs to the king's chamber, swept the guards aside, and stormed into the room, crying, "O King, you have shamed me! You have stamped shame upon the faces of all your men who went into battle for you and saved your life, and the lives of your sons and your daughters, and of your wives. Why do you do this? Why do you weep and keep yourself solitary? Do you love your enemies and hate your friends? If Absalom had lived and we all had died by his command, would that have pleased you more?"

"Is this how you speak to your king?" said David. "Have I merited this?"

"You know how I love you," said Joab. "And how many times I have risked my life for yours and spilled my blood for you. Again today I went into battle for you, and saw men die in that battle, men I led in your name. I cannot bear it, King. I shall put this sword through my own heart unless I see you accept your victory as you should."

"What do you wish me to do?" said David.

"Arise! Go out and praise your men for their service this day. I swear to you that if you do not, you will not have one man left by evening."

"Forgive me," said David. "You are right. My heart is torn, but the time of grieving is past. I will go out to the men."

David went out and spoke to his men, thanking them and praising them. Then he led them out of Gilead over the Jordan, back to Jerusalem in a triumphal march.

But the wound in his heart did not heal. For many years he mourned Absalom. And it was not until Solomon, son of Bathsheba, his youngest son, grew to be a beautiful youth, also, and a wise and gentle youth, that David was able to forgive himself for his victory over Absalom. Seeing Solomon grow up into such splendid manhood, he realized that God had not meant Absalom to take the throne of David — that he and his sons were all part of a great design, and that Solomon was meant to be king after him.

SOLOMON

David ruled over Israel for forty years. When he knew he was dying, he called for Solomon and said: "Son of Bathsheba, you are not my eldest son, but you are the child of the woman I have loved best. God has chosen you to be my heir and to rule over His people."

"No, my father!" cried Solomon. "I am not ready for you to die; I am not ready to be king. Do not leave us."

David said: "I go the way of all flesh, my son. Be strong, therefore; show yourself a man. Keep the charge of the Lord, your God: Walk in His ways, keep His statutes, obey His commandments and His judgments and His testimonies, as is written in the law of Moses. Do this, and you will prosper in all things."

Solomon was about twenty years old when he was crowned king. The Lord appeared to him in a dream and said: "What shall I give you?"

Solomon said: "You showed David, my father, great mercy. He walked before you in truth and in righteousness. You secured his throne and overthrew his enemies. Now, O Lord, my God, you have made me king. And I am but a little child; I do not know how to go out or come in. I rule over a great people, the people you have chosen, a people who cannot be numbered or counted because of their multitude. I ask only this of you: Give me an understanding heart to judge your people, that I may discern between good and evil."

God answered, "Because you have asked this thing, and have not asked for a long life, or great riches, or for the life of your enemies, but only an understanding heart and a discerning judgment — because you have done this, behold, you have pleased me and I will give you what you desire. You shall have a wise and understanding heart. You shall be wiser than any man who came before you; nor shall there be any like you afterward."

Solomon awoke, and knew that he had dreamed, and rejoiced in the dream.

His wisdom was soon tested. There came to him two women. One of them carried a child. The other one said: "Oh, my lord, this woman and I dwell in one house. I was delivered of a child. Three days later this woman bore a child, also. There was no one else in the house, only we two and our two infants. Now, this woman rolled over in her sleep and smothered her child, and he died. Then she arose at midnight and took my son from me as I slept, and laid my child upon her breasts and put her dead child in my bed. When I arose in the morning to nurse my child I saw that he was dead. But when I looked more closely I saw that it was not my babe, but hers."

"No!" cried the other woman. "You lie, you whore! You were the one who rolled over and smothered your child. My son lives. Yours is dead."

"It is you who are lying," said the first woman. "O King, I appeal to you for justice. I speak the truth."

Solomon studied the faces of both women. He looked at the baby. It seemed to resemble neither woman, but he could not tell. He thought for a moment, then said to his servant: "Bring me a sword."

A sword was brought to him. "Now," said the king, "I cannot tell which of you is lying and which tells the truth. Therefore, I shall cut the child in two and divide him between you."

"No!" cried the first woman. "No, my lord, no! Don't cut the child in half. I withdraw my claim. Let her have him."

The second woman said: "You are just, O King. Cut him in two and give me my half."

Solomon said: "Woman, you who have refused to let the child be slain have produced the only valid claim to motherhood, which is love. I award the child to you."

God smiled upon Israel. Everything prospered. The people were busy, peaceable, full of joy and pride. And Solomon felt his heart bursting with gratitude.

"I will use my wealth to build a house for God," he said. "Such a temple as has never been seen."

He sent for skilled workmen from every land, from Egypt and Tyre and Sidon, from the lands to the south and the east: carpenters, silversmiths, goldsmiths, and those who worked in stone. He had decided that no base metal should be used in God's house — no tool of iron, no hammer, axe, adze, nor any nail or bolt or rivet of copper or iron. This meant that all the timber had to be cut and shaped, all the stone hewn and polished before reaching Jerusalem. It also meant that the huge beams had to be notched and tapered so that they might fit into each other and hold together of their own weight without spike or nail. The massive hewn stones had to be taken from the quarries of the Dead Sea,

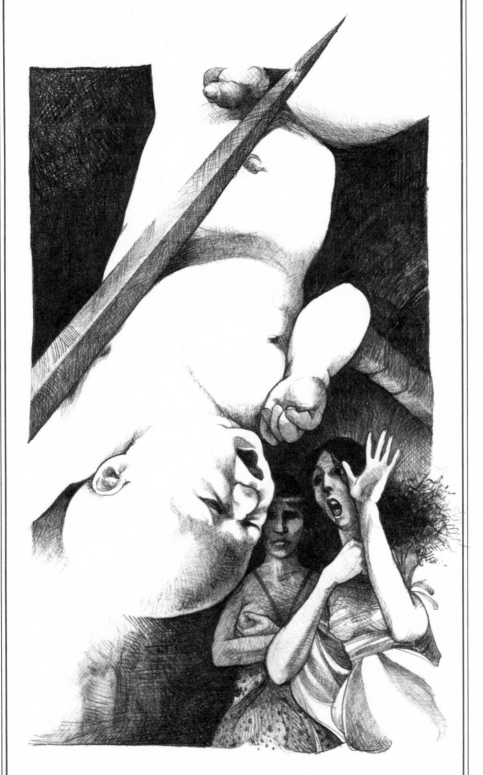

263

carried by ox cart across the desert, and by mule train up the Judean hills. And the great timbers, the tremendous dressed planks of cedar and fir, had to be taken by mule down the hills of Lebanon, then by ox cart to the ports of Sidon and Tyre, loaded on barges, and floated down to the Red Sea port of Ezion-Gabor — then by ox wagon across the desert to the Judean hills, then uphill on mule-back to that courtyard in Jerusalem that was to become the spiritual navel of the world.

Solomon put an army of men to work — one hundred and eighty thousand of them. They worked for seven years. And in that wide, sunny courtyard on the eastern slope of the city's easternmost hill, stone and timber were fitted together, and a building began to grow into the shape of the vision that burned in Solomon's mind. In the city taken by his father, David, and dedicated to God, in Jerusalem, a huge temple arose. Of cedar was it made, and fir, and hewn stone. Roof and wall and pillars were covered with gold leaf, pure gold beaten thin as leaves. The temple stood on its hill in Jerusalem, a pillar of golden fire in the sunlight, dazzling the eyes of all who looked upon it.

Solomon decided to make the dedication of this temple the largest, most impressive, most joyous occasion that the world had ever seen. He sent messengers throughout the land and summoned the tribes to assemble in Jerusalem. In that vast throng stood, also, the kings of earth or their ambassadors — from Tyre, Sidon, from Egypt, Persia, Sheba, and Edom. There, before that multitude, Solomon faced the altar and stretched his arms to heaven and prayed to God to enter His house and bless His people. He did not speak loudly, but his voice was like music, and everyone heard every word, even those standing on the farthest hill. And those listening felt that they were hearing not the words of king or priest but the whispered aspirations of their own hearts magnified to an eternal pledge. And the congregation wept, but the tears were of joy.

"Blessed be the Lord, who has given rest unto His people, Israel, according to all that He promised. May the Lord our God be with us as He was with our fathers, and not forsake us. May He incline our hearts to Him so that we walk in His ways and keep His commandments, that all the people of earth may know that the Lord is our God and there is none else."

Then, upon his signal, the priests bore in the ark of the covenant, that ancient box holding the two tablets of stone upon which Moses had engraved the words God spoke to him on Mount Horeb. The priests brought the ark into the sanctuary under the wings of stone cherubs. And it is said that when the ark was laid in that place, the stone cherubim stretched their stone wings, covering the ark.

The torches went out. The candles blew out. There was darkness in the temple, and no man spoke. For they knew that God had entered His house and stood there in a cloud so that He might not blind them with His radiance. Standing there in that thick darkness, Solomon heard a voice: "This is a rich and gorgeous house you have built for me. But you know that my real dwelling place is in man's heart. And, in time to come, if the children of Israel turn from my way, then this strong house will be cast down; it will be torn apart stone from stone, and passersby will hiss at the place where once it stood But, O Solomon, I have heard your prayer and supplication. And I have hallowed this house that you have built, and my name shall be here forever, and my eyes and heart be here perpetually."

The darkness departed. All was bright again. And the people feasted and rejoiced.

Like his father, David, Solomon reigned for forty years. He became the most powerful king in the world, and Israel the strongest nation. Nevertheless, as happens to many kings, Solomon lost his wisdom before he lost his power. In his old age, when his wits were befuddled, he allowed some of his young concubines to tempt him into the worship of Ashteroth. He raised strange altars, and dedicated them with orgies.

Whereupon the spirit of God departed from him; he sickened and died. And, after his death, ten tribes of Israel revolted against his son and the kingdom was divided — never again to be united.

THE PROPHETS

After Solomon, when Israel was divided and both thrones were occupied by a series of weak and wicked kings, moral authority passed to those angry old men who came to be known as the prophets.

Who were these prophets? They were men who in some way had tapped that vein of intellectual and moral energy that they called the holy spirit, and through private vision had gained access to God's moods and intentions. Their courage was so total that they did not even think of themselves as courageous. They thought of themselves simply as God's messengers, and, after coming away from that gigantic presence, everyone else, including kings and queens, seemed very small indeed.

It was not only kings they outraged. They preached against lawlessness and sinfulness wherever they found it, and they found it everywhere. The mob hated them as much as the courtiers did; they were often stoned in the streets. Nevertheless, they persisted, warning the people of Israel that an angry and disappointed God would return them to the exile and slavery from which He had taken them, and embroidering their predictions with hideous detail of the disasters to come. That their dire prophecies proved totally accurate did not make them more popular.

The great names that have come down to us are Elijah, Elisha, Isaiah, Jonah, Jeremiah, Ezekiel, and Daniel. Perhaps the most remarkable of these men was Elijah.

Elijah

After Solomon died the kingdom passed to his eldest son, Rehoboam, who inherited his father's wealth but not his wisdom. He laid heavy burdens upon his people, and oppressed them. Rebellion flared. Rehoboam marched against the rebels, but, being as weak in warfare as he was arrogant in civil affairs, was driven from the field. He lost the larger part of his kingdom, retaining only the territory of Judah and Benjamin, including Jerusalem, and this became the kingdom of Judah. The land held by the other ten tribes — a much larger territory — was known as Israel. Thus Israel, which had grown mighty under David and mightier under Solomon, was rent in two, and was not to become whole again until three thousand years had passed.

After the kingdom was divided, three generations of wicked kings ruled over Israel. Then came the wickedest of all, a man named Ahab. But even more evil than this evil king was his wife, Jezebel. She was the daughter of Ethbaal, king of the Sidonians, a country where the stone idol, Baal, was worshipped with horrid rites. And when Jezebel came to Israel, she brought Baal with her. She easily persuaded Ahab. He liked the idea of human sacrifice and temple orgies and gave her a free hand in religious matters. From Sidon and from other lands to the north and east of Israel she imported four hundred and fifty priests of Baal and four hundred priestesses of Ashteroth.

The priests of Baal built idols of stone and worshipped them with murderous ceremonies.On feast days they went among the prisoners and slaves and selected men and women — picking those in the prime of life, and without blemish — bound them with ropes, and laid them on the stone altar before the stone idol. Then, with stone knives, they cut their throats, howling prayers to Baal as blood ran into the trenches of the altar.

Ashteroth also enjoyed the savor of blood, but, with more delicate taste, she preferred blood warmed by caress. She was the moon goddess, mistress of harvest. On the night of the first spring planting, each priestess led out a youth selected for his strength and beauty. In one hand she held a pruning knife, with the other she clasped the lad and led him into the field in the blaze of the rising moon. She peeled his tunic off, then cast off her own robes. Naked in the moonlight, the woman embraced the lad and drew him to earth. Still embracing him, she stabbed him with many wounds, and his blood ran into the furrows of the plowed field. All this was to please Ashteroth so that she would grant fat crops.

Thus was Israel, land of the covenant, land favored by the living God, infected by alien cults, and her holy places profaned.

The priests of Israel went raging to Ahab and demanded that those who served Baal and Ashteroth be driven from the land. Ahab sat on his throne and listened to them. He said: "My queen, Jezebel, handles these matters. Go to the walled courtyard. She will receive you there, and, in her wisdom, deal with your complaints."

They went into the walled courtyard, all but fifty, whom the king's steward, Obadiah, led by a secret way out of the palace. One hundred of the priests of Israel, pious and learned old men, went into the courtyard. There was Jezebel on a litter held on the shoulders of four tall slaves. There also were the queen's guard, picked warriors who served Jezebel. She raised her arm; her bracelets flashed in the sunlight. Her men drew their swords, fell upon the priests of Israel, and hacked them to pieces. Only those smuggled out by Obadiah escaped.

Now no one dared raise a voice against the rites of Baal and the orgies of Ashteroth.

Yet one man dared. He dwelt in the flinty corner of Judah called Gilead, and his name was Elijah. He went to the palace, forced his way into the throne room, stood before Ahab, and cried out: "As the Lord lives, there shall not be dew or rain upon this land until I give the word!"

Ahab stared, astonished. Wielding death, he was feared like death; no man or woman in Israel — except Jezebel — dared look him in the face. And here was this uncouth old man with tangled hair and beard standing before the throne, threatening him. He tried to speak but the words were strangled in his throat. And by the time Ahab was able to roar "Seize him!" Elijah was gone. The king sent his guard to search every house in the city, but the old man had vanished.

The season of rains came, but no rain fell. No clouds covered the face of the sun, which knelt low, parching the earth, drinking up the rivers. The priests of Baal prayed for rain. The women who served Ashteroth, mother of harvests, prayed to her for rain. But no rain fell. No dew fell. The rivers dried; the brooks and streams dried. People began to starve.

Ahab called his captains together, and said: "Lo, the old man came here and cursed us with drought. He vowed that no rain would fall until he gave the word. Now we must find him. We must search every corner of the land, go into every house, every sheepfold, every cave. We must search wood and slope and the desert places. We must find this man. Then I shall torture him until he utters the word that brings rain."

Elijah was wandering in the waste places. He did not dare go to his home in Gilead because he knew that the king's men were searching for him. He was weak from hunger and thirst, but he did not dare go to any house to ask food, for Ahab's men were all about — and he knew that they were searching for him more desperately than ever.

"What shall I do, O Lord?" he said.

A voice spoke out of the burning sky: "Leave this place. Journey eastward to Jordan, and hide yourself near the brook, Cherith."

Hiding by day and traveling by night, Elijah walked eastward and crossed into Jordan. The river had dried up, and he was able to cross the riverbed on foot. But the brook, Cherith, still held a trickle of water. Elijah hid in a stand of trees near the brook, and drank of the brook. But he was faint with hunger. The sky blackened. He thought he was swooning, but it was a flock of ravens. They settled near him. He saw that each black bird carried food in its beak. As he watched, wondering, a bird alit on his shoulder and put food into his mouth. It was lamb's meat, roasted and savory. Another raven came and sat on his shoulder and put food in his mouth. It was bread. And so the ravens fed him until he was satisfied. Then they flew away. But they returned twice a day, bearing bread and meat. Twice a day the birds came and brought him food enough to restore his strength. And he drank of the brook and thanked God for His mercy.

Still no rain fell. Each day the brook dwindled. Finally, there was only a handful of mud. Elijah squeezed the water out of this; then there was no more water. The ravens came with food, but he could not eat it because he was too thirsty. "What shall I do, O Lord?" he said.

Again a voice spoke out of the sky: "Arise! Go to Zarephath in Sidon, over the border in Jezebel's own country. You will find a widow there and she will harbor you."

Elijah journeyed toward the border of Ahab's kingdom and finally crossed into Sidon. A few huts still clung to this place, where once copper had been mined and smelted. But the drought had stretched into Sidon, and no one had strength to work the mine, and the little village was almost empty. He approached the village at dusk, and saw a woman gathering sticks. He went to her and said: "Fetch me, I pray, a little water that I may drink."

She looked at him silently, then turned and walked away. He called after her, "Bring me, also, I pray, a morsel of bread, that I may eat."

She turned then and said: "I have no bread. We are starving here. All I have is a handful of flour in a barrel, and a little oil in a cruse. Now I am going home to make a fire with these two sticks and make a last small loaf of bread for myself and my son. We shall eat it, then wait for death."

"Fear not," said Elijah. "Take your two sticks and go home and build

269

your fire, and bake your loaf. Do not eat of that loaf or feed your son, but bring it to me. Then go home and make another loaf for yourself and your son."

"But I have meal enough and oil enough for only one small loaf," said the woman.

"Woman," said Elijah, "widow woman, listen to the word of the Lord, which He has spoken to me. The barrel of meal shall not go empty nor shall the cruse of oil run dry. You shall have flour in your barrel and oil in your jar until the day that the Lord sends rain to the earth again."

She said nothing more, but left. Elijah waited. Dusk deepened; it was night. She came back, bearing a newly baked loaf of bread, and silently put it into his hand. He devoured the bread. She looked at him and wept.

"You do not believe me, do you?" said Elijah. "Go back to your house now and put your hand in the barrel and you will find flour. And you will find oil in the cruse. Go home and start baking. I shall go with you and share what the Lord provides."

For many months, then, Elijah dwelt with the widow and her small son. He slept in the loft and came down for his meals. And the barrel of flour filled itself each time it was empty, and the jar of oil never ran dry.

One night the little boy fell sick. By morning he burned with fever. The breath caught in his throat; he gasped for air. The woman screamed at Elijah, "Why have you come here, you man of a dread god? Do you remind your god of my sins? Why does he slay my son?"

"Give me your son," said Elijah.

He lifted the boy off the bed, slung him over his shoulder, and climbed the ladder into his loft. He laid the strangling child on his own bed, and cried, "O Lord, my God, have you brought evil upon the widow? Are you killing her son?"

The boy's face was blue. He did not seem to be breathing at all. A chill wind blew. Elijah touched the boy's face; it was ice cold. He covered the boy with his own body to warm him, crying, "O Lord, my God, I pray you, let this child's soul come back into his body!"

Three times Elijah cried out. He heard a whimpering beneath him, and raised himself. Color had returned to the boy's face. A pulse throbbed in the thin throat. Elijah touched him with his great veiny hand. The boy was warm again, but not feverish. And as he stroked the boy's face, the mouth opened and the chest stirred. The child breathed again.

"Thank you, God," said Elijah. He lifted the child and climbed down the ladder and gave him into his mother's arms. "See," he said. "Your son lives."

The woman cradled the child in her arms, and rocked him, sobbing with joy.

"Now, by this," she said to Elijah, "I know that you are a man of God, and that the word of the Lord in your mouth is the truth itself."

For two years Elijah dwelt with the widow. All this time, no rain fell, no crops grew. People died of thirst; they starved to death. But in the widow's house there was always food and drink. Then, in the third year, the word of the Lord came to Elijah, saying, "Go to Ahab, and I will send rain upon the earth."

Elijah said farewell to the widow and departed. He passed through Samaria on his way to Ahab's palace. And he grieved as he saw the dry rivers and the parched earth, the skeletons of cattle and of men.

Now, shortly before this, Ahab had called his steward, Obadiah, to him and said: "Go out of the city and search for grass. Go to all the fountains of water and all the brooks, and look for a fountain that still springs and a brook that still runs. Take men and go. I will take men and search in another direction. For we must find grass, or all our cattle and horses will die."

And, as Obadiah rode through Samaria, he saw an old man clad in a tattered robe. He carried a staff; his hair and his beard were white and tangled, and his eyes smoldered in their deep sockets. Obadiah bowed to the ground and said: "Are you my lord Elijah?"

"I am," said Elijah. "Go say to the king, 'Behold, Elijah is here.' "

"This message means my death," said Obadiah. "Do you not know that Ahab has sent men to seek you throughout Israel and Judah and all the nations whose borders touch ours? He has ransacked the earth for you, so that he may take you and torture you into saying the word that will bring rain again."

"Then he should be happy to know that I am here," said Elijah. "Go tell him."

"And if I go to tell him," said Obadiah, "and if the spirit of the Lord should carry you here or there while I am on my way? If I tell Ahab that you have come, and we cannot find you, then he will slay me. It is not just. I have feared the Lord all my life. Have you not heard of my deed? When Jezebel slew the prophets of Israel, it was I who saved fifty of them — led them out of the palace by a secret way and took them to a cave and fed them. It was I, Obadiah, who did this. Now you say go tell the king that you have come back. It is my death. The king will draw his sword and slay me where I stand."

Elijah said: "As the Lord of hosts lives, and as I stand before him, I will show myself to the king this day, and you shall be spared."

Obadiah hurried off and informed Ahab that Elijah had returned, and Ahab went to meet him. Elijah waited for the king. He saw a whirl of dust and horsemen coming. Ahab reined up and dismounted and stood before Elijah. His men sat their horses, drawn swords glittering in their hands.

Ahab said: "Are you he who troubles Israel, who stops the rain and blights the crops, causing men and cattle to die?"

"I do not trouble Israel," said Elijah. "I have been sent to trouble you and your father's house because you have forsaken the commandments of the Lord and have followed Baal."

"Do you dare to tell me this?" whispered the king. "Do you dare to stand there and speak these words to me, you who have cursed my land with drought and done such evil?"

"The Lord has spoken to me," said Elijah. "And I repeat his words. Now, if you wish the rain to return, O King, I will tell you what to do. Call together all the people of Israel and bring them to Mount Carmel. Also, bring the four hundred and fifty priests of Baal and those four hundred women who serve the groves of Ashteroth."

"And if I do not?" said Ahab. "If, instead, I cut you to pieces with my sword and leave you for the jackals to eat? What then?"

"Then you shall have no rain," said Elijah.

"Do you promise to bring rain if I do as you say?" said Ahab.

"I promise not to if you don't," said Elijah. "Go, call the people together, and bring them to Mount Carmel. And the priests of Baal, and the priestesses of Ashteroth."

Ahab did all that Elijah commanded. He sent proclamations throughout Israel and gathered all the people together in a mighty throng at the foot of the mountain. He brought the four hundred and fifty priests of Baal and the priestesses of Ashteroth to the mountain, also.

Elijah stood halfway up the slope of the mountain and spoke to the people: "How long will you waver between two opinions?" he said. "If the Lord is God, follow Him. But if Baal be God, then follow Baal."

There was a great hush. No one spoke. "Here am I alone," said Elijah. "One man alone, who is the prophet of the Lord. But Baal's priests number four hundred and fifty. Now bring us two bull calves. Give one to the priests of Baal and one to me. They will dress their calf and lay it on the wood before the altar, but put no fire to the wood. And I shall dress my calf and lay it on my stack of wood, and not kindle the wood."

The people brought two calves, and gave one to the priests of Baal and the other to Elijah. Now Elijah turned to the priests of Baal and roared, "You who serve the stone idol, you priests of Baal, dress your calf and put it on the wood, and call on your god to light a fire under your offering. I will do likewise, and call upon my God, also. We shall see who lights the first flame."

The priests of Baal flayed their calf and dismembered it, and laid the pieces on a tall stack of wood. It was still early morning. The priests raised their voices, calling to Baal, crying, "O Baal, hear us! Send fire!"

There was no answer. The priests of Baal leaped upon the altar and danced upon it, crying to Baal. But there was no answer. They danced until noon, waving their arms and frothing at the mouth and calling to Baal. And the huge throng of people stood there watching; no one moved. At noon, when the sun stood directly above, Elijah mocked the priests: "Cry aloud!" he said. "Cry out to your god. Either he is talking, or chasing someone, or simply taking a journey somewhere. Or, perhaps, he is asleep and must be awakened."

Then all the priests of Baal cried out in one voice, a mighty wailing cry. They drew their knives and slashed themselves until their blood flowed. They did this from noon until evening, offering the blood of their own bodies to Baal. But he did not answer.

Then Elijah spoke to the people: "Come near," he said.

Like one man, the multitude surged forward. Elijah took twelve stones, one for each of the sons of Jacob, who became the tribes of Israel. With these stones he built a new altar, for the other had been fouled by the priests of Baal. He dug a trench about the altar. Then he cut his bullock in pieces, laid the pieces upon the wood, and said: "Fill four barrels with water and pour it on the bullock and on the wood."

Two men came out of the crowd. They filled four barrels with water and poured it over the calf and over the wood. "Do it again," said Elijah. They did it again. "Do it a third time," he said. Again they filled the barrels with water and drenched the calf and the wood. The water ran off the altar and filled the trench. Now it was time for the evening sacrifice. Elijah, the prophet, stood before the altar and raised his hands to the sky, and said: "Lord, God of Abraham, of Isaac, and of Israel, let it be known this day that you are the true God and that I am your servant, and that I have done all these things at your word. Hear me, O Lord, hear me, that this people may know that you are the Lord God! Make them a sign, I pray. Revive their hearts!"

He fell silent. He waited. No one stirred. Lightning hooked from the cloudless sky. A great fang of fire split the evening air and touched the wood, which burst into flame. Fire crackled beneath Elijah's calf. Fire leaped. The wood was consumed. The stones took fire, and the dust. The flame licked up the water. And all the people of that multitude fell to the ground, crying, "The Lord is our God!"

"Arise!" cried Elijah. "Take the false prophets! Take them all!"

The mob broke and seized the four hundred and fifty priests of Baal and dragged them away from the mountain, away from the altar, down to the brook, Kishon. They broke branches off the trees and clubbed the priests of Baal to death. The lightning kept flashing. Thunder crashed. The sky blackened and rain fell — great sheets of rain. Elijah went to Ahab and said: "Baal has fled. The Lord lives. There is an abundance of rain."

Ahab stood white-faced and bareheaded in the downpour. He did not answer Elijah, but lifted his face and drank the rain. Elijah said: "Prepare your chariot and return to your palace before the plains are flooded."

A strong wind blew, driving the rain flat. Ahab mounted his chariot and drove back to Jezreel, where his palace was. Now the hand of the Lord was upon Elijah, directing him past his own knowledge. The old man found himself running before Ahab's chariot through the wind and the rain to the gates of Jezreel.

That night, Ahab told Jezebel all that had happened at Mount Carmel, how Elijah had tested the priests of Baal, how he had vanquished them with his fire from heaven and had provoked the people to kill them. Jezebel stormed at Ahab, crying, "He is your enemy and you have held your hand from him because you fear his lord! Where is he now?"

"Here. Beyond the gates. Squatting in the rain and praying."

"Well may he pray. I do not fear his invisible god. I will kill him." She sent this word to Elijah: "Troublemaker, prepare to die. I will slay you as you slew my priests."

Now Elijah was full of terror. He knew that Jezebel was crueller even than Ahab, and less easily swerved from her intention. Elijah left Jezreel and fled to Judah. "Stay here," he said to his servant. "I go into the wilderness."

He went a day's journey into the wilderness and sat under a juniper tree. "I am weary, Lord," he said. "I have had enough. Take my life now and let me join my fathers."

He lay down and slept. In his sleep an angel touched him and said: "Arise, and eat."

He sat up. He saw a fire of twigs, and a flat stone over the fire, and on the stone a newly baked loaf of bread. A pitcher of water stood there, also. He ate and drank, and slept again. Again the angel came and touched him and said: "Arise and eat, because the journey is too great for you."

He ate and drank and journeyed to the mount of God called Horeb, where, six hundred years before, Moses had received the law. There Elijah found a cave. He went into the cave and dwelt there for forty days and forty nights, waiting for the Lord to speak again.

The word of the Lord came to him: "What are you doing here, Elijah?"

"O God," said Elijah, "I have been zealous in your service. The children of Israel have forgotten your covenant, thrown down your altars, and slain your prophets with the sword. I alone am left, and now they seek my life."

"Go forth," said the voice. "Stand upon the mountain."

He arose and stood at the mouth of the cave. A wind came and lifted the rocks off the mountainside and dashed them together, breaking them into pieces. But the Lord was not in the wind, and Elijah waited. Then, looking down from the mountain over the wide plain, he saw the earth tremble. He saw the earth quake and split. But the Lord was not in the earthquake. Elijah stood there and waited. A storm of dust arose and became particles of fire. Bushes burned, brambles burned, fire ran along the ground. But the Lord was not in the fire, and Elijah waited.

After the fire came a still, small voice. When Elijah heard it, he wrapped his face in his mantle. "Why do you wait here?" said the voice.

"I await your word, O God," said Elijah. "Of all your priests only I am left alive. And Jezebel's men hunt me up and down the land. What shall I do?"

God answered, "Go. Go into the wilderness to Damascus. There anoint Hazael to be king of Syria. And Jehu, son of Nimshi, shall you anoint to be king of Israel. Then find a man named Elisha and anoint him to be prophet in your place. And this shall come to pass. Him who escapes the sword of Hazael shall Jehu slay. Him who escapes the sword of Jehu shall Elisha slay. For know this: In Israel are left seven thousand who have not bent the knee to Baal or kissed their hand in homage to the great whore of the grove who is called Ashteroth. For the sake of these who have kept the faith, you must live though your journey be long and your way be weary. You must live and speak my word until I give you leave to fall silent."

Elijah went off the mountain and journeyed toward Damascus. On the way he passed a young man who was plowing with a yoke of oxen. Elijah stopped and looked at him. He had never seen him before, but this young plowman looked as beautiful as a son to Elijah, and he loved him and pitied him and was proud of him all at once. The young man pulled up his oxen and bowed low to Elijah.

"What is your name?" said Elijah.

"I am Elisha," said the young man.

Elijah took off the mantle he was wearing and cast it upon the young man. It was a tattered old sheepskin mantle, hairy side out, but to the young man it was as though a robe more gorgeous than any king's robe had fallen upon him. Elijah turned and walked away.

The plowman did not hesitate. He unhitched his oxen, the fine strong beasts he had worked all his life to buy. He killed them where they stood, and flayed them and cut them up and gave them to his neighbors to eat. And his neighbors rejoiced, for they were poor. Then the young man followed Elijah, and caught up with him. He stayed with the old man, and would never leave him, but attended to him, and studied all his ways.

Now, there was a man named Naboth who lived in Jezreel. He owned a small vineyard near Ahab's palace. Naboth loved to work the earth. He worked very hard, plowing, sowing, nourishing the earth with manure; weeding, watering, and destroying pests. His vineyard flourished. His vines were heavy with purple grapes. They were sweet to taste.

One day, Ahab rode past the vineyard. He reached down and broke off some grapes and ate them. He was king and had vast lands of his own, but now he coveted this little vineyard. He called Naboth to the palace and said: "Good Naboth, I want your vineyard. I want it for a garden of herbs. I will give you another piece of land for it, much larger. Or I will pay you for it in gold, if you prefer."

277

"God forbid that I should sell my inheritance," said Naboth. "This land was my father's; it will be my son's. At the risk of your displeasure, O King, I cannot sell it."

Ahab scowled and turned away. Naboth left the palace full of foreboding. It was not a light thing to defy a king like Ahab. But Naboth was a stubborn man, and resolved not to give up what was his.

Ahab was not used to being thwarted. He lay on his bed, face turned to the wall, and did not rise to eat.

"What is the matter?" said Jezebel. "Why do you refuse to dine?"

"There is a man named Naboth who owns a vineyard nearby. And I want it for my own. I have offered him more than it is worth, but he will not sell it."

"Why, then, you must take it," said Jezebel. "Get rid of this Naboth, and take it."

"I cannot," said Ahab.

"Of course you can," said Jezebel. "You are king."

"Even as king I cannot take what belongs to another," said Ahab. "It is the ancient law, received by Moses on the mountain."

"You are king," said Jezebel. "Your will is law. That was the custom of kings for many thousands of years before this Moses of yours. And it is still the way of kings."

Ahab grew thoughtful but did not answer. "Do not trouble yourself," said Jezebel. "Leave the matter to me. Now rise, and eat, and be merry."

Jezebel took advantage now of a statute that she hated. After Elijah had vanquished the priests of Baal, and had roused the people of Israel against Baal and Ashteroth and all their works, the king had been forced to ban all worship of these false gods on the pain of death. This had been a blow to Jezebel, but now she stood the law on its head. She wrote letters to certain elders of Jezreel, informing them that Naboth was a secret worshipper of Baal and practiced the forbidden rites.

Jezebel was queen, and the men she wrote to were courtiers. They believed her without investigating. They caused Naboth to be bound and taken to a public square. There people formed a circle about him and hurled rocks at him, until he was battered to the ground by the rocks and crushed to death beneath them. Then the crowd went its way. Dogs came, and licked up the blood from the stones.

The Lord spoke to Elijah: "Ahab and Jezebel have killed a man and taken his little vineyard. Go and tell them the meaning of their deed."

Elijah went down into Samaria, sought out Ahab, and stood before him. "Have you found me, O my enemy?" said Ahab.

"I come in the name of the Lord," said Elijah. "Have you killed, O King, and have you taken possession?"

"I have done what I have done," said Ahab.

"You have done evil in the sight of the Lord," said Elijah. "Now He will bring evil upon you. He will rend your kingdom from you and wipe out your house. In the place where the dogs licked the blood of Naboth shall they lick your blood, also. As for your wife, the dogs shall eat Jezebel by the wall of Jezreel. Her body shall be flung like dung upon the field, and dogs shall lick up her blood from the stones."

Elijah said nothing more, but departed. Now, Ahab had learned that what Elijah said always came true. So he was in great terror. He had reason to be; it all happened. Ahab was cut down in his pride, leading a chariot charge against the Syrians. He was pierced through by a spear and bled to death in his chariot. His charioteer brought him back to Jezreel. The dead king was lifted from the chariot, and the chariot was washed clean. The king's blood ran down into the gutter, and dogs licked it up as they had licked up the blood of Naboth.

Nor did Jezebel have long to reign as a widowed queen. A young captain named Jehu, to whom Elijah had promised the kingdom, gathered men and marched against the sons of Ahab. He defeated them and stormed the palace.

Jehu sat his horse in the courtyard and sent his men into the palace. He heard a hawk shriek. He looked up. It was no hawk; it was a woman, standing on the battlement screaming down at him. She wore a gown of samite sewn with diamonds and pearls; on her head was a golden crown. And he knew she was the queen. She was old now. Her eyelids were painted silver and her mouth was a scarlet gash. She cursed him with the curse of Ashteroth the Disabler. He would be blighted in the flower of his youth. His tongue would wither at the roots; his arms and legs would rot off his body.

As she screamed down at him, he saw his men go up behind her and seize her. "Throw her down," he said.

They threw her down. She fell near Jehu, who reared up his stallion and made it strike down with its hoofs, trampling the woman into the ground. Then Jehu went in to take possession of the palace and to eat and drink. He told his men, "Go bury that woman. She is a king's daughter."

His men went out to bury her. All they found was her skull and her feet and the palms of her hands. The dogs had eaten her flesh and licked her blood off the stones.

Elijah was old now. It was very painful for him to walk; he could barely eat. He had kept himself alive to speak the Lord's word, but upon this day in Gilgal he felt his strength going fast. He said to Elisha: "Stay here, for the Lord sends me to Beth-el."

"I will not leave you," said Elisha.

They went to Beth-el and were met by a group of young men studying under the prophets. One of them said to Elisha: "Do you not know the Lord will take away your master today?"

"I know it," said Elisha. "Hold your peace."

Elijah said: "Stay here, Elisha. The Lord sends me to Jericho."

"I will not leave you," said Elisha, and went with him to Jericho. Now, word had gotten out, and a great throng followed Elijah and Elisha. They halted at the edge of the Jordan. The river was high, and there was no bridge. Elijah took his mantle and struck the waters. The stream divided. The waters shrank away from the mantle, leaving a strip of dry ground across the river. Elijah and Elisha passed over the river to the other side.

"I am going now," said Elijah. "What can I do for you before I depart?"

"I pray you," said Elisha, "look upon me as an elder son, and leave me your wealth — which is your spirit."

"It is a hard thing," said Elijah. "The spirit is difficult to bequeath, difficult to inherit. Nevertheless, if you see me when I am taken from you, you shall have what you ask for. If you do not see me, you shall not inherit."

Just then a hot wind blew, too hot to bear, and they heard a sound of chariots. But the plain was empty, and the mountain slopes. They looked up. There above them stood a chariot of fire, drawn by horses of fire. Elijah climbed the air and mounted the chariot. Elisha stood watching him, and cried, "My father, my father! The chariot of Israel and the horsemen thereof!"

The wind became a whirlwind. The horses galloped upward, drawing the chariot into the sky. Elisha watched it until the last flame had disappeared into hot blueness. Then he rent his clothes from his body and wept.

Elijah had dropped his mantle when he was taken up into the fiery chariot. Elisha picked up the mantle and went back to the river Jordan. The river was high again. He cast the mantle upon the waters, crying, "Where is the Lord God of Elijah?"

The waters parted. Elisha crossed over on the river bottom between the taut walls of water. The young men who waited on the other side bowed low to him and said: "The spirit of Elijah rests on Elisha."

Jonah

Jonah was a prophet in Israel. A squat, balding man, he was passionately honest and very stubborn. The word of the Lord came to him: "Arise. Go to Ninevah, that great city, and cry out its sins. The people there are very wicked, and if they do not repent in forty days they will be destroyed. Go to Ninevah. Speak my word."

Jonah was discontented. "Nobody heeds me in my own land," he said to himself. "What can I expect in Ninevah? I shall rant and rave and preach myself blue in the face, promising disaster and urging repentance, and no one will listen. They will mock me and revile me and assault me with sticks and stones, and pursue their evil ways in perfect disregard of my warnings."

He pondered a while longer, then said to himself: "Also, I do not view the destruction of Ninevah as an unmixed disaster. The Assyrians are a fierce and warlike people. One day they will descend upon us like wolves in a sheepfold. No! I do not like this errand. God must find another prophet. I will flee this place."

And Jonah went down to the seaport in Joppa. Since Ninevah lay to the northeast, he looked for a ship heading southwest. He found one leaving for Tarshish. He paid his fare and boarded the ship, and tried to sail out of the Lord's presence.

But the Lord had prepared a rough voyage for Jonah. He sent a great wind, and the sea boiled up in fierce waves. The ship buffeted back and forth. Its sails were torn into rags; its masts snapped. It was driven onto its side and could barely right itself. And the crew was afraid. Every man cried out to his god. They were from many places and believed in many gods. And each man prayed to his own for safety in the tempest.

They threw the cargo overboard to lighten the ship. All were terrified but Jonah, who was in his hammock asleep. The captain went below and found him sleeping. He grasped his shoulder and shook him awake, crying, "What do you mean, O sleeper? Arise! Call upon your god like everybody else. For if some god does not call off this wind, we are finished."

The wind grew stronger, and now the ship was about to sink. The captain said: "There is someone here the gods pursue. They will drown all of us for the sake of this one loathed fellow. Let us draw lots to find out who has brought this evil upon us."

The captain tore paper until there was a piece for everyone aboard. On one of the pieces of paper he put a dot. He folded the papers and cast them into a hat. Then each man drew. And Jonah drew the fatal dot. He was not surprised. The captain said: "Tell us, I pray, who are you? What is your occupation? Where do you come from?"

Jonah said: "I am a Hebrew. I worship the one God, God Almighty, who has made the sea and the dry land. And I fear Him, and flee His face."

Terror mounted in the crew when they heard these words. The captain shuddered. "Why do you flee?" he whispered to Jonah. "Have you aroused his anger?"

"I have disobeyed Him," said Jonah. "He sent me on an errand to Ninevah, and I embarked for Tarshish. His wrath be upon me."

"His wrath is upon all of us," said the captain. "What shall we do? Another few minutes of this wind and we must all drown."

"Get me off your ship," said Jonah. "Cast me into the sea. I alone will drown and the wind will fall."

But the captain was a kindly man and the crew were good-hearted men. They tried to row the ship toward shore, for they did not wish to cast Jonah into the sea. But the wind blew harder and harder. The ship foundered and began to take on water. The captain cried, "We beseech you, O Lord, let us not perish for this man's misdeed. Neither do we wish to kill him."

The wind blew harder. Jonah said: "Cast me into the sea! Cast me overboard or you all perish!"

"Do so," said the captain. The men seized Jonah and threw him overboard. But the Lord did not wish Jonah to drown; He had other plans. He had prepared a great fish for Jonah. The fish was waiting. It was longer than the ship. A monster fish, it was called a leviathan then.

Today we would call it a whale. Jonah never hit the water. The whale took him like a trout taking a fly, and swallowed him up.

It was very dark in the whale's belly. Jonah saw only an occasional flash of daylight far up the long tunnel of the whale's throat, when it opened its mouth to swallow something else. Jonah was as brave as he was stubborn. He did not despair. He sat down in the darkness of the whale's belly, and said: "O God, I cry to you out of the belly of hell and you hear my voice. For I was in the deep, in the midst of the sea, in the midst of the tempest, and the waters hungered for me. The depths called to me to drown. But you have delivered me out of the deep and you have put me into this safe place. Thank you, O Lord, for your mercy — which takes strange forms."

And the Lord found Jonah's prayers bittersweet. They were stubborn and contentious, but they were knotted with the man's own peculiar conscience, and in them was a questioning, a struggle for light. God directed the whale toward the shores of Assyria. The great fish turned northeast and swam to the shore that the Lord had intended as Jonah's destination. The whale stood offshore and sounded. It leaped out of the water, and, at the highest point of its leap, vomited Jonah out. Jonah flew through the air and landed on the shore of Assyria, unhurt. There were people who saw this and ran to spread the report of a miracle, of a great fish breaching and vomiting out a man, who landed unharmed. A man with a bald head and an angry face and a long, white beard.

As Jonah sat on the shore and looked about, the voice of the Lord came again: "Arise. Go to Ninevah, that great city, and preach what I have told you."

Jonah journeyed inland and came to Ninevah. It was then the greatest city in the world. Sixty miles around were its walls and twenty miles across. It teemed with people. There was a clamor in the streets, and great wealth, and great poverty. The king was arrogant beyond belief, and his princes worse. The king's huntmaster trained his young lionhounds on prisoners who had been released from their dungeons and forced to run across the plain. The dogs pursued; those whom they caught they were permitted to devour. And every day twenty slaves died of exposure, fetching snow from the mountaintop for the king's sherbet.

Ninevah was a mighty pageant night and day; the city never slept. It burned like a furnace, this fat city, and wallowed in sin. Men and women coupled like dogs in the street, and on the rooftops, and wherever they

happened to meet. There were unlikely combinations, also. Men and men, women and women, man and cow, woman and bull. All the things that were forbidden they did with great zest.

"Unclean!" bellowed Jonah. "Filth! Abomination!"

A crowd gathered to hear him. No man had ever spoken like this in Ninevah. "Abomination!" he roared. "You are the worst sinners on the face of the earth! The Lord has prepared a flaming death for you, even as befell Sodom and Gomorrah. Yea, Sodom and Gomorrah, the cities of the plain. The Lord was displeased with them and loosed a fiery rain upon them, a storm of fire, until they were utterly consumed. Every man, woman, child, house, barn, animal — all, all consumed. And Sodom and Gomorrah were innocent little villages compared to Ninevah. Cease! Cease! You have but forty days, then Ninevah will be destroyed."

A great shriek of rage went up from the crowd. They surged forward, ready to tear Jonah to pieces. But the king was there. And he cried, "Stop! Touch not the hem of this man's robe. He is the man vomited out by the whale. He is the man of that wet miracle. He has come on God's errand and speaks God's word. We must heed what he says or be destroyed."

The king thereupon proclaimed a penance in Ninevah. He forbade pleasures of the flesh. Men and women were to cease their fornications, to put aside all carnal appetite, whatever its form. And by royal decree a fast was proclaimed. The king put on sackcloth and covered his head with ashes, and all the people did likewise. A proclamation went forth to every part of Assyria, to every village and farm in the broad reaches of that land. It read: "Let not man or beast taste anything. Let them not feed or drink water. Let each man and beast be covered with sackcloth and cry mightily unto God. Let everyone turn from his evil way."

Jonah said to the king: "This is not sufficient. You must not only cease your gluttony and your fornications, but you must turn your hand from violence. You must recall your raiding parties and take no more slaves. And the slaves you have must be treated without cruelty. You must not work them to death or lash them to death or treat them like beasts. Let this, also, be proclaimed."

The king did as Jonah said. The people fasted and abstained from sin. And God saw their works and repented of the evil that He had designed against them, and withheld His wrath.

Word came to Jonah of the Lord's mercy, and Jonah was very angry. He spoke to God, saying, "Lord, did I not tell you all this was useless? That is why I fled to Tarshish. For I knew that either my words would be ignored, or that you in your great mercy would spare the city. Yes, for a few bolts of sackcloth and a few buckets of ashes and a few weeks' show of virtue you have spared the wickedest city on the earth. And you have spared a people fierce and warlike, who will surely march south one day against Israel and Judah and vanquish your chosen people. And for this you have spared the Assyrians and the wicked city of Ninevah. Therefore, I pray you, since I do not understand you and am unworthy to be your prophet, I beseech you take my life. It is better for me to die than live."

The Lord spoke: "Is it well for you to be so angry?"

Jonah went out of the city and sat near its east wall. He built a little hut for himself and sat in its shade to see what would happen to Ninevah, how long virtue would be enforced, how long until chastity became intolerable. But when the sun shifted, the hut did not shade Jonah. The sun of Assyria is savage in midsummer, and Jonah grew faint.

God prepared a gourd and made it sprout on a vine — a large, plump gourd, which cast a shade that fell upon Jonah all day long until the sun sank. And Jonah welcomed the gourd and its cool shade.

But in the gourd that God had prepared for Jonah He had also planted a worm. The worm ate the heart of the gourd, and the gourd perished. When the sun arose the next morning God sent an east wind, the hottest wind, the wind that blights. There was no shade and the sun beat upon the head of Jonah. And the ill wind blew, and Jonah swooned. He sank to earth and spoke to God: "It is better for me to die than live," he said.

God said: "Is it well for you to be so angry about the gourd?"

"It is," said Jonah. "I am angry, and I will be angry until I die."

The Lord said: "You have pity on the gourd for which you did not labor. You did not plant the gourd, nor did you make it grow. It came up in a night and it perished in a night. Yet you grieve because it is gone. Then what of me? What of your God? Should I not spare Ninevah, this great city, a city so full of people? Should I not pity them who cannot discern between their right hand and their left hand? Should I not pity their dumb cattle?"

Jonah heard these words and repented in his heart, and sat silent. But God can read hearts, and read Jonah's. And He spared him, and kept him as a prophet. And He sent him back to Israel, where Jonah, doomed to wisdom, preached again.

286

THE HEROINES

ESTHER

Ahasuerus, king of Persia, was the mightiest ruler in all the world. He had swallowed up his neighbors, and sent his armies against Egypt and the land of the Philistines, and Israel and Judah and Syria. He had overthrown those great cities, Ninevah and Babylon. His fleets dominated the Middle Sea, and he held its islands subject. Now his empire stretched from India to Ethiopia. His palace was in the beautiful terraced city of Susa, and Vashti was his queen.

Now, when the Persian armies had overrun Israel and Judah, they had taken out many captives. But Ahasuerus was a subtle man. He had studied the reigns of kings of ages past, and knew how other empires had risen and fallen. And he did not enslave the children of Israel, for he knew what had happened to Egypt's Pharaoh, and knew of the strange disasters that had struck other conquerors who had attempted to enslave the Israelites. Therefore, Ahasuerus did not treat the Jews as he did his other captive peoples, but allowed them to dwell in peace in the cities of Persia. They engaged in trade, and were scholars, and maintained their own customs among strangers, worshipping their own God, refusing to defile themselves or to eat unclean food. Since they were very quick at languages, and keen merchants; since every one of their children was taught to read and write and was trained in habits of industry, they prospered in Persia. They dwelt in every city of the land. Their prosperity caused them to be disliked in many quarters. Still, they were protected by the king's edict, and suffered no harm.

There was a man named Mordecai, who dwelt in Susa, where the king's palace was. He was employed by the court, and, being a master at numbers, served the revenue officer. He was in his middle age, severe, suspicious, very stubborn, with an inquisitive eye and a caustic tongue. He also had a loving heart. He had taken into his house his uncle's orphaned daughter, Hadassah, and raised her as his own daughter. And Hadassah loved him as though he were her own father. For, although she was extremely beautiful, he cherished her more for her wit than for her beauty. He loved above all things to spend long hours in discourse with her. He told her the ancient tales of her people, and searched the stark events for their hidden meanings. She hung on his words and was entranced by the old tales, and questioned him closely about how this

291

happened, and that, and why they happened the way they did.

So beautiful was Hadassah that the young men of Susa prowled like tomcats around Mordecai's house. But he never allowed them to approach the girl.

It was Mordecai's habit to tell her the gossip of the court when he came home after the day's work. Upon this day, he was bursting with news. The king was in a terrible rage, for Vashti, his queen, had refused his summons to appear at a feast, and had kept to her own chambers. Now, it was said, the king was thinking of putting her aside as wife, and stripping her of royal honors.

This is what had happened. There had been a feast at the palace that had lasted seven days and seven nights. On the seventh night, when all the men were boasting about the beauty of the women they had known, the king had said: "Princes, captains, and nobles, you are men of valor, and have known fair women. But fairest of them all is my wife, Vashti." Then he had said to a servant: "Go fetch the queen. Tell her to come here and show her matchless face before my guests."

The messenger hurried to Vashti, who struck him across the face, crying, "They have caroused for seven days and seven nights. They are sodden with drink and of bestial appetite. Am I summoned now to show myself before this vile mob? Am I queen or dancing girl?"

She struck the messenger again and drove him from the room. He returned to the king and told him how his message had been received. Ahasuerus, who was never befuddled no matter how much he drank, simply said: "It is well. She shall be neither dancing girl nor queen."

The next day, the king called his council together to prepare an edict of divorcement. That evening, Mordecai went home and said: "It is done. He has cast her off as wife. She is queen no more, and will no longer live in the palace."

Now it was proclaimed throughout the land that the most beautiful young virgins would be selected from every city and province, and be taken to the palace to be trained for the king's pleasure. This was customary; it took place every few years. What was unusual was the further announcement that the king was seeking not only concubines, but a bride — that she who most pleased him would become queen in Vashti's place.

Mordecai knew that Hadassah would be taken to the harem, for no one had seen a girl so beautiful. He spoke to her privately: "Hearken to me, my cousin, my daughter, most beloved of daughters. As surely as night follows day, this edict means that you will soon find yourself in the royal harem. You will be near the king, the source of power. Now, where power abides, men conspire. That palace is a web of plot and counterplot. You must do this: Put aside the name Hadassah. Take up your Persian name of Esther, and allow yourself to be thought of as Persian. Do not reveal that you are of Judah."

"Why not?" she cried. "It is a proud thing to be a daughter of Judah! Who would be heathen who could be Hebrew?"

"Listen to me. A faction has formed in the court that hates the Jews and seeks to rouse the king against them. Allow yourself to be regarded as an orphan girl, ignorant of her roots."

"You are very wise, cousin," said the girl. "And I shall accept your counsel, as I have always. But tell me, beloved kinsman, am I to be separated from you totally now, never to see you, never to speak with you?"

"For the first six months you will be kept in seclusion in the women's quarters in the palace. That is the custom. But I will not lose sight of you for a day. Each day, at a certain hour, I will stand at the gates of the palace near the women's court. Perhaps I shall glimpse you; perhaps we shall be able to exchange a glance."

They embraced each other and wept. The next day, Hadassah, who now called herself Esther, was taken to the women's court in the palace. There she dwelt with the other maidens, undergoing the rites of purification, according to the royal law of the Medes and the Persians. The maidens were bathed in sweet waters and anointed with oil of myrrh and other precious scents. They were trained to play the lute and sing and dance, and their ways were polished so that they would be fit for a king's chamber.

Each day, as he had promised, Mordecai went to the palace and stood at the gate near the women's court. Sometimes he glimpsed Esther, sometimes he was glimpsed by her.

At the end of a year, the maidens were summoned to the king, one by one. Some he rejected on sight. Others he took to his chambers for the night. But not one of them did he call back a second time. Finally, Esther was summoned. When the king saw her, he smiled and beckoned her near. He rose to meet her, and took her hand, and said: "Truly are you named. For you burn like a star in the summer sky."

She entered his chamber that night, and did not leave in the morning. The king held no court that day. He did not appear in his throne room. For three days and three nights he stayed in his chamber with Esther. He became like a youth again. His jaded appetite revived. After three days he led her forth and declared, "Esther shall be my queen." He set the royal crown upon her head and ordered a great feast where the rites of marriage were performed, and Esther became queen in Vashti's place.

Everyone did the new queen honor, not only because of her rank, but because they began to love her. She remained modest and gentle-spoken, and was never cruel. Mordecai rejoiced privately at Esther's triumph. But he boasted to no one about their relationship, nor disclosed who she really was. He held his own counsel, and each day went to the palace and stood in the gate, hoping for a glimpse of her.

But now that she was a queen she was able to leave the palace and visit whom she pleased. Often she would visit Mordecai's home. And they would embrace each other and converse for hours, as in days gone by. But he would not allow her to reveal herself as his kinswoman, or to use her influence for his advancement in office.

Standing each day at the palace gate, the shrewd Mordecai picked up current and cross-current of intrigue. His keen ear caught whispers; his sharp eye spotted secret gestures. He noticed who spoke to whom. He read faces, studied entrances and departures, sudden friendships, quarrels. One evening, when Esther came to visit him, he had something important to tell her.

"There are two among the king's chamberlains, Bigthana and Teresh, who are plotting against your husband. Their duty is to keep the door of the king's chamber. But they plan to open that door and admit armed men who will kill the king, and elevate one of the princes to the throne."

Esther hurried back to the palace and told the king what had been told her. He immediately ordered an investigation. The plot was uncovered. Bigthana and Teresh were hanged from a tree. Then the entire matter was inscribed in the book of records. And Mordecai's part in breaking the conspiracy was written down, also, at Esther's dictation. But the record was sealed and the king did not read it.

Now the king promoted a man named Haman to be chief counselor. He was a wily man, Haman, belonging to the Amalekites, a tribe that had always hated the children of Israel. He was proud, ambitious, ruthless to his enemies, and as single in his purpose as a sword blade. The king, dismayed by the treachery of his two most trusted chamberlains, put Haman in charge of all the palace staff. Haman gathered power in his hands. He labored night and day, and acted for the king in all things, and made his name so feared throughout the land that people bowed to him as though he were the king himself.

But Mordecai had observed Haman for a long time, and loathed him, and did not bow to him when he passed through the gate. A servant of Haman raged at Mordecai, "Who are you that you do not bow to this man who stands next to the king?"

"That is not bowing," said Mordecai. "That is prostration. You cast yourself on your face in the dust before this man. I am a Jew. I prostrate myself only before God."

This was told to Haman, who did not seek to avenge himself immediately upon Mordecai, for he sensed a greater opportunity. He went to the king and said: "O great Ahasuerus, you who are king of kings and hold empire over land and sea, know that my one purpose is to serve Your Majesty."

"I know it," said Ahasuerus.

"Then I must tell you a grievous thing, O King. There are those in your realm who do not recognize your sovereignty. They refuse to do you homage as everyone else does, and refuse to honor those whom you honor."

Ahasuerus frowned. "Who are these people?"

"A rebellious people," said Haman. "A peculiar people, who separate themselves always from their neighbors and follow their own god and their own ways. They are the Jews. Lo, you have protected them against adversity. In the shelter of your compassion they have prospered and multiplied. Now they mock you. May I do you one more service and rid you of this pest?"

"Bring me a blank scroll," said the king. "I will stamp it with the royal seal. Then you may write upon it whatever you wish, and do to this people what you will."

Haman, the Amalekite, believed in moody gods. He believed in lucky days and unlucky days. Before doing anything important, he had his astrologers consult the stars and his soothsayers cast lots. Now he wished to choose the right day for the massacre. He wanted to kill every Jew throughout the land suddenly and completely in one bloody stroke. He had his soothsayers write the names of the months on pieces of paper and number the days of each month, and cast lots to find the best day.

Numbers were drawn. The day that came up was the thirteenth day of the twelfth month. But months were numbered differently then. The twelfth month was not December but March, a beautiful month in Persia, a month when the almond trees blossom. Then Haman prepared proclamations for every city and every province, naming the thirteenth day of the twelfth month a day of massacre, when every Jew in every place would be hunted out and killed — every man, every woman, every child.

Mordecai, with his uncanny quickness, learned what the proclamations were going to say before they were written. He rent the clothes from his body, put on sackcloth, and covered his head with ashes. Then he returned to stand at the palace gate. Esther's maid saw him there and went and told Esther how the tax officer who always stood at the gate was now clad in sackcloth and ashes, and was weeping as though a loved one had died. Esther sent him down fresh garments to wear, but he refused them and said to the queen's servant: "Send me Hathach, the queen's chamberlain."

Hathach went down, and Mordecai said: "I have a message for the queen."

"Who are you to send messages to the queen?" said Hathach.

"A man with something to say that she will want to hear," said Mordecai. "Whoever I am, she will thank you."

There was something in Mordecai's face that told Hathach, who was a man of discernment, that this matter merited the queen's attention. "Take this scroll to Queen Esther," said Mordecai. "Upon it she will read tonight what the governors of the provinces and the governors of the cities will read in five days, the words of a proclamation by Haman. Take it to her quickly."

Hathach took Esther the scroll. She read it, put on a dark cloak, and went out of the palace. They met at Mordecai's house. "You must stop this thing," said Mordecai. "You must use your influence with the king."

"Alas," said Esther, "I do not know how much influence I still have with the king. He has not called me to him for thirty days."

"Do not wait for his summons," said Mordecai. "Go to him."

"I cannot," said Esther. "He is in the inner court. You know the law of the Medes and the Persians, that when the king is in the inner court no one may enter without permission. And whoever enters will be put to death."

"Death will find you, anyway," said Mordecai. "Haman has declared that all Jews must die. And when massacre is in the air, the nose of the Jew killer is sharpened, and he smells out Jewish blood no matter how well concealed. Haman will know you as a daughter of Judah; he may already know it. You will die, also. Listen to me, Esther, my daughter, my queen. Listen to me, beloved girl. God has a way of preserving His people. He will not let us all be destroyed. But if you do nothing to save your people, then God's hand will be upon you. Who can fathom His deep intention? Perhaps you have been elevated to the throne for precisely this occasion — that you may be the instrument of your people's salvation. Go to the king."

Esther stood tall and looked in Mordecai's face. "I am not afraid of death, only of failure. I will seek the king, even in the inner court. Now I have instructions for you in turn, my father. Gather all the Jews of Susa, and fast for three days and three nights, and pray that I may be strengthened to do what I must. And I and my maidens will also fast, and pray to God. Then I will go to the king in the inner court, and if I perish, I perish."

Esther returned to the palace. Mordecai gathered the Jews of Susa and they began their fast. After three days, Esther clad herself in her most queenly garments and put the gold crown on her head. She made her way to the inner court. The guards crossed their swords in front of her. She put a hand on each sword and pushed them aside, and they did not dare bar her way. She went through the gate into the courtyard, where the king sat on his judgment throne. All voices stopped. The courtiers looked at Esther in amazement. Haman stared at her. All knew the law; all knew that she had transgressed; all knew that her transgression meant death.

Ahasuerus went stony with surprise. Who was this who dared defy the ancient law of the Medes and the Persians and enter the inner court without invitation? Whoever it was deserved death. The king raised his scepter high, intending to bring it straight down, rapping its haft on the paving stones in a sign that meant "kill."

But as the king raised his scepter something gripped his arm, and held it upraised. He could not lower his arm. The courtyard tilted; the king's vision spun. When it cleared, he saw who it was who had parted the swords of the sentries and was approaching the throne. It was Esther. Her face burned on the gray air, and was more beautiful than it had ever been before. And the goggling courtiers saw their king turn his scepter in the air and hold it toward Esther, knob first, changing the sign of death to the sign of mercy.

Esther went close to him and touched the knob on top of the scepter. Then, as on the day when he had first seen her, the king smiled at her, and descended the steps of the throne, and took her hand, and kissed her cheek.

"What is it, Queen Esther?" he said. "It must have been a mighty reason that brought you here. What do you want? Whatever you want, you shall have."

"I come only for this," said Esther. "If it please you, my lord, come to my chambers tonight, to a banquet — and bring Haman with you."

"I thank you," said the king. "I am pleased to go to your banquet. I know that Haman will be pleased."

Haman was delighted to hear these words. For, despite the high favor he had found with the king, he sensed that Esther disliked him. And, knowing her influence with the king, he had always tried to ingratiate himself with her. But she had never smiled upon him. Now he was overjoyed by this invitation. He went home and called Zeresh, his wife, and his closest friends, and began to speak almost as if he were drunk, babbling and boasting. He told them how rich he was, and how many fine children he had; how the king had honored him and promoted him.

"What's more," cried Haman, "Esther, the queen, gives a banquet tonight. She has invited only the king and myself. And it is said she has prepared every dish with her own hands to do us special honor."

"You are fortunate above all men," said one of his friends.

"I am," said Haman. "And should be the happiest of men, except for this: Mordecai, the Jew, still stands at the gate. And when I pass through that gate tonight on my way to the banquet, he will do me no honor. He alone will refuse. He will not bow to me. By the gods, I will not wait for the massacre! He must be dead by tomorrow."

Haman called to his men and said: "Let a gallows be built. Build it taller than any tree, reaching high above the gates. Let a high gallows be raised, and tomorrow let Mordecai be hanged there."

Now, before the banquet Esther sent her servant to the king, with the court record telling how Bigthana and Teresh had plotted against him, and how Mordecai had uncovered the plot and revealed it, saving the king's life. The king read this for the first time and said to his chamberlain: "I have not known the whole truth of this matter. What reward has Mordecai received for his service to me? Has he been enriched? Dignified by office?"

"He has received no reward," said the chamberlain.

The king sent for Haman, and said: "As my chief advisor, tell me this: What should be done for the man whom the king delights to honor?"

That's *me*! thought Haman. Whom would the king delight to honor more than me? And Haman answered: "O bestower of gifts, whom you delight to honor should be dealt with in this fashion: Royal garments should be taken to him. And a horse given to him, as fine as the king's own stallion. Then, wearing a golden crown, this man should ride through the streets conducted by princes. And heralds should call out before him: 'Behold the greatest man in the kingdom!' so that all the people should know it. Thus would I deal with this worthy man."

"Your words are full of sense," said the king. "All shall be done as you advise. Now go; we meet at the queen's banquet tonight."

Haman hurried off to garb himself, more joyful than ever.

That night, the king and Haman and Esther sat at a table. Gold and silver plates glittered on the table. Tall tapers burned, scenting the air. Servants passed food and wine. The savor was delicious. For Esther, knowing every shade of the king's taste, had prepared every dish herself. And she had never been more beautiful. She wore a gown of white samite, and had twined diamonds and pearls in her long black hair. The king was very pleased.

"O Queen," he said to her, "thank you for this delicious repast."

"Tell me, my lord," said Esther, "what would you do to a man who threatened my life?"

"Threatened your life?" said the king. "The life of my queen? Of my star? Of my beloved? Why, I do not know what I would do to him. There are those who serve me who are expert in torment. I would give him to them with special recommendations. In an hour he would be pleading for death. But why do you ask me such a question? Who could possibly threaten you? Have you had a bad dream?"

"No dream," said Esther. "The threat is real. You have never inquired of my origins, O King. But I am a daughter of Judah, cousin to Mordecai, for whom a gallows has been built beyond the palace gate. This man of

whom I speak seeks to hang Mordecai first, then to slaughter all of my people, every man, woman, and child. He has assigned the day of massacre, and that day is two days from now, the thirteenth day of the twelfth month."

"Who is this man?" cried the king, leaping to his feet. "Who is he? Who?"

Esther rose, too. She stretched her arm and pointed at Haman. "Behold the man! Your chief advisor, Haman!"

The king clapped his hands. Armed men rushed into the room. "Take this man," said the king. "Hang him from the gallows that he built for Mordecai."

Then the king sent for his chief scribe and dictated these words to him: "Out of those children of Israel and Judah who sojourn in this land, two people have come forth, a man who has saved your king's life, and a woman who has made that life worth living. I speak of Mordecai, son of Jair, of the tribe of Benjamin, and of his cousin, Esther, who is my queen. Therefore, know this: That the Jews dwell in Persia in the shelter of my special gratitude, and that he who touches a hair of the head of one of these people shall immediately be seized and taken to a place of execution, and there hanged."

The scribe hurried off. "Now let Mordecai be sent for," said the king. His chamberlain went down to the palace gate and brought up Mordecai. He was still clad in sackcloth; ashes were in his hair. Esther went to him and took him in her arms. The king embraced him, also. Then servants led Mordecai away. He was bathed and anointed and clad in the king's own colors, which were blue and white. He was given a royal stallion to ride. Heralds ran before him in the streets, proclaiming, "Hail, Mordecai! Hail the man whom the king delights to honor!"

And so Mordecai took Haman's place as chief advisor to the king. He lived a long and busy life, and under his guidance the kingdom prospered.

For the rest of Ahasuerus' reign the Jews of Persia lived in peace. Since that time the thirteenth day of the twelfth month has been celebrated. For some twenty-five hundred years now, it has been a Jewish holiday, a time of feasting and rejoicing. It is called "Purim" after the Persian word "pur," meaning the casting of lots.

JUDITH

The king of Assyria was known simply as the Great King, for he had sent his armies against the most powerful nations in the world and had overthrown them. He had conquered the Medes, the Persians, the Babylonians. Their kings ruled only by his consent, and paid him yearly tribute. The palace of the Great King was at Ninevah, a walled city, enormous and strong, on the east bank of the Tigris. His court was the richest and most brilliant in the entire world.

The Great King sent for his chief captain, Holofernes, and said: "Behold, my son, you have led my armies and overthrown my enemies. Now I have another task for you."

"To hear is to obey, O King."

"I have planned great works. I would build a summer palace set among a hundred gardens. I would build an artificial lake there, also, with a pleasure garden in the center of that lake, swans upon the lake, and peacocks in the garden. Also, the walls of Ninevah need repairing. I plan a string of fortresses and a great road from the city to the southern border. We shall require thousands of slaves for this work. And I must stuff my treasury again. Therefore, Captain, take an army. Take spearmen, horsemen, iron chariots, and march against those rich countries that do not yet pay us tribute. Go into Egypt. Go into Syria and Lebanon. Make yourself master of these nations. Destroy their armies. Sack the treasure cities of Pithom, Rameses, Tyre, and Damascus. In the vaults of Jerusalem, also, will you find much treasure. Kill the weak, the old, the sick — those unable to work. Bring the able-bodied here as slaves."

"A noble task, sire," said Holofernes. "I will do all that you command."

"As for those of Judah," said the king, "know this: They are clever and rebellious and make dangerous slaves. Therefore, kill every man, every male child in that land. But the women are lovely. They talk too much, but a taste of the whip cures that. So choose the most beautiful of the women and maidens of Judah, and bring them here for my harem."

Holofernes departed and mustered men for battle — a hundred and twenty thousand picked warriors, spearmen and horsemen and charioteers, and twelve thousand mounted archers. He took camels and donkeys to bear supplies; sheep and goats and oxen to feed the army.

He struck the borders of Cilicia and wiped out all resistance. He went into the lands of Arabia. He swept across the plain of Damascus at the time of wheat harvest, burned the fields, destroyed flocks and herds. He sacked the Syrian cities and enslaved their inhabitants. Fear and dread went before him. The kings of Tyre and Moab and Ammon, and the Pharaoh of Egypt, sent ambassadors to him, saying, "Do not come with fire and sword, great Captain. We submit ourselves to you without battle, our houses and our fields of wheat, our flocks and herds, our tents and our cities. Use them as it pleases you. And those who dwell in our lands, from highest to lowest, shall prostrate themselves before your king. He can put his foot upon our necks and we will be his servants."

So Holofernes was master everywhere in the name of his king. He came down the sea coast and set garrisons in the cities, and took slaves without number. The people did not resist at all. They received the Assyrians with garlands and with dances and the music of timbrels.

Holofernes sent men through all these lands to destroy every temple they could find, every sacred grove, every wayside altar, every place of worship. He decreed that no god should be worshipped anywhere; only the Great King of Assyria could be worshipped as god. The decree was obeyed. People everywhere shunned their old gods and worshipped only the Great King of Assyria.

Now all the nations were conquered except the smallest one, Judah, and this seemed an easy thing. Holofernes gathered his forces and marched toward Judah. He paused on the shore of the great strait and prepared for invasion.

Now, the children of Israel who dwelt in Judah knew that Holofernes was coming against them with the mightiest army ever assembled, and they were very fearful. But their minds were troubled beyond fear. They had faced invasion and captivity before, but word had reached them that Holofernes was defiling temples, forbidding worship of any god but the king of Assyria — that he was planting statues of the Great King in all the holy places, and forcing the people to pray to the statue and sacrifice to it.

This the Jews were forbidden to do. God Himself had forbidden it. And they feared the wrath of God more than man's cruelty. Therefore they decided to resist. Word was sent to the villages of Samaria and Judah. Men began to fortify their villages and build strong places upon the hills. They stored up provisions against siege. The high priest of Jerusalem wrote to the elders of Beth-el and to the elders of other walled cities among the mountains, charging them to guard the mountain passes. These narrow passes were the only entrance to Judah, and a few brave men could hold them against vast numbers of the enemy.

The city and villages were fortified. Grain was stored. Then all who dwelt in the land, every man, every woman, every child, prostrated themselves in their temples, and put ashes upon their heads, and spread sackcloth before the altar. They begged God not to deliver them up to the Assyrians for slaughter. For three days they fasted and prayed, then left the temples and waited for the enemy.

Messages came to Holofernes that the children of Israel were preparing for war, that they had shut off the mountain passes and fortified the hilltops, and had dug chariot traps in the plains. Holofernes was enraged. He called the princes of Moab, and the captains of Ammon, and the governors of the seacoasts, and said: "Tell me now, you sons of Canaan, who are these stubborn hill people? What are the cities they inhabit? How large is their army? Where lies their power? Why do they refuse to submit to me like all the rest of the world?"

A man named Achior answered. He was a captain of the Ammonites. "O Holofernes," he said, "they who oppose you are descended from the Chaldeans. One family of them refused to worship the stone gods of the Chaldeans and left that land and went into Mesopotamia. There they began to worship an invisible god. The family grew and became many tribes. They were conquered but never dispersed, enslaved but never subdued. In Egypt they broke the bonds of slavery and wandered again in the wilderness, and the Egyptians who pursued them were drowned in the sea. Then, it is said, their god spoke to them from a mountain and gave them many laws. They marched through the wilderness toward Canaan. And when they kept the law of their god, it is told, they prospered. They triumphed in battle. When they disobeyed their god, they were vanquished. Now this generation has returned to its god, and has come together from all its places of exile, and has taken the city of Jerusalem again and the hill country of Judah. It was desolate but these people restored it, and they dwell there, worshipping their god."

Holofernes roared with fury, "Man, I ask you a simple question and you stand there ranting and raving like a maniac! What do I care about their invisible god and their ridiculous history? I want to know about troops, chariots, archers, spearmen — where their forts are and who their captains are. For, know this: There is no god but the king of Assyria, and these Israelites will be kissing the toe of his statue before a week has passed." Holofernes turned to his men and said: "He's a Jew in his heart. Bind him. Take him to the foot of that hill. Leave him there so that he may be found by the Jews and killed before he has a chance to tell them how much he loves them."

The guards seized Achior and bound him and took him into Judah until they came to the foot of the hill. But when the men of the mountain city of Beth-el saw the horsemen, they took up their weapons and rushed out of the gates, and the horsemen galloped away, leaving Achior there. The Israelites went down; they loosed his bonds and brought him into the city. They knew the man had something to tell, and they called an assembly. Achior told his story, how Holofernes had questioned him and how he had answered — and how the Assyrians were preparing to attack.

"Behold!" cried Ozias, the high priest. "This Ammonite is our friend. He has done us a service this day." They made Achior welcome. Then the entire assembly went to the temple to pray.

Holofernes kept questioning the princes and captains of Canaan. An Edomite spoke up: "My lord, do not attempt to attack this land by marching through its mountain passes. These passes are narrow. You will find them blocked by walls of rock and defended by spearmen who will make a hedge of spears in the narrow way. And while you are attempting to dislodge the spearmen, lo, others of Judah, lurking on the hillsides, will shoot arrows down upon you and hurl huge boulders down, crushing man and horse, crushing your chariots like beetles. We Edomites have attempted these passes, and we have seen our armies destroyed. Also, if you force these passes with a great loss of men, you will find the entire population of each city arrayed behind its walls — women and children fighting alongside the men. Those who cannot handle weapons will pour boiling water on the heads of your men, and ladles of burning pitch, and drop heavy objects upon them."

"Are you saying they cannot be taken?" growled Holofernes.

"Not at all, my lord," said the Edomite. "I am suggesting this: The city can be taken by a simple trick. The city of Beth-el, which sits upon the first hill commanding the passes, takes its water from springs that gush at the base of the mountain. Therefore, send men secretly at night and stop up these fountains. The people will have no water to drink. They will die of thirst. Their cattle will die of thirst, and the people will starve. So the city will fall to you without a fight."

"Good counsel!" cried Holofernes. "We shall do this. We shall stop up their fountains."

He sent men that night. They went to the base of the mountain and stopped the springs of water. Then Holofernes threw siege lines around the hill so that no one could come down out of the city. He kept to his tent, and waited for the city to surrender.

The cisterns dried up in Beth-el, and the people thirsted. Water was rationed; it was measured out cup by cup, and no one had enough to drink. People swooned and fell down in the streets. The men no longer had strength to bear arms. They cried out before Ozias and the elders; "Make peace! Make peace! God has sold us into the hand of the Assyrian. Therefore, send a message to Holofernes. Open the gates! Let us submit! We cannot wait here and see our infants die before our eyes. Anything is better."

Ozias spoke: "Do not lose courage so quickly. Let us endure five days more and see whether God turns merciful toward us. After five days, if God still withholds salvation, then I will do as you say, and open the gates to the enemy."

Now, there was a woman of that town named Judith. She was a young widow. Three years before, her husband had died of a heat stroke while harvesting barley. She was the most beautiful young woman in the city, tall and graceful, with pearly skin and long black hair. But no man looked upon her beauty. When her husband died, all the passion of her heart was turned to grief. She plunged into mourning as she had into marriage, and shunned everyone except her servants. She made a tent on the roof of her house and wore sackcloth, and rarely left her tent, and never left the house. No one violated her privacy or spoke evil against her, for she had been highly esteemed in the city.

Judith did not attend the assembly, but her serving woman brought her the news. She went down out of her tent of grief into the house and sent messages to the elders, and to Ozias, the high priest, inviting them to call upon her. They came.

She said: "The people have spoken out of their agony, calling upon you to surrender. And you have asked for five days to give God a chance to save us. O wise men of Beth-el, you have done wrong! You cannot put a time limit upon God's mercy. He is beyond our time as He is beyond all our measurement. It was He who wrought the firmament and hung our sun and moon, which make our night and our day and mark our time. He cannot be bound by such small artifacts, such small ideas. You cannot threaten God, you cannot hasten Him; you will only provoke Him to greater angers."

"Sage words," said Ozias. "But what would you have us do?"

"We must keep up our courage and implore God's mercy, which He will grant us in His own good time, if it pleases Him. This generation has not strayed from His way. We have not run after the gods of the Canaanites, stone Baal and Ashteroth of the grove. We have not done this, and God should not abandon us. Let us go to the temple and thank God for testing us in His mysterious way, and beg Him to deliver us from the enemy."

"Your understanding is deep; your heart is good," said Ozias. "But the people thirst. They have made us swear to surrender the city within five days unless help comes. If we refuse, they will slay us and surrender the city themselves. All I can say to you, Judith, is pray. Pray for rain. Perhaps God will listen to you."

Standing there among the defeated old men, Judith suddenly felt herself changing. She felt as though the spirit of God were shining upon her — like the sunlight lancing through the window. She was filled with gaiety and with courage. She knew what she had to do.

She said: "I have prayed, and I think my prayers have been answered, or are beginning to be answered. Listen now. Open the gate for me tonight. I shall go out with my waiting woman. Within the five days that you have given yourselves before surrender, I will bring the vengeance of God upon our enemies."

"How?" cried Ozias. "What do you mean to do?"

"Do not ask me," said Judith. "For I cannot tell you. I must act in secrecy, and alone."

"You shall act as you see fit," said Ozias. "God knows, there is no one else with a plan."

They departed. Judith fell upon her face and cried out: "O God, O my God, hear me. The Assyrians glory in the strength of their spearmen; they trust in chariots, in sword and bow and sling. They do not know that you are the Lord of battle who breaks down shields and tramples chariots. Behold their pride and send down your wrath upon their heads. Deliver them into my hand; let the great captain be brought down by the hand of a woman."

307

308

She listened. She heard a great hush. But there was a fullness in it, not a silence. She cried out again, "O God, God of the afflicted, helper of the oppressed, upholder of the weak, protector of the forlorn, savior of them who are without help, I pray you, I pray you, give me strength for the deed I must do."

She arose. She pulled off the sackcloth, put off her garments of widowhood, and washed herself with the last water in the house. She anointed herself with sandalwood and myrrh. She braided her hair and threaded jewels in its blackness, and put on a gown of scarlet and gold. She put on armlets and bracelets and rings and earrings. She looked at herself in the glass for the first time in three years and wept when she saw herself, for she was as radiant as on her bridal day. She took a bottle of wine and a cruse of oil, filled a leather bag with parched corn and figs and bread, and gave it to her servant. They went to the city gates.

She went down the mountain path into the valley. A man came toward her, bearing a spear. He wore a tall plumed helmet. He was an Assyrian. "Who are you?" he said. "Where do you come from, and where are you going?"

"I am a woman of the Hebrews," she said. "And I am fleeing from them. Now take me to Holofernes, your captain. I know a secret that will deliver the city into his hands."

The man stared. In that moonlight she was beautiful beyond all dreams of beauty. He trembled with desire. But he did not touch her. He knew that Holofernes would delight in the sight of her, and thoughts of advancement danced in his head.

"I will escort you to the captain's tent," he said. He conducted her through the sentry post to the tent of Holofernes. Word flashed among the captains and among the men.

"If there be others like her in Beth-el," said one young man, "I will scale this mountain and batter down the walls of the city singlehanded. An hour with such a woman is worth the torments of eternity."

She was ushered into Holofernes' tent. The great warrior rested on his bed under a canopy of purple and gold silk. Silver lamps burned in the tent; bowls of incense smoldered. Judith sank to the earth before Holofernes.

"Rise," he said. "Arise, fair visitor, and do not fear. But tell me why you have fled your city and come to us."

"I have left my city because I know it will fall," said Judith. "In my soul I despise losers."

Holofernes roared with laughter. "Truly, victors are to be preferred," he said. "Your wit matches your beauty."

"I have come to tell you how you may take Beth-el without losing a man," said Judith. "It is secret knowledge; he who possesses it must vanquish us despite our hills and our narrow passes, and our men of valor. You heard the words of the Ammonite whom you cast out. He spoke truth to you, but partial truth. We are a special nation. No one can prevail against us unless we sin against our God."

"Are these your words of good counsel?" said Holofernes. "Is this why you have left your city and come through the night, to tell me this, that I must wait for your people to sin before I can vanquish them?"

"Do not be angry, my lord, but hear me out. For they must sin. And you must prevail. You have stopped up the springs; the cisterns fail. They suffer thirst. They hunger. Now, human flesh can bear just so much. They fear God; they fear to break His laws, and they will hold out longer than you might think possible. But finally their hunger and thirst will drive them to eat unclean meat and drink its blood. Thus they will sin against God and He will punish them. You are their punishment."

"Now your words begin to please me," said Holofernes. "Speak on."

"If you attack before they have committed their sin, you must lose many men. But I can assist you. I am versed in matters of ritual. I shall stay here in your camp, if you permit me. And each night I shall go out, go to the city gates and observe what is happening inside. When I see the people of the city sinning, when I see them eating forbidden food and defiling themselves, then I will come straightway to you and lead you through the passes, and God will open the gates of Beth-el to you."

"So be it," said Holofernes. "You shall be given a tent, and permission to come and go as you please. But each night after you have visited the city, you must report to me here in my tent."

Judith dwelt in the camp of the Assyrian. Each night she went out, but did not go up to the city. She tarried on a hillside, then came back, and went to Holofernes' tent and said: "Well, my lord, I climbed the hill to the gates and looked into the city. They suffer but do not sin. It is not yet time." She looked full into his face as she spoke, and sat near him. Each movement of her body, each glance of her eye uttered meaning beyond the words she spoke.

Holofernes was intoxicated with her beauty. On the fourth night he could wait no longer. He had his servants prepare a small feast and pour out the finest wines, and he sent a man to Judith. "My lord, Holofernes, invites you to dine in his tent," said the man. "To drink wine and be merry with him, and to be received this night as a daughter of the Assyrians and a noblewoman in the house of the Great King."

"Tell your lord that I am honored," said Judith. "I shall change my garments and go to him."

Her servant bathed her and anointed her, and scented her with sandalwood and myrrh and essence of the night-flowering jasmine. She plaited diamonds and pearls in Judith's black hair, and clad her in a gown of blue and silver.

When Judith went to the tent, she found Holofernes there alone. The table was set and the wine was poured, but he had dismissed his servants. Tapers burned in the tent; there was a heavy musk of incense.

Holofernes wore no armor. He was clad in cloth of gold. His beard was braided in the manner of the Assyrian court and he wore a lotus flower in his hair. He was a huge man, powerful as a bull, and of ravenous appetite. He had never wooed a woman before. Next to the king he was the greatest man in the empire. Men trembled at his look, and women hastened to obey him before he spoke. A woman like Judith, of wit, understanding, and bold, free spirit, was a total novelty to him. She not only awoke his lust but caught his imagination. For the first time in his life he was in love.

She sat near to him and spoke with him. She told him stories out of her girlhood, how her father, Simeon, had killed a man who had leaped upon her in the field, loosening her girdle and trying to force her to the ground. Her father had drawn his sword and cut down the man where he stood. And she had burned her dress, which was stained with the stranger's blood.

She told her story, and lifted a goblet of purple wine to her lips, and pretended to drink. She encouraged her host to drink. He tossed off goblet after goblet, and grew more and more delighted. He was on fire with the need for her. He was a sword of desire, and knew that he would soon be sheathed in the coolness of her beauty.

She urged him to drink more and more. He became very drunk. "Lie down, my lord," she said. "Lie down while I quench the tapers. I would come to you the first time in darkness."

He flung himself upon the bed. But he had drunk too much, eaten too much. As soon as he touched the bed, he fell asleep.

Judith went to the bed and looked down upon the sleeper. His face was red and swollen, glazed with sweat. His lips were purple. Four carved wooden pillars held up the gorgeous silken canopy of his bed. On one of these pillars hung Holofernes' sword. It was a curved scimitar, bright as the new moon.

Judith lifted down the scimitar. She wound her left hand into his hair. "Strengthen me, O Lord," she whispered. She raised the scimitar high and slashed down at his neck with all her might. She did not cut through. She wrenched the blade from his thick neck, raised it again and cut down again. This time she sliced through the neck. His head was cut from his body.

Holding the bloody head by its hair, she reached up and tore down the canopy — and rushed out of the tent. She gave the head to her servant, who stuffed it in the leather meatbag. Stars blazed overhead. There were no sentries at Holofernes' tent, for he had told them not to come near that night.

Judith wiped her hands on the canopy and looked up at the night sky. This canopy was flung over the world and sewn with stars. "Thank you, God," she murmured. Then the two women hurried out of the camp through the valley and up the hill.

They came to the city gates. She saw the watchman upon the wall. "Open now!" she called. "Open the gate! God is with us!"

Her call rang through the city. The elders hurried from their houses to meet her at the gate. People came running with torches; there was a throng in the streets. Her voice was still unnaturally loud, loud as a trumpet, and she cried, "Praise God, praise God, I say! He has not taken His mercy from the house of Israel, but has used me to destroy our enemies this night."

She reached into the leather bag and pulled out the head. "Behold Holofernes," she cried, "chief captain of Assyria's king! Behold the canopy under which he lay in his drunkenness. Behold the hand that smote him, the hand of a woman. And, as the Lord lives, although I deceived him with my beauty, yet I killed him before he could defile me."

No voice answered. The torches flickered. The crowd was silent, struck mute with astonishment. Finally, Ozias came to her and said: "O daughter, blessed are you above all the women on earth. Thanked be the Lord God who has created the heavens and the earth, and who guided your hand that held the sword."

312

313

"Let me say one more thing while the spirit is upon me," said Judith. "Then I will return to the quiet ways of widowhood. Do this now: Hang this head high upon the city wall. Let every fighting man take his weapons and go down the valley and occupy the heights above the camp of the Assyrian. But do not attack, not yet. At the first light of dawn, beat your spears upon your shields and blow blasts upon your trumpets and make a great clamor. The Assyrian captains will think you are about to attack and rush to the tent of Holofernes for instruction. Entering the tent, they will see the headless body of their great leader, and terror will strike them. They will fall into a panic. They will not know what to do. All will be confused. Then you must attack. March upon them and smite them. They will flee before you."

A man took the head from her. Another man took the canopy. She went through the crowd toward her house. But she stopped. She saw a man lying on the stones. She knelt to him. It was Achior, the Ammonite. She raised his head. His eyes opened.

"Forgive me," he said. "I am a warrior and have seen many men die before my eyes. But when you pulled the head of Holofernes, the great Holofernes, from that leather bag, then I fainted dead away. O Judith, blessed are you in the tabernacle of Israel. In all nations, men, hearing your name, shall be astonished."

She bent and kissed his face. "Thank you," she said. "Of all this multitude you are the only one, I believe, who can picture my deed this night."

She arose and went to her house. Achior gazed after her. "Truly," he said to himself, "there is only one God, the God of Israel. There is also only one woman in the world for me, that bloody-handed beautiful widow. I will turn Jew and woo her."

That very night he went and got himself circumcised and became a Jew.

The head of Holofernes was hung from the highest place on the wall. At the first light of dawn, the warriors went out of the city and took up positions on both ridges of the valley overlooking the Assyrian camp. Then, as Judith had instructed, each man smote his spear upon his shield, making a great clamor. And the trumpeters blew great blasts upon their horns. The Assyrian camp awoke. The captains rushed to the camp of Holofernes, crying, "They attack! They attack!"

The men burst into his tent. They gaped in dismay. The canopy had been stripped from its pillars. The table was overturned. Spilt wine mixed with blood. The headless body of their captain lay sprawled among the litter.

"It is the strange god!" they cried to one another. "The invisible god of the Hebrews! He has struck in the night, lifting our captain's head from his body."

They were seized by a great fear. Panic spread like wildfire among the men of the Assyrian host. It infected the animals. Camels plunged, breaking their lines. Horses fled from those who would saddle them. Cattle stampeded. And the men stampeded like cattle, rushing out of their camp, out of the valley, fleeing north, fleeing east. The men of Israel pursued and cut them down as they fled.

The men returned and unstopped the springs at the base of the mountain. The fountains of Beth-el flowed again; the cisterns filled.

The elders went to Judith's house, bearing loot from the sacked camp, for they wished to give her the greatest share of it. They gave her what was taken from the tent of Holofernes, silver and gold plate, his silks and his jewels, and said to her: "You are the exaltation of Israel; you are the rejoicing of our nation."

Judith parceled out the gold and silver plate and the silk and jewels among the women of Beth-el. The canopy and the curved sword of Holofernes she gave as relics to the temple. The women blessed her and swept her into a dance. They put a garland of olive leaves upon her head. She held an olive branch as she danced. She danced in the street and all the women danced, following her. The men joined, dancing in their armor, with garlands on their heads and song in their mouths. Achior came to Judith and danced with her.

The end of the story is lost in the mists of time. Some say that Judith remained a widow all her days. Others say that she married Achior and lived to be a hundred and five years old, thus attaining widowhood again. But all the tales agree that, widow or wife, Judith was honored throughout Israel. In the years to come there were to be other invasions, other defeats, other victories. But the Assyrians never came again. Their power was broken forever.

ISRAEL IN EXILE

DANIEL

Nebuchadnezzar, king of Babylon, was a mighty warrior and had conquered most of the world. Now he invaded Judah and laid siege to Jerusalem. And the king of Judah was a weak and empty man who ignored God's word and broke His statutes, and the people had followed him. The spirit of the Lord had departed from the children of Israel. Their hearts were without valor and their arms without strength. Jerusalem fell.

The troops of Nebuchadnezzar violated the temple and took certain golden vessels, cups, and ewers, which were used in the sacred ceremonies, and bore them off to the king's treasure house. The king spoke to his chief officer, saying, "You have brought me gold and silver and gems, but have not possessed yourself of the Hebrews' greatest treasure, which is their secret wisdom. I need this wisdom; my wise men have lost theirs. My sorcerers do no sorcery. My astrologers read no special meaning in the pattern of the stars. We need new knowledge, new magic. Now, there are those among the Hebrews who are masters of sorcery, who delve into hidden places and who read dreams — who divine secrets, raise demons, do marvels. Go, then, among their young princes and those of the king's seed, and choose me the worthiest of these youths — those without blemish, well favored, and wise beyond their years. We will take them to Babylon and train them to be kings' counselors, and teach them the tongue of the Chaldeans."

The cream of Israel's youth was taken to Babylon. There another selection was made, and the best of these were separated. They received meat from the king's own table and wine from his bottles. They received special teaching for three years. And of these selected youths there were four who shone among the rest. Their names were Daniel, Hananiah, Mishael, and Azariah. Of these four Daniel was the leader.

The head eunuch who was in charge of the young men called Daniel to him and inquired the meaning of these names. Daniel answered, "My name, Daniel, means 'God is my judge.' Hananiah means 'God has been gracious.' Mishael means 'Who is equal to God?' Azariah means 'God has helped.' "

"The king wishes you to take Babylonian names," said the head eunuch. "It will be difficult to find those as elevated as your own, but I shall try. You, Daniel, will take the name of Belteshazzar. Do you know what that means?"

"A prince of Baal," said Daniel. Rage bit him at the sound of the name, but he allowed none of it to show. For Baal was a stone idol and the name was an abomination to Daniel.

"Hearken to me," said the eunuch. "These shall be the names of your three friends, and you may inform them of the change: Hananiah shall be named Shadrach. Mishael's name shall be Meshach. And Azariah shall now be called Abednego. Is it all clear? Very well, Belteshazzar, you may go and tell your friends the good news. And it *is* very good news. It means the king has deigned to notice you."

"My gratitude is too great for utterance," said Daniel. "And I know that the others will feel the same."

Daniel went to the others and told them their new names. They were all sorely grieved, for each of the names was an abomination. Shadrach meant "servant of the moon." Meshach meant "shadow of the prince." And Abednego meant "servant of Ishtar," nymph goddess of midsummer and mistress of orgies.

Daniel said: "Let us be of good cheer. We know our names. God, who is the theme of our names, knows them. We are captives in Babylon, despite the princeliness of our raiment and our royal fare, and these names are part of the ceremonies of defeat. But if our bodies are captive, our hearts and minds belong to us and cannot be taken. And our own names — to be spoken in secret and among us only — these names, whose syllables proclaim God, shall be like another prayer to us, pleasing to the Almighty."

Nevertheless, Daniel was angered by these Babylonian names, and that night questioned God more earnestly. And he received an answer. The next day he went to the head eunuch and said: "I would ask a boon."

"If it is in my power, I will grant it," said the eunuch, who esteemed Daniel. "Speak."

"Please withhold the king's portion of meat and wine, and allow us to subsist on our own simple fare."

"You turn back delicacies from the royal table?" exclaimed the eunuch in horror. "You will offend the king!"

"On the contrary, our one wish is to serve the king," said Daniel. "The king, in his graciousness, is training us to be counselors. Now, among us wisdom comes from God. He grants it only to those who are pure in spirit. And our God views the body as the temple of the spirit. We must keep our bodies pure, also. Food is a sacrament to us. Certain food defiles us, and clouds our wits. Allow us our simple fare, I pray you. It will strengthen us for the king's purpose."

"But what will you eat? What is this simple fare?"

"Bread and herbs, chiefly. Honey. Cheese. Milk, water. But scant portions of all."

"A starvation diet!" cried the eunuch, who was fat. "You will waste away without meat and wine. The king will see you looking less comely than is your wont, and he will strike the head from my body."

"Let it come to proof, then," said Daniel. "Allow us to feed ourselves in our own way for ten days. If our appearance has suffered after ten days, then we shall partake again of the royal fare."

"So be it," said the eunuch.

Daniel and his friends ate their own food for ten days. At the end of this time, the eunuch called them to him and was amazed at their appearance. They were radiant with health, and had lost no weight. "Well, you seem to flourish on that cattle fodder," said the eunuch. "I shall never understand you Hebrews. Eat what you like."

Nevertheless, he feared to inform the king of this and ate the meat that had been intended for them, and drank the wine, and grew fatter than ever.

Now, it came to pass that Nebuchadnezzar dreamed a dream and was very troubled. He called together his magicians and astrologers and soothsayers and the wise men of the Chaldeans, and said: "I have dreamed a dream that troubles me. Tell me its meaning."

And the eldest of the sorcerers said: "Tell us your dream, O King, and we will tell you its meaning."

"I have forgotten the dream," said the king. "But all of you here are supposed to know things that other men do not know. I have honored you and made you rich for this special knowledge. I have forgotten my dream. It has gone from me. But it was full of terror and I want to know its meaning. You must tell me what I dreamed and then tell me what it means."

"Impossible," said the sorcerer.

"You had better make it possible," said the king, "or you will all be cut into many little pieces, and your houses will be made a dunghill. But if you recall my dream from its darkness and read it for me, then you shall receive gifts and honors."

The sorcerer answered, "O King, there is not a man upon earth who can read your dream if you do not tell him what it is. No king who has ever lived has asked such a thing of any magician or astrologer or Chaldean."

The king dismissed them. And, in his fury, he commanded that all the wise men and magicians and astrologers and Chaldeans in the kingdom be killed. The decree went forth that they be slain. And Arioch, captain of the king's guards, sought Daniel and his friends to slay them, also.

Daniel said to Arioch: "Why this hasty decree? Why do you seek to slay all the wise men of the kingdom?"

Arioch told him what had happened.

"Take me to the king," said Daniel. "I have some skill at dreams and may be able to tell him what he wants to know."

"I shall inform the king that you seek audience," said Arioch. "If he refuses, you must die along with the others."

He departed. Daniel went to his house and made the thing known to his friends. They all prayed to God for wisdom. Daniel fell asleep and dreamed. And he knew that this sleep vision was the one the king had been sent. Daniel said: "Blessed be the name of God forever. He changes times and seasons; He removes kings and sets up kings; He gives wisdom to the wise and knowledge to them that know. He reveals deep and secret things. He knows what is in the darkness, for light dwells in Him. I thank you and praise you, God of my fathers, for you have made known to me now what the king must know, and have saved my life."

There was a knocking on the door. It was Arioch and a company of guards. "The king grants you audience," said Arioch. "Come." They took Daniel to the palace, and he was ushered into the throne room.

"Are you Belteshazzar?" said the king.

Daniel bowed low and said: "I am now. I was formerly known as Daniel."

"Are you able to make known to me the dream that I have forgotten, and to read its meaning?"

Daniel said: "What you have asked cannot be accomplished by all your wise men and your astrologers and your sorcerers. But there is a God in heaven who reveals secrets and makes known what is to be in the days to come. This is the vision that God sent to your bed. In your dream you saw an image, huge and bright and terrible. Its head was of fine gold, its breast and arms were silver, its belly and thighs of bronze. Its legs were of iron, and its feet partly iron and partly clay. As you admired this image, a stone came hurtling out of the darkness and smote the image upon its feet. The image fell and was broken — the iron, the clay, the bronze, the silver, the gold were broken into pieces and became like chaff on the threshing floor. The winds blew the pieces away, and the idol was gone. And, as you watched, the stone that had smote the image grew into a great mountain."

The king stared at Daniel in wonder. "It is true," he whispered. "This is what I saw. I remember now. What does it mean?"

"This is the meaning," said Daniel. "Your dream is a parable of four kingdoms. The first of these kingdoms is your own, and yours is a golden kingdom, signified by the head of gold on the image. For you are the greatest of kings. You have power and strength and glory. All the places men dwell, and the beasts of the field and the fowl of air, have been given into your hand by the God of hosts, and you rule them all. You are this head of gold. But your kingdom shall vanish. After you shall rise another kingdom, a lesser one, signified by the silver arms on the image. And that, too, shall vanish, and after that kingdom shall come another; this one of bronze and lesser still. Then a fourth kingdom shall rise. This one shall be strong as iron, breaking the other material into pieces. The iron men of this kingdom shall march everywhere, breaking, bruising, prevailing. These are the names of the kingdoms: After the golden kingdom of Babylon comes the silver kingdom of Persia. Then the bronze kingdom of Greece. And then the terrible iron kingdom of Rome. And Greece and Rome are names unknown to you; they lie in the future. But they will come."

"Speak, wise youth. What of the stone, the dreadful stone that broke the image to pieces, and the iron, also?"

"The stone . . ." said Daniel. "The stone is God's wrath hurled upon the arrogant kingdoms of men — none of which shall endure. For God in heaven shall raise up people to destroy them, to break them into pieces and consume them. Then God shall make another kingdom. And that one shall stand forever. God's own kingdom! And it shall endure. The Lord sent you this knowledge, for He wanted you to know."

"My sorcerers and astrologers and wise men are babbling children compared to you," cried the king. "I honor your god, and I honor you whom he has sent to reveal secrets. I will make you a great man in my kingdom, and your friends, also."

The king did as he had said. He made Daniel the chief man in Babylon after himself, the head of all the governors in the kingdom, and the chief among his wise men. And Daniel's friends, whom the king knew as Shadrach, Meshach, and Abednego, were made governors.

Now, there were at court certain princes and captains and counselors who envied Daniel and feared the growing influence of the Hebrews — and plotted their downfall. The occasion was ripe, for the king had bade his jewelers to make the largest golden idol ever wrought. It was seventy feet high, cast in solid gold, with eyes of sapphire and a ruby set in its navel. It stood on the plain of Dura, and when the sun hit the golden idol its light dazzled the countryside. The king was very proud of this great jeweled image, which had no rival in any other kingdom. And he readily approved a decree offered by the wicked counselors. A herald went throughout the land, proclaiming: "To you it is decreed, O people, ye of all nations and languages within the realm of Babylon, that when you hear the music of cornet, flute, or dulcimer, you shall fall down and worship the golden image that the king has raised. Whosoever does not fall down and worship the image shall be cast into a fiery furnace and given to the flame within an hour of his refusal."

This the herald proclaimed in every corner of the land. Musicians went out to all cities and villages, and walked along the streets playing flute, cornet, and dulcimer. And when the music was heard the people prostrated themselves and worshipped the golden idol.

Then a prince of the realm went to Nebuchadnezzar and said: "Behold, O King, certain of your subjects ignore your decree and fail in their worship of the golden idol. They hear the music and walk through it as if they were deaf, and do not bow down to the great image."

"If this be true, they die," said the king. "Who are they?"

"They are the Jews whom you chose to govern — Shadrach, Meshach, and Abednego."

"Bring them here!" said the king.

Shadrach, Meshach, and Abednego were taken before the king. He said: "It has been reported to me that you disobey my edict concerning the golden idol, and do not prostrate yourselves and worship the image when you hear the sound of its music."

"It is true," said Shadrach. "We have not bowed down and worshipped the golden idol."

"According to my edict," said Nebuchadnezzar, "you should immediately be cast into the furnace. However, because of my esteem for Belteshazzar, whom you call Daniel, I will pardon you on condition that you obey my decree hereafter, and prostrate yourselves when you hear the music, and worship my golden idol."

"You are gracious, O King," said Meshach. "But our God, maker of heaven and earth, has uttered laws and commandments to us. The first of these is that we worship Him only, and do not bow down to any idol made of wood or stone or gold or brass, or any material that can be wrought by man."

"Do you choose the furnace?" said the king.

"We do not choose; we are chosen," said Abednego. "We cannot serve your gods or worship your idol."

Nebuchadnezzar was full of fury, and ordered his men to heat the furnace seven times hotter than it had ever been heated, and bade them bind the three Hebrews and cast them into the flames. The soldiers seized them. They were bound and carried to the furnace in an open cart. A great crowd gathered in the streets and followed them to the furnace to watch them burn. Men stoked the furnace, piling on wood to make it seven times hotter than it had ever been. The flames grew so hot that tongues of it shot out of the furnace belly and licked up the men who were stoking it, and consumed them. But other men took their places and threw wood upon the fire.

The flames mounted higher. Then Shadrach, Meshach, and Abednego were taken by the arms and legs and flung into the midst of the fire. And the tongues of flame licked out and enwrapped the soldiers who had cast them into the furnace, and consumed these men. And the king was smitten with wonder. For he saw Shadrach, Meshach, and Abednego standing upright in the midst of the flame, even in the belly of the furnace. They were standing and conversing, and they were unbound because their ropes had burned. Nor were their garments burned.

As he watched, as he gazed into the furnace and felt its heat on his face, he saw a fourth among them — the figure of a taller man formed from the flame itself and casting a light that made the fire look dark. And Nebuchadnezzar whispered, "Oh, I see four men loose, walking in the midst of the fire, and they are unharmed. And the form of the fourth is like an angel of god."

325

326

Then, despite the terrible heat, the king went closer to the furnace and shouted, "Shadrach, Meshach, and Abednego! You servants of the most high god, come forth!"

The people watching saw the three of them walk out of the furnace and bow to the king. Not a hair of their heads was singed, nor were their garments charred. Nor did they smell of fire. Nebuchadnezzar said: "Blessed be the god of Shadrach, Meshach, and Abednego, who has sent his angel to deliver his servants out of the fiery furnace. I praise your god, who caused you to break my statute and give your bodies to the flame rather than serve any other god except your own. And this is my decree, to be proclaimed throughout my realm: Anyone who speaks anything amiss against Shadrach, Meshach, and Abednego shall be cut to pieces and his house made into a dunghill."

The royal guards rounded up all the princes and captains and counselors who had been plotting against the Hebrews, and they were put to the sword in a single night. The king restored Shadrach, Meshach, and Abednego to their posts and sought Daniel's counsel more eagerly than ever. And Daniel and his friends governed Babylon, and the country was at peace.

Again, Nebuchadnezzar dreamed, and again he was troubled. He remembered his dream this time, and called in the wise men, the astrologers, and the soothsayers. He told them the dream and asked for an interpretation. They pondered and conferred for three days, but they could not read what had appeared to the king at night. He dismissed them and called Daniel. He said: "O Belteshazzar, master of magicians, I know that the spirit of the holy god is in you and no secret defies you. Read me my dream, I pray."

"Do you remember it?" said Daniel.

"I do," said the king. "I beheld a tree, but its girth was thicker than that of any tree, and it stood taller than any tree I have ever seen. Its leaves were delicately shaped and of a beautiful green. Its boughs were hung with fruit, gold and red globes of fruit. There was enough to feed the fowls of air. And the shadow of its boughs was enough to shelter the beasts of earth. Then there was a flash of light and the sound of thunder. And a bright one descended from the sky. He was a watcher and a holy

King in the Grass

one, an angel of god. He stood at the tree and held a flaming sword. He cried, 'Hew down the tree and cut off its branches! Shake off its leaves and scatter its fruit! Let the beasts depart and the fowls fly away!' And the beasts went from the shade of the tree and the birds flew upward. And the angel cried, 'Leave the stump of the tree in the ground, and let its roots be untouched. Bind the stump with a band of iron, and let it stand in the tender grass of the field. Let it dwell among the beasts and the grass. I say this by the decree of the watchers and the demand of the angels so that all men may know that God rules, that His wrath is flame, and that all must shelter in the shadow of His law.' That is what I saw in the night, O Hebrew, and what I heard. I do not know what it means, but my spirit is troubled. Read me the dream, I pray."

Daniel was astonished, listening to the king. He was troubled by what he heard. He pondered for a while but hesitated to speak. The king said: "I know that this vision is a terrible one. Do not fear to tell me its meaning. I am king and must be prepared to hear the worst."

"My lord, I wish that your enemies had dreamed this dream, and that I could apply its meaning to them," said Daniel. "The great tree you saw, whose top reached the sky, whose fruit was abundant, whose branches sheltered the birds and whose shade invited the beasts of earth, that great beautiful tree, O King, was you, Nebuchadnezzar. For you are grown strong and great. Your stature reaches to the sky, your dominion to the end of earth. And the angel came and said: 'Hew the tree down, but leave the stump in the ground to stand among the beasts and the grass.' And this stump is what you will become, O King."

"Must I be hewed down?" whispered Nebuchadnezzar. "Must I die even in the flower of my years?"

"No," said Daniel. "You have displeased God, but He does not punish you with death. The stump shall remain, as the angel decreed. You shall live and you shall keep your kingdom. But first you shall be punished. You shall be driven from mankind. Your dwelling shall be with the beasts of the field. You shall eat grass like an ox, and be wet with the dew of heaven. You shall sleep in the fields and rise in them, and be as an ox among cattle. And you shall live so for seven years. Afterward you shall be a man again, a king. And, if you break off your sins and raise no more idols, and practice righteousness, and cancel your wickedness by showing mercy to the poor — then you shall be allowed to reign, and all your greatness shall be restored to you."

The king was silent. Daniel departed. Then Nebuchadnezzar, sitting alone on his golden throne in the great throne room, cried out: "O god whom I do not know, who appears to me in the night, am I worthless in your sight? Have I not built this great Babylon? Am I not clothed in power and majesty?"

A voice spoke: "You have heard the word, Nebuchadnezzar. The kingdom has departed from you. Put off your crown now. Divest yourself of your kingly raiment. Leave this palace and get into the field. Do not let night find you in this place, or you die."

In the same hour Nebuchadnezzar ceased to be a king and ceased to be a man. He was in a field eating grass. His body was wet with dew. And he grazed in the field and lay down in the field at night and lived among the cattle. His hair grew out like feathers; his nails were like bird claws.

So it was for seven years. Men thought that the king had died and that his body had vanished. The king's son was too young to take the throne, and a regent ruled in his stead. But the regent was not sure that the king was dead, and did not dare to change his edicts or to trouble the Hebrews. At the end of seven years Nebuchadnezzar lifted his head from the grass and looked at the sky. And he felt himself flooded with understanding. The feathers dropped off his body, his claws shrank, and he was a man again. His hair was his own and his hands were a man's hands.

"O God," he cried, "your dominion is everlasting. Your kingdom passes from generation to generation. I bless you, Most High One. I praise and obey you."

Honor and brightness settled upon Nebuchadnezzar, and he returned to his palace. He clad himself again in his kingly robes and sat on the throne and ruled. He heaped honors upon Daniel and upon his friends. And the children of Judah lived in peace among the Babylonians.

Nebuchadnezzar died and his son, Belshazzar, became king. And the young king did not follow the ways of his father. He did not esteem the Almighty God and inclined toward idols. He gave a mighty feast; his guests were a thousand lords and princes. They glutted themselves and drank wine. And the king served the wine not in his own goblets but in the gold and silver vessels taken from the temple in Jerusalem. These sacred vessels were filled with wine, and the king and his princes, his wives and concubines drank out of them. As they drank, they praised the idols that had been cast down, and Belshazzar promised to raise them again, mightier than before — to make them of gold and of silver, of wood, brass, and stone.

A great, golden candlestick stood in the middle of the table. It held a tall candle of wax. Lesser candles stood about on the table and cast light for the feasting. Then the king rose to his feet, shouting, "Let us drink to the old gods, to the splendid ones of gold and brass that I will raise again!" As he shouted this and lifted the golden goblet that had been taken from the temple in Jerusalem, all voices were stilled. All eyes were fixed in astonishment upon a man's hand that formed itself out of air and floated over the table. A man's hand, but larger. The hand came down and picked up the golden candlestick with its tall candle and clove through the air to the wall, and there wrote in letters of flame these words: MENE, MENE, TEKEL, UPHARSIN.

The hand went back to the table and set the candle down and vanished. But the words remained written in letters of flame upon the wall: MENE, MENE, TEKEL, UPHARSIN.

The king was terrified. "Depart!" he shouted. "The feast is ended!" And the joints of his body were loose; his knees knocked against each other. "Bring on the astrologers!" he cried. "And my soothsayers!"

They came, the wise men of Babylon, the sorcerers and astrologers and soothsayers. The king said: "Whoever reads this writing and interprets it shall be clothed in scarlet and wear a chain of gold about his neck and shall be the third ruler in the kingdom." The sorcerers and the astrologers and the soothsayers tried, but the script was strange to them; they could not pronounce the words or even guess at their meaning.

The king was wrathful, and dismissed them from his sight. He was very troubled. He went to his chamber, but was restless and could not sleep. His thoughts were in a fever. The queen said to him: "There is a man in your kingdom who is old now. But the spirit of the gods is in him. In the days of your father he spoke words of wisdom and read dreams and unciphered secrets. Your father honored him and made him master of the magicians, and called upon him for counsel whenever he was troubled."

"Who is this man?" said the king.

331

"He is a Hebrew. His name is Daniel. He is old but he still lives. He has not come to the palace since your father's death."

"I will send for him," said the king.

Daniel was sent for and brought before the king, who said: "Are you that Daniel who is of the children of Judah, whom my father brought out as captives?"

"I am."

"I have heard of you," said the king. "I have heard that the spirit of the gods is in you, that you are a man of understanding and wisdom. Do you see the writing on that wall?"

"I do," said Daniel.

"We were feasting," said the king, "and a hand came and picked up a candle and wrote those words in letters of fire. My wise men cannot read them, nor my magicians, nor my astrologers. And I know that they were written for a purpose and must be read. If you can read them, you shall be clothed in scarlet and wear a chain of gold about your neck and shall be the third ruler in the land."

"You may keep your gifts, O King," said Daniel, "and distribute your rewards elsewhere."

"Will you not read the writing?" cried the king.

"I will," said Daniel. "But your bare request is sufficient. Hearken, O King. Your father, Nebuchadnezzar, pleased God at first, and God gave him a kingdom and majesty and glory and honor. All nations trembled before him. He was master everywhere. But when his heart swelled with vanity and his pride hardened, the spirit of God departed from him. He was toppled off his throne; his glory was taken from him. He was driven from among men and was made into a beast, and dwelt among cattle. He ate grass and was a beast, in mind and body. And so he lived for seven years — until God forgave him and restored him to his throne. Now you, Belshazzar, have also offended God. You have taken the vessels of His house and filled them with wine, and given them to your lords and your wives and your concubines to drink out of. And you have no word for the high God, but praise the idols of gold and silver and brass, of iron, wood, and stone, which do not see or hear or understand. And the living God, maker of heaven and earth, the God who holds you in His hand, Him you have not glorified. Therefore, these words were written in letters of fire on your wall. The words are MENE, MENE, TEKEL, UPHARSIN. This is what they mean: MENE — God has counted the sins of

Babylon and found them many; TEKEL — You are weighed in the balances and are found wanting; UPHARSIN — Your kingdom will be divided and given to the Medes and the Persians."

The king was afraid. He resolved to humble himself and repent before God. He clothed Daniel in scarlet and put a chain of gold about his neck and appointed him to be his chief counselor.

But it all came to pass as Daniel had said. Darius, king of the Medes, marched against Babylon and besieged the city. It was a mighty, walled city, strongest city in the world. It had withstood every siege because a river flowed through it, and its water could not be cut off and the inhabitants made to yield because of thirst. But Darius was a master of strategy. And God had turned His face from Babylon. Darius set a thousand men to work to bend the river from its course. Then they crept along the dry riverbed that ran under the wall. They passed under the mighty wall and entered the city, ten thousand armed men coming suddenly by night. They surprised the sleeping Babylonians and slaughtered them and took the city. And Darius reigned.

F rom his Medes and his allies, the Persians, Darius chose one hundred and twenty princes to govern the provinces of Babylon. Above all these he set Daniel. For it had been told to him that Daniel had predicted his victory and was the wisest man in the kingdom.

But the princes were jealous and conspired against Daniel. They conferred together, and the craftiest of these princes said: "This man is old and very wise and virtuous. We shall not find any error in him whereby we can damage his position and overthrow him. But he is a Jew, and the children of Judah recognize no law that was not uttered a thousand years ago by their own god on some mountain. Now, I propose this: That we persuade the king to decree that all petitions, all requests be addressed to him, the king, Darius — and that whoever will petition any god or man for any reason will be cast into a den of lions." The princes shouted approval. They understood that such a decree would lead Daniel to defiance.

They went to the king and proposed their decree. Now, Darius was proud. His armies had vanquished all others and he was full of himself. He established the decree. It was proclaimed throughout the land that anyone who would address any prayer or petition or request to any god or man except to Darius would be cast into a den of lions.

Daniel did not protest against the decree; he ignored it. He did what he had always done. Three times a day he went into his house and into a chamber whose windows looked toward Jerusalem. He opened these windows and faced toward Jerusalem and prayed. Nor did he do this secretly, but openly as always.

The princes went to the king and said: "O King, there is a man who breaks your law every day, three times a day. He ignores your word and tramples upon your edict."

"Who is this man?" said Darius.

"He is the man whom you have honored and set above us all. He is Daniel, the Jew Daniel. Three times a day he prays to his god in defiance of your statute."

The king was troubled. He regretted the edict that he had been persuaded to utter. But he did not wish to diminish his power by changing any of his decrees. He said to the princes: "Let him be punished according to the law. Let him be cast into the den of lions."

Daniel was seized and bound with ropes, and taken on a cart out of the city into the wilderness, to the foot of a mountain. There he was put into a den where lions dwelt. A huge stone was rolled before the mouth of the den, closing it up. And Darius stamped the stone with a royal seal so that all men might know what had been done.

The king went back to the palace and passed the night. But he was troubled, and did not call for his musicians or permit any guests. He arose early and rode with his escort out of the city to the mountain. When he came to the lion's den he cried, "Daniel! Are you there?" expecting only silence. But he heard Daniel's voice, saying, "O King, I greet you. May you live and prosper."

The king bade his men roll the stone from the mouth of the den. There, standing in the cave, was Daniel. He was erect and easy in his bearing, and smiled at the king. There was no mark of tooth or fang upon him. Three lions gamboled about him, fawning upon him like hounds, and licking his hands.

"God sent an angel," said Daniel. "He came into the cave and shut the lions' mouths. And they did not devour me. Know this, O King. I have in no way harmed you any more than the lions have harmed me. I have served you faithfully. But I must maintain my own customs and worship my own God and no other — not an idol made of stone or brass or gold, or a king upon his throne."

And Darius feared Daniel's God. He ordered Daniel restored to his place as high governor of Babylon, and ordered that the princes who had conspired against him be cast into the den of lions. This time no angel appeared. The lions' hunger was not thwarted. And the wicked princes were devoured.

And Daniel governed Babylon all through the reign of Darius and into the reign of Cyrus, the Persian. He lived many years and grew in wisdom. God sent him visions, and these visions burned in him. And he uttered searing words — prophecies in the form of stories and fables. He spoke of man and God and the ways of man before God. He also told of things to come. To those who listened to him and heeded what he said, his speech was marvelous.

But, as always, there were only a few who listened. After many generations the Jews came out of their exile in Babylon and returned to their own land. They rebuilt their temple in Jerusalem. But other enemies came. There were victories and defeats, but more defeats than victories. Then, finally, a Roman emperor destroyed the Second Temple, and the Jews were driven out of their land and scattered among the nations of the earth. And they began to live out the terrible prophecy uttered by Moses fourteen hundred years before, when the children of Israel danced before the golden calf:

"You shall be left few in numbers, whereas you were as the stars of the earth for their multitude. The Lord shall scatter you among all people from one end of the earth even unto the other. And among these nations you shall find no ease, neither shall the sole of your foot have rest; but the Lord shall give you there a trembling heart, and failing of eyes, and sorrow of mind. Your life shall hang in doubt before you, and you shall fear day and night. In the morning you shall say: Would God it were evening! And at night you shall say: Would God it were morning!"

And to those who, mystified by disaster, cry out to God in their agony, questioning His purpose, He answers: "Who is this that darkens counsel by words without knowledge? Gird up your loins now. Where were you when I laid the foundations of the earth? Declare if you have understanding. Who has laid the measures? Who has stretched the line upon it? Whereupon are the foundations thereof fastened? Who laid the cornerstone, when the morning stars sang together, and all the sons of God shouted for joy?

"Who shut up the sea with doors when it broke forth, and said: Thus far shall you come but no farther; and here shall your proud waves be stayed?

"Have you entered into the springs of the sea, or have you walked in the search of the depth? Have the gates of death been opened to you? Have you seen the doors of the shadow of death?

"Have you entered into the treasures of snow? Have you seen the treasures of the hail? Have you seen by what way the light is parted, which scatters the east wind upon the earth?

"Who has divided a watercourse for the overflowing of waters, or a way for the lightning and thunder?

"Can you bind the sweet influences of the Pleiades or loose the bands of Orion?

"Can you lift up your voice to the clouds, that abundance of water may cover you? Can you send lightning?

"And who has put wisdom in the inward parts? Who has given understanding to the heart?

"Does the hawk fly by your wisdom and stretch her wings toward the south? Does the eagle mount up at your command and make her nest on high?

"Have you an arm like God? Can you thunder with a voice like Him? Can you deck yourself with majesty and excellency, and array yourself with glory?

"Shall you contend with the Almighty? Shall you instruct Him? Shall you reprove your God? Declare yourself to me.

"Will you annul my judgment? Will you condemn me that you may be righteous?"

But these questions have also been questioned. Each generation has questioned them — and been variously answered.

CHRONOLOGY

Entering Bible time, we have come into a place where our clocks and calendars are useless; we have entered myth. Its numbers dance away from our arithmetic.

We can put a date on those Egyptian records that first used the word *Hebrew* to describe a loose federation of tribes dwelling in the hills of Canaan. The date for Abraham, then, would be about 2000 B.C. And Abraham's father, Terah, might have listened to the tales of a very old man named Methuselah, who would have told him tales he had been told in his boyhood by a very old man named Noah, his great-great-grandfather's great-great-grandfather. Now, since Methuselah lived for about nine hundred years, and Noah eight hundred, we can count backward until we come to Creation, which would have been about 4000 B.C.

However, we are told that the world is much, much older than this — although those who tell us so allow themselves a margin of error of several billion years without blinking an eye. We shall simply have to accept that Bible time is Bible time, and real time is God knows what.